PHYSICS
in Context
An Integrated Approach

VISIT US ON THE INTERNET
www.cord.org

CORD
Leading Change in Education

CORD Staff

Director: Michael Crawford, Ph.D.
Program Manager: John Souders Jr., Ph.D.
Chief Scientist: Leno Pedrotti, Ph.D.
Applications Specialist: Nick G. Carter
Applications Specialist: Bonnie Rinard
Educational Specialist: Lewis Westbrook
Educational Specialist: John Chamberlain

Consultants

Joanne Langabee
Papillion LaVista High School
Papillion, Nebraska

Les Steger
Leander High School
Leander, Texas

Clint Stephens
Escalante High School
Escalante, Utah

George Taliadouros
Minuteman Science-Technology High School
Lexington, Massachusetts

© 2001, 2005 CORD
7 8 9 10

Published and distributed by
    CORD COMMUNICATIONS
    324 Kelly Drive
    Waco, Texas 76710
    800-231-3015 or 254-776-1822
    Fax 254-776-3906

ISBN 1-57837-275-5

Contents

Chapter 2 Work   82

Chapter 3 Rate   120

Chapter 8 Waves and Vibration   352

Chapter 9 Radiation   384

Chapter 10 Light and Optical Systems   422

CHAPTER 1

THE PRIME MOVERS

A **force** is a push or a pull. We use forces all the time. When you lift a book, when you walk, when you breathe, you use force. In industry and sports everything depends on force.

Cranes use force to lift containers.

High jumpers use force to push off the ground.

In this book, we describe the effects of forces in four types of **energy systems**. In **mechanical systems**, a force acting on an object can result in a change in the object's motion. For this reason, we call force the **prime mover** in a mechanical system.

A **fluid system** is one in which a fluid such as air, steam, water, oil or gasoline is moved—usually through pipes, lines or tubes. In a fluid system, forces are distributed on a surface. **Pressure** is the force on a surface divided by the area of the surface. Fluids move in a fluid system because of pressure. When blood moves through arteries, it moves because of blood pressure. When water travels through a fire hose, it does so because of water pressure. A hot-air balloon rises or falls because of air pressure.

Air pressure causes a hot-air balloon to rise or descend.

An **electrical system** is one in which electric charge (electrons) moves through wires or through complex circuits. Charge moves in an electrical system when electrons experience an *electric potential difference*, or **voltage**. When you turn on a television set, voltage causes electric charge to flow through the circuits in the set to create pictures on the screen. When you turn the ignition key in a car, voltage causes electric charge to flow through the starter motor, which then turns the engine.

A **thermal system** is one in which *heat* flows from one place (a hot object) to another (a cold object). Heat flows in a thermal system because of a **temperature difference**. When a hot object is placed in contact with a cold object, heat flows from the hot object (high temperature) to the cold object (low temperature). For example, if a welding torch increases the temperature of one end of a metal rod, the temperature difference causes heat to flow from the hot end of the rod to the cold end. When cool air flows over a car's radiator, temperature differences cause heat to flow from the hot water to the metal in the radiator to the cooler air.

1.1 FORCE IN MECHANICAL SYSTEMS

Objectives

- Define force, and describe how forces are measured.

- Describe what happens when forces on an object are balanced and when they are unbalanced.

- Explain the meaning of Newton's first law of motion.

- Define scalar, vector, weight, mass, and torque.

- Determine the resultant force on an object when two or more forces act on it.

- Solve problems involving force, lever arm, and torque.

INTERNET *connection*

To find out more about force in mechanical systems, follow the links at **www.learningincontext.com.**

Forces are used in all mechanical systems. Forces are transmitted by a variety of mechanical parts—such as gears, belts, valves, chains, pulleys, screws, cams, linkages, rods, sprockets and pistons. These parts are interconnected in various ways to form mechanical systems.

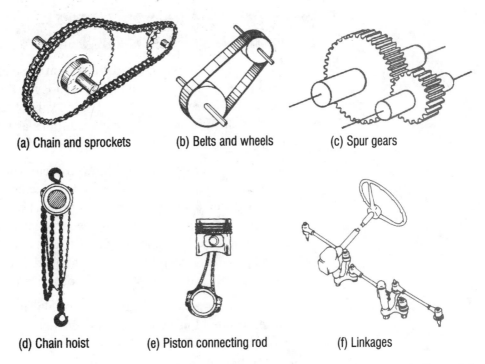

(a) Chain and sprockets   (b) Belts and wheels   (c) Spur gears

(d) Chain hoist   (e) Piston connecting rod   (f) Linkages

Figure 1.1
Mechanical parts transmit forces in mechanical systems.

A bicycle is a mechanical system. Can you identify the forces used to move a bicycle forward? Or to stop a bicycle? What part do the legs play? How are the forces exerted by the feet on the pedals transmitted to the back wheel of the bicycle? What mechanical parts are involved?

Figure 1.2
A bicycle is a mechanical system.

Measuring Force

Most of the world uses the **metric system** in science, engineering, industry, medicine, and sports. The metric system is the most convenient set of measurements because it is based on powers of ten. The metric system provides units for measuring such quantities as length, mass, and liquid capacity.

But there are many more than three physical quantities that must be measured. For example, speed is a ratio of length over time. Acceleration is a ratio of speed over time. Force is a product of mass and acceleration. Thus, measurements and units of speed, acceleration, and force are dependent on the fundamental, or basic units of length, mass, and time. In fact, all physical quantities can be described as combinations of length, mass, and time, plus four other basic quantities.

In 1971, the International Bureau of Weights and Measures, in Sèvres, France, selected **base units** for the seven basic quantities. These are called the **SI** base units, from Le Système International d'Unités. Table 1.1 lists the seven SI base units.

Table 1.1 SI Base Units

Quantity	Unit	Symbol
Length	meter	m
Mass	kilogram	kg
Time	second	s
Electric current	ampere	A
Temperature	kelvin	K
Amount of substance	mole	mol
Luminous intensity	candela	cd

Other units are **derived** from the base units. For example, the SI unit of speed is m/s (length/time), acceleration is m/s^2 (speed/time), and force is the **newton**. You will learn in Chapter 4 that force equals mass (kg) times acceleration (m/s^2). So the newton (N) is defined as

$$1 \text{ N} = 1 \text{ kg} \cdot 1 \text{ m/s}^2 \quad \text{or} \quad 1 \text{ N} = 1 \text{ kg} \cdot \text{m/s}^2$$

Some industries in the United States still use the **English** system of units. The English unit for force is the **pound** (lb). In this book, we will use both SI and English units.

Some useful information on units is organized in two tables that follow. Table 1.2 lists SI and English units for length, time, mass, and force. Table 1.3 lists some useful data for converting weight and mass units. You may want to refer to these tables later.

Table 1.2 English and SI Units

	Length	Time	Mass	Force
ENGLISH	foot (ft)	second (s)	slug	pound (lb)
SI	meter (m)	second (s)	kilogram (kg)	newton (N)

Table 1.3 Weight and Mass Conversions

1 pound = 16 ounces	1 kilogram weighs 9.80 N or 2.2 lb
1 pound = 4.45 newtons	1 slug weighs 32.2 pounds
1 kilogram = 1000 grams	1 slug = 14.59 kg

You can measure force with a spring scale. The spring in the scale stretches an amount proportional to the force applied to it. Thus the scale can be calibrated to read force directly. In Figure 1.3, a spring scale is used to measure the weight of a batch of nails. The weight of the nails is a force, directed downward. **Weight** is a force caused by the Earth's gravity.

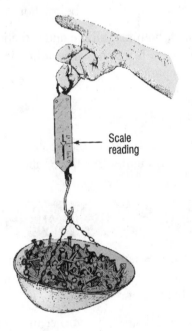

Scale reading

Figure 1.3
A spring scale measures force.
Here, it measures the weight of a batch of nails.

Spring scales can measure force in units of either newtons or pounds. It doesn't matter which system we use, as long as we don't mix units in the same problem. For example, a weight of 30 pounds added to a weight of 20 newtons doesn't equal either 50 pounds or 50 newtons. We can't mix units. We must add pounds to pounds or newtons to newtons to find the correct answer.

Force Is a Vector

When you exert a force, for example by pushing on a book, you can push hard or gently. You can push to the right or left, forward or backward, up or down. The effect the force has on the book depends on two things: (1) the **magnitude**, or strength of the force, and (2) the **direction** of the force. When we describe a force, we always give its **magnitude** and its **direction**. A quantity that must be described by both a magnitude and a direction is called a **vector**. Force is a vector quantity. Displacement, velocity, acceleration, and momentum are also vectors. You will learn more about these quantities in Chapter 3 and Chapter 7.

Some physical quantities are described by only a magnitude. These are called **scalars**. Temperature, elapsed time, pressure, and mass are examples of scalars.

The following are correct ways of describing forces:

> 20 lb to the right
> 35 N northeast
> 115 N at an angle of 45° below horizontal

For each force, both magnitude and direction are specified. On the other hand, temperature is a scalar. The following are not correct ways of describing temperatures:

> 68° F west
> 20° C to the left

Such statements have no meaning, since temperature doesn't have a direction. We say simply that the temperature is 68°F or 20°C.

How Do We Represent Forces?

A vector is represented—or drawn—as an arrow. The length of the arrow is proportional to the magnitude of the vector. The arrow points in the direction of the vector.

As an example, consider the worker in Figure 1.4 pulling a cart. The worker pulls with a force of 30 pounds along the rope, and the rope makes an angle of 30° above the horizontal. How would you draw an arrow to represent the force the rope applies to the cart?

The length of the arrow must be proportional to the magnitude of the force, 30 pounds. So choose a convenient scale—such as one inch equals 10 pounds. Then draw the arrow three inches long, to represent 30 pounds.

Since the force makes an angle of 30° above the horizontal, draw the arrow in the same direction. The final drawing should look like the arrow in Figure 1.5.

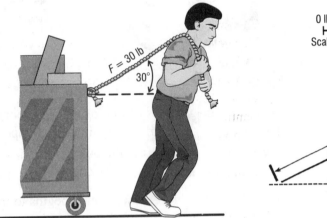

Figure 1.4 Force along rope pulls on cart.

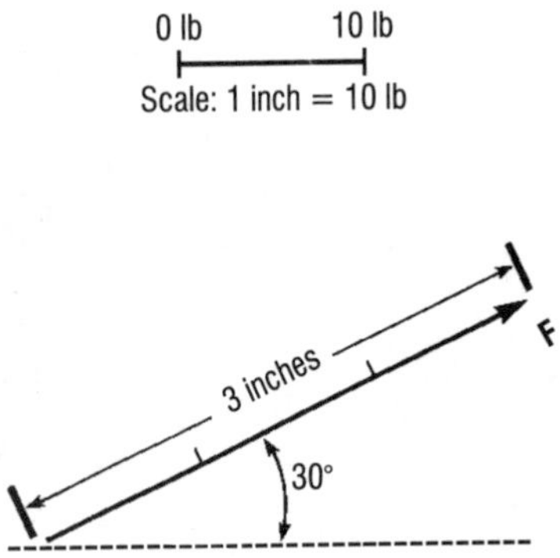

Figure 1.5 Arrow drawn as a vector to represent a 30-lb force acting at an angle of 30° above the horizontal

Balanced and Unbalanced Forces

Figure 1.6 shows two situations where opposing forces act on an object. In one case, two people pull in opposite directions on a door. In the other case, a lawnmower is pushed forward by its engine but there is an opposing force of friction. The vectors representing the forces on each object are drawn below the figures. We use a boldface letter to represent a vector. We use the same variable, but not boldface, to represent the magnitude of the vector. For example, **F** represents a vector force, and *F* represents the magnitude of **F**.

Why is it that the door does not move but the lawnmower begins to move forward?

$\mathbf{F}_{engine}$ $\mathbf{F}_{friction}$

Figure 1.6
Balanced and unbalanced forces

$\mathbf{F}_{left}$ $\mathbf{F}_{right}$

Notice the magnitudes of the forces. The door doesn't move because the force to the left $\mathbf{F}_{left}$ is equal in magnitude and opposite in direction to the force to the right $\mathbf{F}_{right}$. Therefore, the pull on one side is balanced by an equal and opposite pull on the other side. The forces acting on the door are **_balanced_**.

On the other hand, the lawnmower begins to move because the push of the engine, $\mathbf{F}_{engine}$ is greater than the opposing force of friction $\mathbf{F}_{friction}$. The forces on the lawnmower are unbalanced, so the lawnmower begins to move.

Balanced and unbalanced forces determine how a parachutist falls. As shown in Figure 1.7, two forces are acting on the parachutist—air drag, $\mathbf{F}_{drag}$, and weight, $\mathbf{F}_{gravity}$. Since weight is the force of gravity, it is directed downward. Air drag is always in a direction opposite to the motion, so it is directed upward. When the parachutist first exits the airplane, the two forces are unbalanced. Weight is greater than air drag, $F_{gravity} > F_{drag}$, and the parachutist falls faster and faster. After the parachute opens, air drag increases and soon equals the parachutist's weight, $F_{gravity} = F_{drag}$. Now the two forces are balanced. From then on the parachutist's speed remains constant.

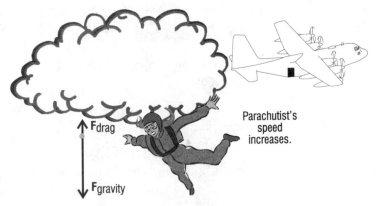

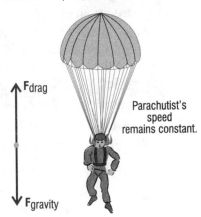

(a) Unbalanced forces (weight is greater than drag)

Figure 1.7
Balanced and
unbalanced forces

(b) Balanced forces (weight equals drag)

To determine what effect more than one force has on an object, we must find the sum of the forces. The sum is called the **net force** acting on the object.

- If the net force is *not zero*, the applied forces are *unbalanced*. In this case, the net force will cause a change in the object's speed or direction. Which situations in Figures 1.6 and 1.7 show net forces not equal to zero?

- If the net force equals zero, the forces are balanced—they cancel each other out. If there is no net force, the body is in **equilibrium**. There is no change in the object's speed or direction. Which situations in Figures 1.6 and 1.7 show net forces equal to zero?

Newton's First Law of Motion

The motion of a body in equilibrium is described by **Newton's first law of motion**:

> *Every object will remain at rest, or will continue to move in a straight line with constant speed, unless the object is acted on by a net force.*

This is the first of three laws of motion written by the English scientist and mathematician Isaac Newton in 1686 in the *Philosphia Naturalis Principia Mathematica* (usually just called the *Principia*.)

Newton's first law is sometimes called the law of *inertia*. **Inertia** is the property of an object to resist changes in its motion. If a body is at rest, it tends to remain at rest. If a body is moving at constant velocity, it tends to keep moving at that velocity.

Example 1.1 Forces in Equilibrium

A yo-yo weighing 0.25 lb hangs motionless at the end of a string. Draw the forces acting on the yo-yo.

Solution: The yo-yo is the system. The forces of gravity and the string act on the system. Draw a **free-body diagram** of the system, as follows:

- Draw a dot to represent the yo-yo.

- Draw each force acting on the system with an arrow representing the vector. Draw the tail of the arrow on the dot, and point the arrow in the direction of the force.

- Draw the length of each arrow proportional to the magnitude of the force.

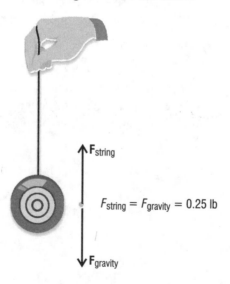

F_{string}

$F_{string} = F_{gravity} = 0.25$ lb

$F_{gravity}$

Figure 1.8
Free-body diagram
of the forces acting on a yo-yo

Since the yo-yo is not moving, the system is in equilibrium. The forces acting on it are balanced, and the magnitude of the net force is zero. The force exerted by the string is equal and opposite to the force of gravity.

Adding Forces That Act Along a Line

We add forces to find the net force acting on an object. Forces are easy to add if they act along the same line—either in the same direction or in opposite directions.

- If two or more forces act in the same direction, add their magnitudes to get the net force. The direction of the net force is the same as the direction of the added forces.

- If two forces act in opposite directions, subtract their magnitudes to get the net force. The direction of the net force is the same as the direction of the larger force.

Example 1.2 Tug-of-War Problem

Five people compete in a tug-of-war. Three people on the left side each pull with 230 N of force. Two people on the right side each pull with 300 N of force. Who will win the tug-of-war?

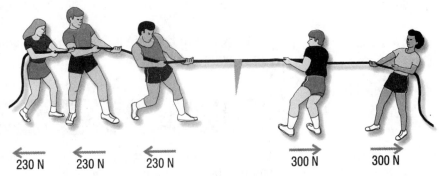

230 N   230 N   230 N   300 N   300 N

Figure 1.9
Unbalanced forces in a tug-of-war

Solution: The system is the rope, and five forces are acting on the system. Find the vector sum of the five forces. If the sum is zero, the rope will continue to be at rest. If the sum is not zero, the rope will begin to move.

Let $\mathbf{F}_1$ represent the total force exerted by the two people on the right. These two addend forces act in the same direction, so add their magnitudes to find $\mathbf{F}_1$.

$\mathbf{F}_1 = 300 + 300 = 600$ N to the right

Let $\mathbf{F}_2$ represent the total force exerted by the three people on the left. These three addend forces act in the same direction, so add their magnitudes to find $\mathbf{F}_2$.

$\mathbf{F}_2 = 230 + 230 + 230 = 690$ N to the left

Figure 1.10
Free-body diagram of the forces

Since $\mathbf{F}_1$ and $\mathbf{F}_2$ act in opposite directions, subtract their magnitudes to find the magnitude of the net force $\mathbf{F}_{net}$. The direction of $\mathbf{F}_{net}$ is the same as the direction of $\mathbf{F}_2$, since $\mathbf{F}_2$ is larger than $\mathbf{F}_1$. The net force is $690 - 600 = 90$ N to the left.

The rope will begin to move to the left, and the three people on the left will win the tug-of-war.

Adding Forces That Do Not Act Along a Line

If forces on an object don't act along the same line, you can't simply add or subtract their magnitudes to get the net force. But you can solve the problem graphically.

Suppose two people pull a boat with ropes tied to the boat. The ropes form a right angle, as in Figure 1.11. The person on the dock pulls with 40 pounds of force. The person on the shore pulls with 30 pounds of force. What is the net force on the boat?

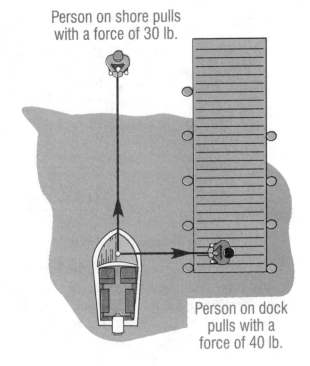

Person on shore pulls
with a force of 30 lb.

Person on dock
pulls with a
force of 40 lb.

Figure 1.11
Two forces that form a
90° angle are applied
to dock a boat.

To find the sum of the two forces, graph the vectors and use the "head-to-tail" method. Follow these five steps:

Step 1: *Draw the 40-lb force.*

Draw a horizontal line on a sheet of notebook paper, or use a horizontal grid line on a sheet of graph paper. See Figure 1.12. Choose a convenient scale, such as "½ inch equals 10 pounds." (The scale used in Figure 1.12 is shown next to the figure.) Mark off the correct number of divisions along the horizontal line to represent 40 lb. Since we've chosen 1 division for each 10 pounds, we mark off 4 divisions, as shown. Draw an arrowhead at the right end to indicate the direction of the 40-lb force. The 40-lb force, drawn as a vector, is represented by the arrow AB in Figure 1.12.

Step 2: *Add the 30-lb force to the 40-lb force.*

The 30-lb force acts at a right angle, or 90°, to the 40-pound force. So the arrow that represents the 30-lb force must be drawn vertically. In the "head-to-tail" method of vector addition, the tail of the 30-lb force is located at the head of the 40-lb force. So draw a line at 90° to the horizontal line at point *B*. Mark off 3 divisions to represent 30 lb. Draw the arrowhead at the top end to indicate the direction of the 30-lb force. Arrow BC in Figure 1.12 represents the 30-lb force acting at 90° to the 40-lb force.

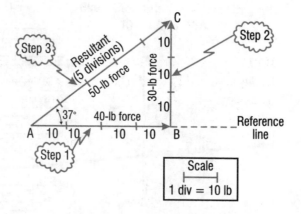

Figure 1.12
Graphical determination
of a resultant force

Step 3: *Draw the resultant force.*

The single vector representing the sum of two or more vectors is called the resultant. When addend vectors are arranged head-to-tail, as in Figure 1.12, the resultant is found by drawing a vector from the tail of the first vector to the head of the last vector. The resultant of the 40-lb force and the 30-lb force is represented by arrow AC.

Step 4: *Determine the magnitude and the direction of the resultant.*

The resultant AC measures 5 divisions on the drawing. Since the scale factor is 10 lb per division, the resultant force must equal 50 lb.

Notice that triangle ABC is a right triangle. Therefore, you can also use the Pythagorean Theorem to calculate the magnitude of the resultant. AC is the hypotenuse, and AB and BC are the legs.

$$AC^2 = AB^2 + BC^2$$
$$= 40^2 + 30^2$$
$$= 2500$$
$$AC = \sqrt{2500} = 50$$

The magnitude of the resultant force is 50 lb.

To find the force's direction, use a protractor to measure the angle AC makes with the horizontal. This angle is 37°.

Step 5: *Now you can draw some conclusions.*

The graphical method has shown us that a 40-lb force and a 30-lb force, pulling on an object (boat) at a right angle to each other, can be replaced by a single force (the resultant) of 50 lb pulling at an angle of 37° measured from the direction of the 40-lb force. Note carefully that the result is not 70 pounds, which would have come from adding 30 pounds to 40 pounds as if they were scalars. The resultant of two vectors is always in a direction between the directions of the two vectors.

Weight and Mass Aren't the Same Thing!

If a net force greater than zero acts on an object that is at rest, it will begin to move. For example, if you push a book with a force large enough to overcome friction, the book will start to move and slide across the table. It takes twice the force to start a stack of two books moving. This is because two books have twice the inertia of one book.

Figure 1.13
Two books have twice the inertia of one book.

The amount of inertia of any object depends on the amount of matter (atoms or molecules) contained in the object. The stack of two books has twice the inertia of the single book because the stack has twice the amount of matter. The mass of an object is a measure of the object's inertia, or of the amount of matter it contains. The SI unit of mass is the kilogram, kg.

Your mass is a measure of the total amount of matter contained within your body. Your weight is a measure of the force of the Earth's gravitational pull on the mass of your body.

Suppose your weight on the Earth is 140 pounds, or 623 newtons, and your mass is 63.6 kg. If you travel to the moon, your weight will be only about 23 lb, or 104 N. This is because on the surface of the moon the gravitational pull is about one-sixth of the pull on the surface of the Earth. But on the moon your body will contain the same number and type of atoms and molecules as on Earth. Therefore, your mass will be the same 63.6 kg wherever you go.

Torque and Rotation

Torque is a quantity that causes rotation in mechanical systems. Gears, crankshafts, flywheels, fans, motors, bolts, and screws all turn or rotate. A torque is the effect of a force applied on a body at some distance from the axis of rotation of that body.

Torques can cause either *clockwise* rotations or *counterclockwise* rotations. Clockwise rotations move like the hands of a clock. The abbreviation for clockwise is "cw." Counterclockwise rotations are in the opposite direction. The abbreviation for counterclockwise is "ccw."

Consider the rotating wheel on a pull starter for a chain saw, as shown in Figure 1.14. A force pulling on a rope that's wrapped around a wheel will cause the wheel to rotate. The torque is caused by the force applied to the rim of the wheel. Torque is equal to the product of the force (F) times the length of the lever arm (AB). The lever arm (distance AB) is always the shortest distance from the rotation axis (labeled "axle") to the ***line of action*** of the applied force. The line of action is a line along the applied force that extends in both directions.

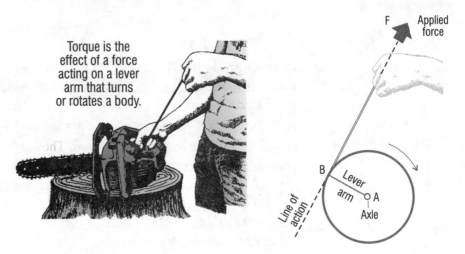

Torque is the effect of a force acting on a lever arm that turns or rotates a body.

Figure 1.14
Torque causes rotation.

Torque is measured in units of force times distance. In the English system, torque is measured in pound-feet (lb·ft); in SI, torque is measured in newton-meters (N·m). We use the Greek letter τ (*tau*) to represent torque.

$$\text{Torque} = \frac{\text{applied}}{\text{force}} \times \frac{\text{lever}}{\text{arm}}$$

$$\tau = F \times L$$

Since torque is equal to the product of an applied force times a lever arm, torque is doubled if we keep the force the same but double the length of the lever arm. Suppose that the nut shown in Figure 1.15a can't be loosened by the wrench when a certain force F_M is applied with a lever arm L. Then the maximum torque applied in an attempt to loosen the nut is $F_M \times L$—not enough to do the job.

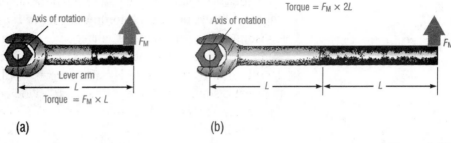

Axis of rotation

F_M

Lever arm

L

Torque $= F_M \times L$

(a)

Torque $= F_M \times 2L$

Axis of rotation

F_M

L L

(b)

Figure 1.15
Increasing lever arm to increase applied torque

How can we loosen the nut? Let's pick another wrench with the same head span but with a handle twice as long (Figure 1.15b). Now, if we apply the same force F_M at the end of this wrench—with a handle $2L$ long—we should get a torque of $F_M \times 2L$ or $2F_ML$. This is twice as much torque as we were able to apply with the shorter wrench. The increased torque may be large enough to break the nut loose.

A gear is a wheel with notches—or teeth—on its rim. A gear is usually mounted on a shaft. The gear turns with the shaft. Two gears are commonly positioned so that their teeth mesh. When one gear turns, its teeth push on the teeth of the other gear. This causes the second gear to move.

In Figure 1.16, the force applied by driving gear A on driven gear B is labeled F_A. The force comes from one gear tooth pushing on another. The lever arm is equal to the radius of gear B, labeled L. The torque that gear A exerts on gear B is then equal to $F_A \times L$, in lb·ft or N·m. Torque is present in all rotating parts of machinery—in gears, pulleys, and crankshafts. Torque is applied by many hand tools—especially a torque wrench.

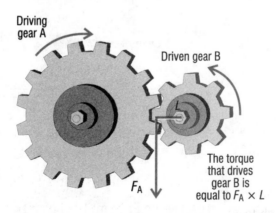

Driving gear A

Driven gear B

The torque that drives gear B is equal to $F_A \times L$

F_A

Figure 1.16
Torque is applied by one gear to turn the other.

A torque wrench is a tool used by automotive technicians to tighten bolts to certain specifications. The automotive technician exerts a force on the handle of the wrench. The handle is a fixed length, so the lever arm is constant. The technician applies different torques to the bolt by varying the force. The larger the force applied on the handle, the larger the torque applied to the bolt. Most torque wrenches found in automotive shops are calibrated in either lb·ft or N·m.

Figure 1.17
Torque wrench used
to tighten bolts

Example 1.3 Calculation of Torque Applied by Torque Wrench

A torque wrench has a lever arm of 1.5 ft. A force of 40 pounds is applied at the end of the wrench to tighten a bolt. Find the torque applied to the bolt in

(a) lb·ft

(b) N·m

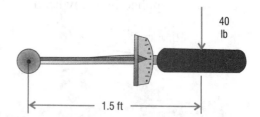

Solution: (a) Torque in lb·ft:

$$\tau = F \times L$$

$$= 40 \text{ lb} \times 1.5 \text{ ft} = 60 \text{ lb·ft}$$

(b) Torque in N·m: First change feet to meters, then change pounds to newtons.

Use the conversion factors:

1 ft = 12 in.	1 in. = 2.54 cm
1 m = 100 cm	1 lb = 4.45 N

$$(1.5 \text{ ft}) \left[12 \frac{\text{in}}{\text{ft}} \right] \left[2.54 \frac{\text{cm}}{\text{in}} \right] = 45.7 \text{ cm}$$

$$(45.7 \text{ cm}) \left[\frac{1 \text{ m}}{100 \text{ cm}} \right] = 0.457 \text{ m}$$

$$40 \text{ lb} = 40 \text{ lb} \left[4.45 \frac{\text{N}}{\text{lb}} \right] = 178 \text{ N}$$

$$\tau = F \times L$$
$$= 178 \text{ N} \times 0.457 \text{ m} = 81.3 \text{ N} \cdot \text{m}$$

Example 1.4 Torques in a Belt-Driven System

The motor pulley in a belt-drive system has a radius of 5 cm (0.05 m). The large pulley attached to the shaft of a machine has a radius of 20 cm (0.20 m). The dragging or pulling force of the belt is 40 newtons. Assume that the belt doesn't slip as the motor and belt drive the load pulley. What is the torque applied to each pulley?

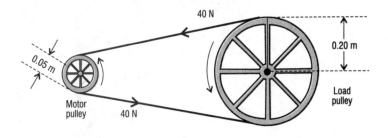

Solution: (a) Motor pulley:
$$\tau = F \times L$$
$$= 40 \text{ N} \times 0.05 \text{ m}$$
$$= 2 \text{ N} \cdot \text{m}$$
             (b) Load pulley:
$$\tau = 40 \text{ N} \times 0.20 \text{ m}$$
$$= 8 \text{ N} \cdot \text{m}$$

Opposing Torques

Often, opposing torques, like opposing forces, act on a rotating system. If the torques cancel each other, the system is a balanced system. It is said to be in equilibrium. That means that, if the system is at rest when the torques are applied, it remains at rest. If it's rotating when the torques are applied, the system continues rotating at the same rate. If the torques don't cancel each other out, a net torque greater than zero exists. The system is then said to be unbalanced. The net torque will cause a change in the rotational speed of the system, by causing it to speed up or slow down.

An example of opposing torques is illustrated by the unequal-arm balance used in truck scales. The forces that cause opposite torques about the axis of rotation are (1) the weight of the truck, and (2) a known balance weight.

Example 1.5 Truck Scales Involve Opposing Torques

A 48,000-pound truck sits on the platform of truck-weighing scales. The truck weight acts on a 0.5-ft lever arm about the pivot point. A 1000-pound balancing weight is hung on the opposite side of the pivot point, 20 ft away. Find:

(a) Torque of truck about pivot point.

(b) Torque of balance weight about pivot point.

(c) Whether or not the torques are balanced.

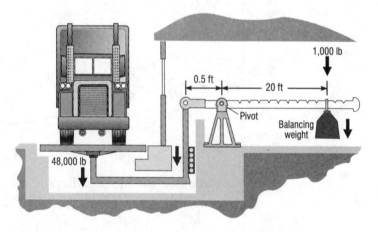

Solution: (a) Torque of truck about pivot

$$\tau = F \times L$$

$$= 48,000 \text{ lb} \times 0.5 \text{ ft} = 24,000 \text{ lb·ft}$$

(b) Torque of balance weight about pivot

$$\tau = F \times L$$

$$= 1000 \text{ lb} \times 20 \text{ ft} = 20,000 \text{ lb·ft}$$

(c) No, torques are not balanced. The torque exerted by the truck is 4000 lb·ft greater. Thus, a net torque of 4000 lb·ft would cause the truck platform to move down. (Can you see that this is like a seesaw?)

Summary

- A force is a push or a pull.

- Force is a vector. It has both magnitude and direction. Its magnitude is measured in pounds or in newtons.

- Newton's first law says that an object will remain at rest or will continue to move in a straight line unless it is acted on by a net force.

- Unbalanced forces result in a net force acting on an object. Balanced forces result in no net force acting on an object.

- If two forces act on an object and the forces act in a straight line, the magnitude of the resultant is either the sum of or the difference between the two forces' magnitudes.

- If two forces act on an object and the forces do not act in a straight line, the resultant can be found using the head-to-tail method of vector addition.

- The mass of an object is a measure of the object's inertia. The weight is a measure of the force exerted on the object by gravity.

- A torque is exerted on a body when a force is applied and the line of action of the force does not pass through the body's axis of rotation. The torque equals the force times the lever arm.

- If no net torque is exerted on a body, it will remain at rest or will continue to rotate at a constant rate.

Exercises

1. Name two units of measure for force.

2. To completely describe a force, what two things must be specified?

3. When you add vectors graphically, you draw arrows to represent the vectors. How do you know how long to draw the arrows?

4. What causes an object to change speed or the direction of motion?

5. Two forces act on an object. The forces have a magnitude of 34 newtons and act along the same line, but in opposite directions. What is the magnitude of the net force acting on the object?

6. Three forces act on an object. If the magnitude of the net force is zero, the object is said to be in _____ .

Use the diagram at the right to answer Exercises 7 and 8.

7. Find the magnitude of the net force (F_{net}) in the diagram shown.

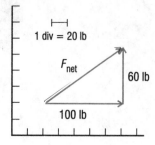

8. The direction of the 60-pound force is north, and the direction is east for the 100-pound force. Describe the direction of the net force.

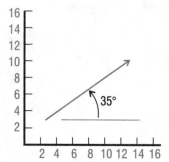

9. Write a complete description of the vector shown in the diagram at the right.

10. A hot-air balloon is acted on by two forces. One force is its weight, equal to 2448 newtons. The second force is a buoyant force acting straight up, equal to 2448 newtons. What change in the motion of the balloon will result from the action of these two forces? Explain your answer.

11. The balloon pilot from Exercise 10 lights the burner, which adds heat to the balloon. The buoyant force increases to 2492 newtons. Write a complete description of the net force on the balloon. What change in the motion of the balloon will result from this net force?

12. Suppose you drive in a straight line 10 km north from home, then turn west and drive 12 km in a straight line. How far are you from home?

13. Suppose you drive 10 km north from home, then turn west and drive until you are 12 km away from home. How far west did you drive?

14. A satellite makes small changes to its position with thrusters. A thruster expels gas through a nozzle, which results in the application of a force to the satellite. To make one change, the satellite fires three thrusters at the same time. Thruster A exerts a force of 20 N directed to the right. Thruster B exerts a force of 30 N directed to the right at an angle of 30° above the horizon. Thruster C exerts a force of 20 N directed straight up.

   (a) Graphically add the forces in the order A + B, then add the result to C. This result is the vector sum A + B + C.

   (b) Graphically add the forces in the order C + B, then add the result to A. This result is the vector sum C + B + A.

   (c) What can you conclude about the order in which the forces are added?

15. Mike's car has a flat tire. He is trying to remove a lug nut that the tire shop overtightened with an impact wrench. Mike applies a force of 80 pounds to the end of a lug wrench that is 1.2 feet long.

    (a) Find the torque applied to the lug nut by the wrench.

    (b) The torque Mike applies to the lug nut does not make it turn. What is the net torque on the lug nut?

    (c) Describe any torques, other than Mike's, acting on the lug nut.

16. Sandra and Maria are loading their ski boat onto a boat trailer. The trailer has a hand winch to pull the boat into position on the trailer. The winch has a pair of gears to multiply the torque Sandra produces when she pulls or pushes on the winch handle. One gear is 2 inches in diameter and the other is 5.5 inches in diameter. A torque of 10 lb-ft is applied to the smaller gear. What torque is produced by the larger gear?

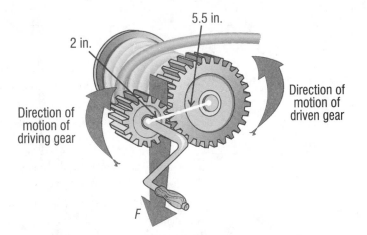

17. Explain the difference between the weight and mass of an object.

18. An astronaut in orbit removes two identical metal containers from a storage compartment. One container is empty and one is full of water. But both containers are "weightless." How can the astronaut tell which container is full of water without opening either container?

19. When you drive your car on the highway at constant velocity, the net force acting on the car is zero. Why must you continue to press on the accelerator?

20. Carlos stands and applies his full weight to a pedal on his bike. A torque of 50.2 newton·meters is applied to the rear wheel. The wheel has a rolling radius of 0.387 meter. What is the magnitude of the force that the wheel applies to the road?

21. The engine of a jet plane applies a horizontal thrust force of 6500 lb to an airplane that weights 12,000 pounds. The wings apply a vertical lift force of 14,500 lb. Find the net force by graphing.

22. The Earth exerts a downward force of 9.8 newtons on an object with a mass of 1 kilogram, and a force of 49 newtons on a object with a mass of 5 kilograms.

   (a) What is the mass of an object if it weighs 22,500 newtons? Show each step in your solution.

   (b) Describe a general method to find the weight of an object on Earth if the mass is known.

23. The ratio of the weight of a object, on Earth, to its mass is 9.8 newtons/kilogram. The ratio of weight to mass is only 1/6 as much on the moon. How much does a 25-kg object weigh on the moon?

24. The jib crane shown in the figure is holding the beam at rest. What is the horizontal force F required at the top of the jib boom to balance the torque on the boom?

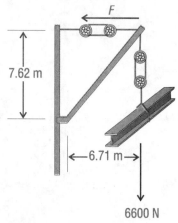

25. The planetary rover shown in the figure has a robotic arm that will pick up a rock and return it to the landing craft. The rock has a weight of 4.1 newtons. What is the magnitude of the vertical force that must be exerted on the rock? When the rock is lifted, how much torque will be applied to the joint at A in the robot arm? How much torque will be applied to the joint at B?

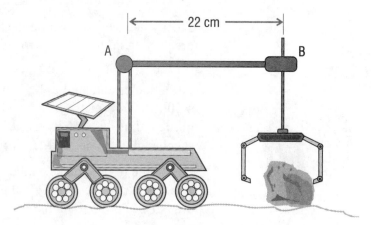

1.2 PRESSURE IN FLUID SYSTEMS

Objectives

- Describe the four states of matter.

- Define density and pressure.

- Explain why pressure in a fluid depends on depth in the fluid.

- Explain why an object submerged in a fluid experiences a buoyant force.

- Predict whether an object will sink or float in a given fluid.

- Explain how a force can be multiplied in a hydraulic lift.

- Explain where atmospheric pressure comes from.

- Describe how a barometer measures atmospheric pressure.

- Explain the difference between absolute and gage pressure.

INTERNET *connection*

To find out more about pressure in fluid systems, follow the links at **www.learningincontext.com**.

Refer to Appendix F for a career link to this concept.

States of Matter

All matter is made of atoms and molecules. Water, for example, is made of molecules that each have two hydrogen atoms and one oxygen atom. A molecule of water is represented by the shorthand H_2O. Matter can exist in four states: solid, liquid, gas, and plasma. Atomic and molecular motion is different in each state.

For example, water is a solid (ice) at temperatures below 0°C (32°F). In a **solid**, molecules are constantly moving, but they do not move around in the solid—they vibrate about fixed positions.

If you add heat to ice, the rate of molecular vibration increases and the temperature increases. Water becomes a liquid when the temperature rises above 0°C. In a **liquid**, the molecules are no longer confined to fixed positions. The molecules continue to vibrate, but they can now easily slide over one another and move about throughout the liquid. This is why the shape of a liquid is not fixed—it takes the shape of its container.

If you continue to add heat to liquid water, the molecules vibrate even more rapidly and the temperature continues to increase. Water becomes a **gas** (water vapor or steam) when the temperature rises above 100°C. In the gaseous state, the molecules move freely about the container. When a molecule in the gas hits another molecule or the side of the container, it bounces like a billiard ball hitting another billiard ball or a wall. The shape of a gas also takes the shape of its container.

If you add enough heat to water vapor, the molecules separate into individual hydrogen and oxygen atoms. Continued heating (to temperatures over 2000°C) causes electrons to separate from atoms. An atom with missing electrons is called an *ion*. A gas containing free electrons and ions is called a **plasma**. The gas inside an operating fluorescent light is a plasma. Plasmas are not commonly part of our everyday lives on Earth, but they are the most common state of matter in the universe. The stars, including our sun, and most intergalactic matter are in the plasma state.

Fluids

Both liquids and gases are fluids. A **fluid** is a material that can flow, has no definite shape of its own, and conforms to the shape of its container.

Fluid systems use liquids or gases to operate mechanical devices or to circulate fluids. The fluid used by the system is called the working fluid. A **hydraulic system** uses a liquid as the working fluid. A **pneumatic system** uses a gas as the working fluid.

A city's water distribution system is a complex hydraulic system made up of elevated water tanks, underground pipes, water meters, and valves. A ventilating system for a building is a pneumatic system. It uses fans to force air through a building's ductwork in order to control temperature and humidity in the building. In the water distribution system, the elevation of the water tank creates pressure that moves water through the pipes. In the ventilating system, the fan creates pressure that moves air through the ducts. Pressure is the prime mover in a fluid system.

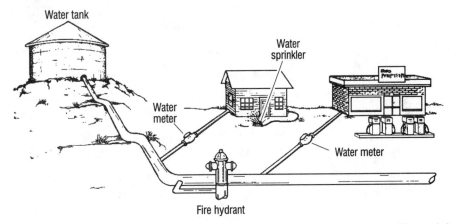

Figure 1.18
A city water distribution system depends on pressure to move water.

Density and Pressure

Have you ever wondered why oil floats on water? Or why a balloon filled with helium or hot air rises? The answer is found in a property of materials called *density*. Density describes how much mass is contained in a given space. The **density** of a material is the amount of matter per unit volume. Density is represented by the Greek letter ρ (*rho*). Density is defined as the mass m of a substance divided by the volume V of the substance.

$$\text{Density} = \frac{\text{mass}}{\text{volume}}$$

$$\rho = \frac{m}{V}$$

In SI units, mass is measured in kilograms (kg) and volume is measured in cubic meters (m^3). Thus, density is expressed in kg/m^3. Mass is also commonly measured in grams (g) and volume in cubic centimeters (cm^3). In these metric units, density is expressed in g/cm^3. The mass of 1 cm^3 of water (at 4°C) is exactly 1 g. Therefore, the density of water is exactly 1 g/cm^3. Can you show why 1 g/cm^3 = 1000 kg/m^3?

In English units, mass is measured in slugs and volume is measured in cubic feet (ft^3). Density is expressed in slugs/ft^3.

The densities of some other liquids and solids are shown in Table 1.4.

Table 1.4 Densities of Several Solids and Liquids

	g/cm^3	kg/m^3
Solids		
Gold	19.3	19,300
Lead	11.3	11,300
Silver	10.5	10,500
Copper	8.9	8,900
Steel	7.8	7,800
Aluminum	2.7	2,700
Ice	0.9	900
Oak Wood	0.8	800
Balsa Wood	0.3	300
Liquids		
Mercury	13.6	13,000
Water	1.0	1,000
Oil	0.9	900
Alcohol	0.8	800

Density is sometimes written as a comparison of an object's weight to its volume. This ratio is called **weight density**. We use ρ_w to represent weight density.

$$\text{Weight density} = \frac{\text{weight}}{\text{volume}}$$

$$\rho_w = \frac{\text{weight}}{V}$$

The SI units of weight density are N/m^3. The English units are lb/ft^3. In English units, water has a weight density of 62.4 lb/ft^3.

Example 1.6 Density of a Fluid

A volume of 500 cm^3 of a certain fluid has a mass of 550 g. What is the density of the fluid?

Solution :

$$\rho = \frac{m}{V}$$

$$= \frac{550 \text{ g}}{500 \text{ cm}^3}$$

$$= 1.1 \text{ g/cm}^3$$

The density of the fluid is 1.1 g/cm^3.

Example 1.7 Calculating Mass from Density and Volume

The graduated cylinder at the right contains alcohol. Find the mass of alcohol in the cylinder.

Solution: From Table 1.4, the density of alcohol is 0.8 g/cm³. The graduated cylinder contains 300 cm³ of alcohol. Use the equation for density, and solve for the mass.

$$\rho = \frac{m}{V}$$

$$m = \rho V$$

$$= (0.8 \text{ g/cm}^3)(300 \text{ cm}^3)$$

$$= 240 \text{ g}$$

There are 240 g of alcohol in the cylinder.

When a fluid is contained in a vessel, the molecules that make up the fluid bounce against the walls of the vessel and exert a force. Since the fluid takes the shape of the vessel, the force is spread over the surface of the vessel. A force applied over a surface is *pressure*. **Pressure** P is defined as the force F divided by the area A on which it acts.

$$\text{Pressure} = \frac{\text{force}}{\text{area}}$$

$$P = \frac{F}{A}$$

In SI units, force is measured in newtons (N) and area is measured in square meters (m²). Thus, pressure is expressed in N/m². This unit is called a **pascal** (Pa), and 1 N/m² = 1 Pa. One pascal is a very small quantity, so the kilopascal (kPa) is more commonly used. One kPa equals 1000 Pa.

In English units, force is measured in pounds (lb) and area is measured in square feet (ft²). Thus, pressure is expressed in lb/ft². Another common unit of pressure is lb/in², often abbreviated psi.

Example 1.8 Comparisons of Forces and Pressures

Two identical bricks, each weighing 32 N, are placed on a table—one on its end and one on its side.

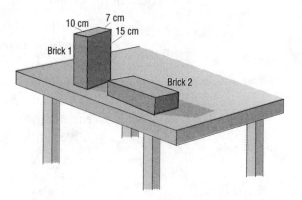

(a) Which brick exerts the greater force on the table?

(b) Calculate the pressure exerted by each brick on the table.

Solution:

(a) The bricks have the same weight, and therefore both exert the same force on the table. This force equals 32 N, directed downward.

(b) In brick 1, the force is distributed over an area A_1:

$$A_1 = (10 \text{ cm})(7 \text{ cm}) = 70 \text{ cm}^2$$

Convert to square meters.

$$A_1 = 70 \text{ cm}^2 \cdot \frac{1 \text{ m}^2}{10^4 \text{ cm}^2} = 7 \times 10^{-3} \text{ m}^2$$

In brick 2, the force is distributed over an area A_2:

$$A_2 = (15 \text{ cm})(10 \text{ cm}) = 150 \text{ cm}^2$$

Convert to square meters.

$$A_2 = 150 \text{ cm}^2 \cdot \frac{1 \text{ m}^2}{10^4 \text{ cm}^2} = 1.5 \times 10^{-2} \text{ m}^2$$

Calculate the pressure exerted by each brick:

$$P_1 = \frac{F}{A_1} = \frac{32 \text{ N}}{7 \times 10^{-3} \text{ m}^2} \qquad P_2 = \frac{F}{A_2} = \frac{32 \text{ N}}{1.5 \times 10^{-2} \text{ m}^2}$$

$$P_1 = 4570 \text{ Pa} \qquad\qquad P_2 = 2130 \text{ Pa}$$

$$= 4.57 \text{ kPA} \qquad\qquad\quad = 2.13 \text{ kPa}$$

The upright brick 1 exerts the greater pressure on the table because its force is distributed over a smaller area.

In Example 1.8, force had both magnitude and direction, because force is a vector. But pressure has magnitude only. We treat pressure as a scalar.

Pressure Increases with Depth

Have you ever dived into a swimming pool and swum to the bottom? You can feel the water exerting pressure against your eardrums. This pressure is caused by the weight of the water above you. As you swim deeper, the weight of water above you increases, and the pressure increases.

You can calculate the pressure at any depth in a liquid using the weight density. Consider a column of liquid, as shown in Figure 1.19. The column has a cross-sectional area A, and height h (also equal to the depth). The volume of the column is Ah.

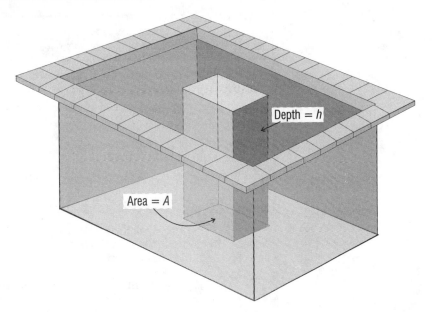

Figure 1.19
A column of water with cross-sectional area A and height h has volume Ah.

The weight density of the liquid is given by the formula

$$\text{Weight density} = \frac{\text{weight}}{\text{volume}}$$

Therefore, the weight of the liquid in the column is given by

$$\text{Weight} = \text{weight density} \times \text{volume}$$

Now write an equation for the pressure at the bottom of the column:

$$\text{Pressure} = \frac{\text{force}}{\text{area}} = \frac{\text{weight}}{A} = \frac{\text{weight density} \times \text{volume}}{A}$$

Since volume = Ah,

$$\text{Pressure} = \frac{\text{weight density} \times Ah}{A} = \text{weight density} \times h$$

You have derived the relationship between the pressure P and depth h in a fluid of weight density ρ_w:

$$\boxed{\begin{array}{c} \text{Pressure} = \text{weight density} \times \text{fluid depth} \\ P = \rho_w \times h \end{array}}$$

Example 1.9 Water Pressure Calculation

The height of the water in a storage tank is 100 ft above a valve. Find the pressure at the valve in lb/ft^2 and lb/in^2.

The weight density of water is 62.4 lb/ft^3.

Solution: $P = \rho_w \times h$

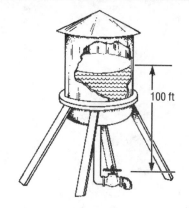

$$= (62.4 \text{ lb/ft}^3)(100 \text{ ft})$$

$$= 6240 \text{ lb/ft}^2$$

To express pressure in lb/in^2, use the relation 1 ft^2 = 144 in^2.

$$P = 6240 \frac{\text{lb}}{\text{ft}^2} \times \frac{1 \text{ ft}^2}{144 \text{ in}^2} = 43.3 \text{ lb/in}^2$$

The units lb/in^2 are abbreviated psi. The pressure at the valve is 6240 lb/ft^2 or 43.3 psi.

Buoyancy and Archimedes' Principle

If you have ever lifted a heavy object under water, you know it appears to weigh less as long as it is submerged. As soon as the object is raised above the surface of the water, it appears to gain weight. This is because, as long as the object is totally or partially submerged, the water exerts an upward force on the object. This upward force is called the **buoyant force**. It is caused by the pressure increasing with depth.

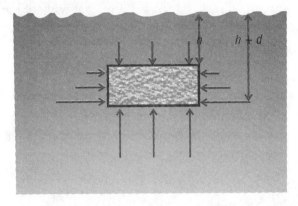

Figure 1.20
A brick is immersed in water. The top surface of the brick is at depth h. The bottom surface is at depth $h + d$, where d is the length of the edge of the brick.

Suppose that a brick is immersed in water, as shown in Figure 1.20. Let d represent the length of a vertical side of the brick. If the top face is at depth h, the bottom face is at depth $(h + d)$. Water pressure exerts forces all along the surfaces of the brick. Since the bottom face of the brick is at a lower depth than the top, the pressure P_{bottom} exerted on the bottom face is greater than the pressure P_{top} exerted on the top face. If ρ_w represents the weight density of the water, the pressures are:

$$P_{top} = \rho_w \times h \qquad\qquad P_{bottom} = \rho_w \times (h + d)$$

The pressures that act along the sides are at the same depth, and cancel each other out. The area A of the bottom face equals the area of the top face. Therefore, the force F_{bottom} acting on the bottom face is greater than the force F_{top} acting on the top face.

$$
\begin{aligned}
F_{top} &= P_{top} \times A & F_{bottom} &= P_{bottom} \times A \\
&= \rho_w \times h \times A & &= \rho_w \times (h + d) \times A \\
&= \rho_w\, Ah & &= \rho_w\, A(h + d)
\end{aligned}
$$

Thus, there is a net force acting on the brick upward. This is the buoyant force $F_{buoyant}$.

$$
\begin{aligned}
F_{buoyant} &= F_{bottom} - F_{top} \\
&= \rho_w\, A(h + d) - \rho_w\, Ah \\
&= \rho_w\, Ah + \rho_w\, Ad - \rho_w\, Ah \\
&= \rho_w\, Ad
\end{aligned}
$$

The product Ad is the volume of the brick V_{brick}. Weight density times volume equals weight. Therefore, the buoyant force equals the weight of water displaced by the volume of the brick:

$$F_{buoyant} = \rho_w \times V_{brick} = \text{weight of water displaced}$$

The buoyant force is the upward force on the brick exerted by the water. If the weight of the brick is greater than the buoyant force, the brick will sink.

If the weight of the brick is less than the buoyant force, the brick will rise to the surface and float. If the weight exactly equals the buoyant force, the brick will stay at the submerged level without moving up or down.

When it is submerged, the brick displaces a *volume* of water equal to the *volume* of the brick. The buoyant force equals the *weight* of this displaced water. This relationship was first discovered by the ancient Greek scientist Archimedes in 212 B.C. **Archimedes' principle** states that:

> *An object immersed in a fluid has an upward force exerted on it equal to the weight of the fluid displaced by the object.*

Notice that the buoyant force does not depend on the weight of the object, but only on the weight of fluid displaced by the object.

When an object such as a block of wood floats in water, the block floats with just enough volume in the water so that the weight of the displaced water equals the weight of the block. If a brick is placed on the block of wood, the block floats lower and displaces more water. The weight of displaced water increases and the buoyant force increases, to balance the increased weight of the block and brick.

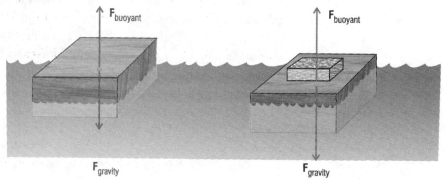

Figure 1.21

You can use densities with a simple rule to predict whether an object will sink or float when placed in a fluid:

1. If the object has a greater density than the fluid, it will sink.
2. If the object has a lower density than the fluid, it will float.

Can you use Archimedes' principle to explain the rule?

A submarine controls its density by changing its mass and weight while keeping its volume constant. To dive, a submarine takes water into its ballast tanks, thus increasing the weight of the submarine. When its density exceeds the density of water, the submarine sinks. To ascend, the submarine removes water from its ballast tanks and replaces it with air. When its density is lower than that of water, the submarine rises.

Use Table 1.4 on page 30 to answer this question: "Will a block of lead float or sink in mercury?"

Pascal's Principle

Figure 1.22 shows a simple fluid system that uses pressure to multiply force. A liquid is confined to two connecting chambers, each fitted with a movable piston.

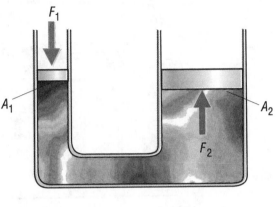

Piston 1   Piston 2

If a force is applied to one of the pistons, the pressure in that chamber increases. The pressure throughout the fluid increases by the same amount. This was discovered in the 1600s by the French physicist and mathematician Blaise Pascal. The rule is now called **Pascal's principle**:

A change in pressure at any point in a confined fluid is transmitted undiminished throughout the fluid.

According to Pascal's principle, if a force F_1 is applied to piston 1 and the pressure is increased, exactly the same pressure increase is felt under piston 2. This pressure causes a force F_2 to be exerted on piston 2. Let A_1 and A_2 represent the areas of the pistons. Since pressure = force/area,

$$P_1 = P_2 \quad \text{or} \quad \frac{F_1}{A_1} = \frac{F_2}{A_2}$$

As an example, suppose F_1 represents a weight of 10 N. What weight can be lifted by piston 2 if $A_1 = 0.1$ m² and $A_2 = 1$ m²? Solve the proportion for F_2.

$$F_2 = A_2 \frac{F_1}{A_1}$$

$$= 1 \text{ m}^2 \times \frac{10 \text{ N}}{0.1 \text{ m}^2}$$

$$= 100 \text{ N}$$

A weight of 100 N can be lifted by a weight of 10 N. The force applied to the small piston is multiplied so that a large weight can be lifted. This is the basis of operation of hydraulic lifts.

Example 1.10 Hydraulic Lift

In a hydraulic lift, compressed air exerts pressure on the hydraulic fluid (oil) in a reservoir. The hydraulic fluid transmits the pressure to a cylinder, and this pressure pushes a piston, which raises the lift.

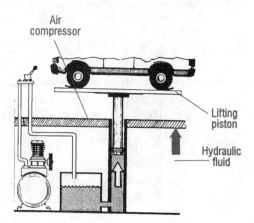

Figure 1.23
A hydraulic lift

If the compressor delivers air at a pressure of 30 psi, and the radius of the cylinder and piston is 6 in., what weight can be lifted?

Solution: The weight that can be lifted is the force F applied to the piston by the hydraulic fluid.

$$P = \frac{F}{A} \quad \text{or} \quad F = PA$$

The cylinder and piston have a circular cross section. So the area A of the piston is

$$A = \pi r^2$$
$$= \pi (6\,\text{in})^2 = 113\ \text{in}^2$$
$$F = 30\frac{\text{lb}}{\text{in}^2} \times 113\ \text{in}^2 = 3390\ \text{lb}$$

The lift can raise a weight of 3390 pounds.

Atmospheric Pressure

On Earth, we live at the bottom of a thick blanket of air. Like the water in a swimming pool, the air in the atmosphere is held to Earth by gravity. Air also has weight, and, just as water pressure is caused by the weight of water above an area, atmospheric pressure is caused by the weight of air above an area. At sea level, a column of air extending up through the atmosphere, with a cross-sectional area of 1 m², encloses about 10,000 kg of air. This mass has a weight of about 1×10^5 N. Thus, atmospheric pressure is about

$$\frac{1 \times 10^5 \text{ N}}{1 \text{ m}^2} = 10^5 \text{ Pa, or 100 kPa at sea level.}$$

Atmospheric pressure decreases with altitude. The change in pressure is what causes your ears to pop when you ride in a car on a mountain highway or in an airplane. For example, at 5.6-km altitude the pressure is about half the value at sea level. At 10-km altitude, atmospheric pressure is about 30 kPa. There are also variations in the pressure of the atmosphere at any given location, due to changing weather. Meteorologists monitor atmospheric pressure constantly in their attempts to predict weather.

A **barometer** is an instrument used for measuring atmospheric pressure. One type is the mercury barometer. In this instrument, a glass tube is filled with mercury and inverted into a bowl of mercury with the open end of the tube below the level of mercury in the bowl. Some of the mercury in the tube drains into the bowl, but no air is allowed to enter the tube. An empty space is created above the mercury in the tube. This empty space is called a *vacuum*.

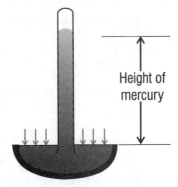

Height of mercury

Figure 1.24
A simple barometer

The atmosphere exerts pressure on the top surface of the mercury in the bowl. This pressure is transmitted to the mercury at the base of the tube (Pascal's principle). This pressure also equals the pressure at the base of the tube caused by the weight of the mercury column in the tube. Therefore, the mercury in the tube must extend to the exact height required to produce a pressure equal to that of the air outside. This height is sometimes used as a unit for atmospheric pressure.

At sea level, the average atmospheric pressure is 101.3 kPa. This equals a height of 760 mm of mercury, and this pressure is called **one atmosphere**. Other units commonly used to measure atmospheric pressure are shown in Table 1.5.

Table 1.5 Units of Atmospheric Pressure

$$1 \text{ atmosphere} = 101.3 \text{ kPa}$$
$$= 760 \text{ mm of mercury}$$
$$= 14.7 \text{ psi}$$
$$= 2117 \text{ lb/ft}^2$$

Absolute and Gage Pressure

When working with fluid systems, pressure measurements often are reported either as *absolute* pressure or as *gage* pressure. It's important to know the difference. For example, if you check the pressure of the air in a tire with a gage, it might read 30 psi. But what does this reading mean?

Absolute pressure is the total pressure measured above zero pressure (a perfect vacuum). **Gage pressure** is the pressure measured above atmospheric pressure. Gage pressure is a measure of how much greater the air pressure inside the tire is than the air pressure outside the tire. Gage pressure is generally measured with a gage, hence the name. Absolute, atmospheric, and gage pressures are related in a simple equation:

Absolute pressure = gage pressure + atmospheric pressure

Suppose a tire gage measures air pressure in a tire as 30 psi. If the atmospheric pressure equals 14.7 psi, the absolute pressure in the tire is:

Absolute pressure = 30 psi + 14.7 psi

= 44.7 psi

The air inside the tire pushes out with a pressure of 44.7 psi. The atmosphere (air on the outside) pushes in with a pressure of 14.7 psi. The difference—30 psi—is the gage pressure. That's what the gage measures.

The tire gage is a useful pressure-measuring device. Its operation is quite simple.

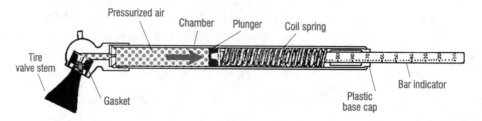

Pressurized air Chamber Plunger Coil spring

Tire valve stem

Gasket

Plastic base cap

Bar indicator

Figure 1.25
A tire pressure gage measures gage pressure.

The tire gage is made of a movable bar indicator and coiled spring housed in a cylindrical tube. When the gage is placed over the valve stem of a tire, the gage chamber and tire become sealed. The pressurized air from the tire flows into the gage chamber. This forces the coil spring to compress. As the spring compresses, it pushes the calibrated bar indicator out of the cylinder housing. When the force of the compressed spring equals the force caused by the pressure within the gage chamber, the forces are balanced. The exposed calibrated bar indicates the gage pressure—the pressure within the tire.

Pressure Is a Prime Mover

All fluid systems have two things in common. First, each system contains a fluid—either a liquid or a gas—that moves through a system of connecting pipes and devices. Second, a pressure difference in the system creates a net force, which causes fluids to move or perform some special function—like pushing a piston or opening and closing a valve. In this sense, pressure is a **prime mover** in fluid systems. Forces are still responsible for moving fluids through the system, but we can usually bypass the vector forces and deal with only the scalar pressures.

Equilibrium in Fluid Systems

Liquid or gas moves in a fluid system when pressure differences exist between different points in the system. If there's no pressure difference, there's no movement. For example, Figure 1.26 shows two tanks connected by a pipe that contains a closed gate valve. The pressure at the bottom of the tanks is different. That's because the water level in tank 2 is higher than in tank 1. Pressure P_2, at the bottom of tank 2, is higher than P_1, the pressure at the bottom of tank 1. The pressure on the left side of the valve is P_1 and the pressure on the right side is P_2. Since P_2 is greater than P_1, there is a pressure difference across the valve. As long as the valve is closed the tanks are isolated. But when the valve is opened, the pressure difference means the system is not in equilibrium. What happens when the valve is opened?

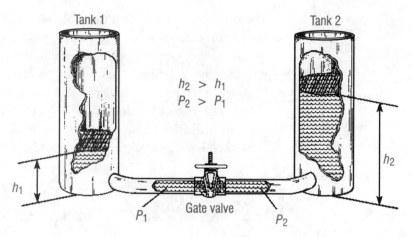

Figure 1.26
Unbalanced pressures across valve

Since P_2 is greater than P_1, there will be a force per unit area on the right side of the valve greater than the force per unit area on the left side of the valve. Water then will be pushed through the valve from tank 2 to tank 1. Water will flow until the levels in the two tanks are equal. When this happens, the pressures at the bottoms of the tanks will be equal and there is no longer a pressure difference in the system. Then, the system will be in equilibrium. This situation is shown in Figure 1.27.

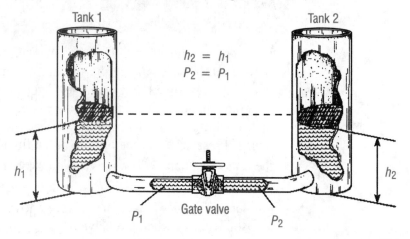

Figure 1.27
Balanced pressures across valve

Now consider Figure 1.28. Here, there are two tanks filled to the same level. Tank 2 has a larger diameter than tank 1, so it contains much more water. But since pressure on the bottom of the tank depends on only height of water contained, the pressure on the bottom of tank 1 and tank 2 is the same. Pressure at any point in a fluid doesn't depend on the shape of the container or the amount of water it contains—just on the height of the water column above the point. What happens when the gate valve in Figure 1.28 is opened?

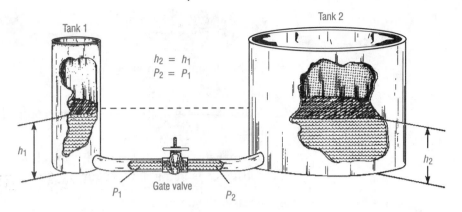

Figure 1.28
Pressure at bottom does not
depend on size or shape of tank.

Summary

- Matter can exist in four states: solid, liquid, gas, and plasma. Liquids and gases are called fluids.

- The density of a substance is its mass per unit volume. The density of water is 1 g/cm^3.

- Weight density is weight per unit volume.

- Pressure is force divided by the area over which the force acts. We treat pressure as a scalar. In SI units, pressure is measured in pascals, where 1 Pa = 1 N/m^2.

- Pressure increases with depth in a fluid. For a given fluid, the pressure does not depend on the size or shape of the container.

- When an object is submerged in a fluid, an upward force is exerted on the object caused by the pressure difference between the top and the bottom of the object. This force is called a buoyant force.

- The buoyant force exerted on a submerged object equals the weight of the fluid displaced by the object.

- A pressure applied to a confined fluid is transmitted throughout the fluid.

- Atmospheric pressure is caused by the weight of the air above a given area. Atmospheric pressure can be measured with a barometer.

- Absolute pressure is the sum of the gage pressure and atmospheric pressure.

Exercises

1. The four states of matter are _____ , _____ , _____ , and _____ .

2. Water can be made to change state from solid (ice), to liquid, to gas (steam) by _____ .

3. The density of a substance describes how much _____ of the substance is in a unit of volume.

4. Pressure is defined as _____ divided by _____ .

5. Fluid systems that use air or some other gas for the fluid are called _____ systems. Fluid systems that use water, oil, or other liquid are called _____ systems.

For Exercises 6–8, you may need to use the fact that 1 kg weighs 9.80 newtons.

6. A steel block has a volume of 1.74×10^{-4} m^3 and a mass of 1.357 kg.

    (a) What is the density of steel?

    (b) What is the weight density of steel?

7. A gallon of water sample occupies a volume of 3.785×10^{-3} m^3. The mass of the water sample is 3.785 kg.

    (a) What is the density of water in kg/m^3?

    (b) What is the weight, in newtons, of one gallon of water?

    (c) What is the weight, in pounds, of one gallon of water?

    (d) Ricardo dives to the bottom of a swimming pool. He is 7 feet below the surface of the pool. How much more pressure does Ricardo feel at the bottom of the pool than at the surface?

8. Karen dives to a depth of 21 meters in fresh water, with a scuba rig. How much does the pressure increase, in kPa, during the dive?

9. When you sit or stand, is your blood pressure higher in your arms or your legs? Explain your answer.

10. Use Table 1.4 to explain why ice floats in water.

11. When a submarine is under water, how does its volume compare with the volume of water displaced?

12. When a submarine is under water, does the buoyant force depend on the weight of the submarine? Explain your answer.

13. An egg will not float in fresh water, but, if you dissolve enough salt in the water, the egg will float.

   (a) Which has the higher density, the egg or the fresh water?

   (b) Which has the higher density, the egg or the salt water?

   (c) Which has the higher density, the fresh water or the salt water?

14. Divers often use helium and oxygen as a breathing mixture for very deep dives. A storage tank containing a mixture of 80% helium and 20% oxygen has an inside volume of 37.85 liters. (1 liter = 1000 cm^3) The gas mixture has a mass of 2.163 kilograms.

   (a) What is the density, in kg/m^3, of the gas mixture in the tank?

   (b) The volume of the whole tank is 40.59 liters. What is the buoyant force, in newtons, when the tank is submerged in fresh water?

   (c) The weight of the tank and gas mixture is 231 N. What are the magnitude and direction of the net force acting on the tank when it is submerged in fresh water?

15. The gage pressure of the gas mixture in the tank of Exercise 14 is 13,700 kPa.

   (a) If the atmospheric pressure is 101 kPa, what is the absolute pressure of the gas in the tank before the tank is lowered into the water?

   (b) The tank is lowered to a depth of 120 m in fresh water. At this depth, what is the pressure exerted on the tank by the water?

   (c) At a depth of 120 m, what is the total pressure exerted on the outside wall of the tank?

16. A petrochemical manufacturing plant uses a 1000-horsepower compressor to compress hydrogen gas to a gage pressure around 1550 psi. The operations computer displays the hydrogen pressure as 1528 psi. At the same time the mechanical gage on the output of the compressor reads 10,500 kPa. Are the two pressure readings substantially in agreement? Explain your answer.

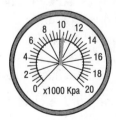

Electrolytic cell pressure	15.06 psi	normal
H2 blower pressure	25.62 psi	normal
H2 compressor discharge	1528 psi	normal

17. A nuclear submarine is running at a depth of 230 meters. The seawater a
its location has a density of 1040 kg/m³.

(a) What is the pressure exerted by the seawater on the outside of the submarine?

(b) What is the force exerted on a circular periscope well door that has a diameter of 60 cm?

18. The pressure in an automotive brake line is 125 psi. This line is connected to a piston, with a diameter of 1.75 in., in the brake caliper. How much force, in pounds, will the piston apply to the brake pad?

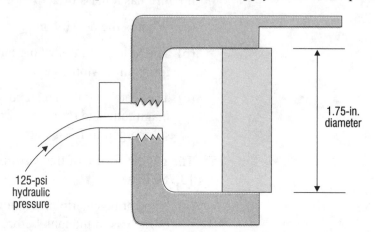

19. The density of substances is often described by stating the ratio of the density of the substance to the density of water. This ratio is called the **specific gravity** of the substance. For example, the density of alcohol is 800 kg/m³ and the density of water is 1000 kg/m³. The specific gravity of alcohol is

$$sg = \frac{\rho_{alcohol}}{\rho_{water}} = \frac{800 \text{ kg/m}^3}{1000 \text{ kg/m}^3} = 0.800 \qquad \text{Specific gravity has no units.}$$

Andrew is preparing a Cessna 206 airplane for a trip that will require an overnight stop in Bettles, Alaska. The temperature in Bettles is forecast to fall to –17°F. At this temperature the specific gravity of the electrolyte in the plane's battery must be above 1.22 to prevent freezing. To determine the specific gravity, Andrew removes an 8.5-cm³ sample of the electrolyte. The sample has a mass of 10.51 grams.

(a) What is the density of the electrolyte?

(b) What is the specific gravity of the electrolyte?

(c) Will the electrolyte freeze if the temperature falls to –17°F? Explain your answer.

1.3 VOLTAGE IN ELECTRICAL SYSTEMS

Objectives

- Explain the similarities and differences between Newton's law of universal gravitation and Coulomb's law.

- Explain how the force between two like charges and the force between two unlike charges are different.

- Describe how to create an electric field. Interpret the information given in a drawing of an electric field.

- Define electric potential difference, or voltage.

- Differentiate between AC and DC.

- Identify the most common source of DC voltage.

- Describe how to connect DC voltage sources so that voltages will add.

INTERNET *connection*

To find out more about voltage in electrical systems, follow the links at **www.learningincontext.com**.

Gravitational force and electrical force are two *universal forces* in nature. They are called *universal* because each force acts the same everywhere in the observable universe. Gravitational forces act between two or more masses; electrical forces act between two or more charges. Although they are not the same kinds of forces, gravitational and electrical forces are alike in many ways. For example, they are both forces acting at a distance. The Earth exerts a gravitational force on the moon even though the two bodies do not touch.

In this section you will learn about electric force, electric fields, and electric potential, or voltage. But first, we introduce force acting at a distance with gravity, since you have experience with gravitational forces.

Gravitational Force

In the 17th century, Newton developed the theory of gravitational force by analyzing the motion of the planets about the sun. The orbits of the planets are approximately circular. Without a force acting on the planets, they would travel off, away from the solar system, in straight lines. Newton proposed that an inward gravitational force is exerted on each planet that causes the planet to travel in a circle about the sun. This force is the same kind of force exerted on an apple that causes the apple to fall toward the center of the Earth when it drops from a tree.

Newton's analysis showed that the source of the gravitational force causing planetary orbits is the sun. He deduced that this force varies with distance in a special way—the force decreases with the square of the distance between the sun and the planet. For example, a planet twice as far from the sun as the Earth would be pulled toward the sun with $1/4$ the force; a planet 3 times as far from the sun would be pulled with $1/9$ the force; and so on. This type of relationship is called an inverse square law. **Newton's universal law of gravitation** is:

Every object in the universe attracts every other object with a force that (for two bodies) is directly proportional to the mass of each body and that is inversely proportional to the square of the distance between them.

Mathematically, the law can be written as

$$F_\text{g} = G\frac{m_1 m_2}{d^2}$$

where m_1 and m_2 are the masses of two objects and d is the distance between them. (See Figure 1.29 on the next page.) The quantity G is called the universal gravitational constant, and its value is

$$G = 6.67 \times 10^{-11}\ \frac{\text{N} \cdot \text{m}^2}{\text{kg}^2}$$

The gravitational force F_g is exerted equally on both masses m_1 and m_2. But the direction of the force is different for the two masses. The force on m_1 is directed toward m_2, and the direction of the force on m_2 is toward m_1. In other words, the gravitational force is always an attractive force.

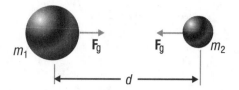

Figure 1.29
The gravitational forces between two spherical masses

Example 1.11 Force of Gravity Between Earth and Moon

The mass of the Earth is 5.98×10^{24} kg, and the mass of the moon is 7.36×10^{22} kg. The average separation distance between the Earth and moon is 3.85×10^5 km. What force does the Earth exert on the moon to keep the moon in orbit?

Solution:

$$F_g = G \frac{m_1 m_2}{d^2}$$

$$= 6.67 \times 10^{-11} \ \frac{\text{N} \cdot \text{m}^2}{\text{kg}^2} \cdot \frac{(5.98 \times 10^{24} \ \text{kg})(7.36 \times 10^{22} \ \text{kg})}{(3.85 \times 10^8 \ \text{m})^2}$$

$$= 1.98 \times 10^{20} \ \text{N}$$

The Earth exerts a force of 1.98×10^{20} N on the moon.

Electric Charge

Have you ever run a comb through your hair on a dry day and seen how the comb can pick up small pieces of lint or paper? Why does a television screen or computer monitor attract dust after being on for a period of time? These forces of attraction cannot be due to gravity, because the gravitational forces would be far too small. They are due to electrical forces. Electrical forces have been studied for centuries. In fact, the word *electrical* comes from the Greek *elektron*, which means amber, the substance used by the ancient Greeks to study electrical forces.

The property of an object that causes electrical force is called **charge**. A great number of experiments on many different materials have shown that electrical forces can be attractive or repulsive. Thus, there must be two types of electric charge. They have been named positive charge and negative charge. If two objects have the same charge, both positive or both negative, they repel. If two objects have opposite charges, one positive and the other negative, they attract. (See Figure 1.30 on the next page.)

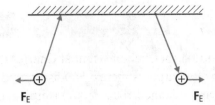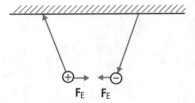

Figure 1.30
Like charges repel. Unlike charges attract.

The origin of electric charge is found in the atom. The nucleus of the atom contains most of the mass, in the neutrons and protons. Neutrons have no charge (they are *neutral*), while protons have a positive charge. The nucleus is surrounded by a group, or cloud, of electrons. Electrons have a negative charge. The mass of an electron is about 1/2000 of the mass of a proton or neutron. But the charge of an electron is exactly equal to the charge of a proton, and of opposite sign. The force of attraction between protons and electrons is what keeps the electrons bound to the nucleus.

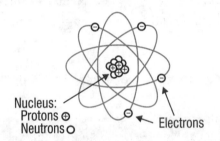

Nucleus:
Protons ⊕
Neutrons ○

Electrons

Figure 1.31
A simple model of the atom, showing its major parts

A normal atom has no net charge—it has equal numbers of protons and electrons and is electrically neutral. The net charge in a system is the algebraic sum of the charges present, or the number of positive charges minus the number of negative charges. The net charge can be positive, negative, or zero (neutral).

You can transfer charge from one object to another because the outermost electrons in the atoms of some substances are not tightly bound to the nucleus, and can be removed. When you run a comb through your hair, friction transfers electrons from your hair to the comb. The comb now has more electrons than protons, and becomes negatively charged. Your hair has fewer electrons than protons, and becomes positively charged.

In this example, you move electrons from one place to another, but you do not create or destroy charge. You can consider your hair and the comb an isolated system. In an isolated system, particles and charge cannot enter or leave the system.

The net electric charge in an isolated system never changes.

This is the **principle of conservation of charge**. Every known physical process conserves electric charge.

Electrical Force

In the 18th century, the French scientist Charles Coulomb made intricate measurements on charged spheres. He discovered a relationship between force, charge, and distance. This relationship is now called **Coulomb's law**:

The electrical force between two charged bodies is directly proportional to the charge on each body and inversely proportional to the square of the distance between them.

Mathematically, the law can be written as

$$F_E = K\frac{q_1 q_2}{d^2}$$

where q_1 and q_2 are the charges on two objects, d is the distance between them, and K is a constant. The SI unit for charge is the **coulomb** (C). The charge on one electron or proton is 1.60×10^{-19} C. This is called the **elementary charge**. When q_1 and q_2 are measured in coulombs, distance is measured in meters, and force is measured in newtons, the constant K has the value

$$K = 9.0 \times 10^9 \ \frac{\text{N} \cdot \text{m}^2}{\text{C}^2}$$

Compare Coulomb's law to Newton's law of universal gravitation. They are both inverse square laws. They both give the magnitude of the force one object exerts on another, which is also the force the second object exerts on the first. In Newton's law, mass m_1 exerts a force on m_2 and mass m_2 exerts the same magnitude force on m_1. In Coulomb's law, charge q_1 exerts a force on q_2 and charge q_2 exerts the same magnitude force on q_1. But, gravitational force is always attractive (there is only one kind of mass), whereas electrical force can be attractive or repulsive (there are two kinds of charge).

The directions of electrical forces are as shown in Figure 1.32. In both cases, the forces act along a line through the centers of the charges. If q_1 and q_2 have the same sign, the force on q_1 acts away from q_2 and the force on q_2 acts away from q_1. If q_1 and q_2 have opposite signs, the force on q_1 acts toward q_2 and the force on q_2 acts toward q_1.

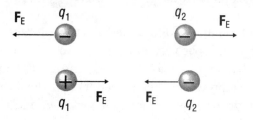

Figure 1.32
To determine the direction of electrical force, remember that like charges repel and unlike charges attract.

Example 1.12 Electrical and Gravitational Forces in the Hydrogen Atom

An electron has a mass of approximately 9.1×10^{-31} kg, and a proton has a mass of approximately 1.7×10^{-27} kg. In a hydrogen atom, the electron and proton are separated by an average of 5.3×10^{-11} m. Compare the electrical force of attraction between the electron and proton to the gravitational force of attraction.

Solution:

$$F_E = K\frac{q_1 q_2}{d^2}$$

$$= 9.0 \times 10^9 \ \frac{\text{N} \cdot \text{m}^2}{\text{C}^2} \cdot \frac{(1.6 \times 10^{-19} \ \text{C})(1.6 \times 10^{-19} \ \text{C})}{(5.3 \times 10^{-11} \text{m})^2}$$

$$= 8.2 \times 10^{-8} \ \text{N}$$

$$F_g = G\frac{m_1 m_2}{d^2}$$

$$= 6.67 \times 10^{-11} \ \frac{\text{N} \cdot \text{m}^2}{\text{kg}^2} \cdot \frac{(9.1 \times 10^{-31} \ \text{kg})(1.7 \times 10^{-27} \ \text{kg})}{(5.3 \times 10^{-11} \text{m})^2}$$

$$= 3.7 \times 10^{-47} \ \text{N}$$

The ratio of electrical force to gravitational force is

$$\frac{F_E}{F_g} = \frac{8.2 \times 10^{-8} \ \text{N}}{3.7 \times 10^{-47} \ \text{N}} = 2.2 \times 10^{39}$$

The electrical force is over 10^{39} greater than the gravitational force.

On a small scale, with distances and masses as small as the atom, electrical forces are important and gravitational forces are insignificant. On a larger scale, with distances and masses as large as the moon, Earth, and sun, gravitational forces are important and electrical forces are insignificant. Gravitational forces govern the structure of planets, stars, and galaxies. Electrical forces govern the structure of atoms, molecules, solids, liquids, and gases.

Gravitational and Electric Fields

Both gravitational forces and electrical forces can act over distance. You can think of the space around a mass like the Earth as being altered in some way, such that another mass like a satellite feels a force. Similarly, the space around a proton is altered such that an electron feels a force. These "alterations of space" are called gravitational fields and electric fields. The satellite is thought of as interacting with the gravitational field created by the

Earth, and the electron is thought of as interacting with the electric field created by the proton.

A field is an imaginary construction used by scientists, engineers, and technicians to help them understand and predict how forces are transmitted from one object to another. For example, imagine placing a "test" mass m at a certain point in the gravitational field of the Earth. The test mass feels a force directed toward the center of the Earth, whose magnitude is given by:

$$F_g = G \frac{m_E m}{d^2}$$

where m_E is the mass of the Earth. The gravitational field is represented by the following equation.

$$\mathbf{g} = \frac{\mathbf{F_g}}{m}$$

Since force is a vector, the field is a vector. The direction of $\mathbf{g}$ is the direction of the force on the test mass. You can move the test mass around, and at every point measure or calculate a different value of $\mathbf{g}$. Thus, at every point in space around the Earth, the gravitational field can be represented by a vector of length g pointing toward the center of the Earth. Notice that, if you substitute the expression for F_g, the m in the numerator cancels the m in the denominator. Therefore, $\mathbf{g}$ does not depend on the size of the test mass.

Now imagine placing a positive test charge q at a certain point in the electric field of a proton. The test charge feels a force directed away from the center of the proton, whose magnitude is given by:

$$F_E = K \frac{q_p q}{d^2}$$

where q_p is the charge of the proton. The electric field is represented by the following equation.

$$\mathbf{E} = \frac{\mathbf{F_E}}{q}$$

The electric field is also a vector. The direction of $\mathbf{E}$ is the direction of the force on the positive test charge. You can move the test charge around, and measure or calculate a different value of $\mathbf{E}$ at every point. Thus, at every point in space around the proton, the electric field can be represented by a vector of length E pointing away from the center of the proton. If you substitute the expression for F_E, the q in the numerator cancels the q in the denominator. Therefore, $\mathbf{E}$ does not depend on the size of the test charge.

One way to visualize a field is with a diagram showing arrows at various locations to represent field vectors. The length of each arrow shows the strength of the field. The direction of the arrow shows the field direction.

Alternatively, fields are illustrated by drawing **field lines**. Field lines for five electric fields are shown in Figure 1.33. The direction of a field at any point is tangent to the field line at that point. Where the lines are close together, the magnitude of the field is high; where the lines are far apart, the magnitude of the field is low. Notice that a field diagram can show only some of the infinite number of possible lines. The field lines in Figure 1.33 are shown in only two dimensions, but the electric field is three dimensional.

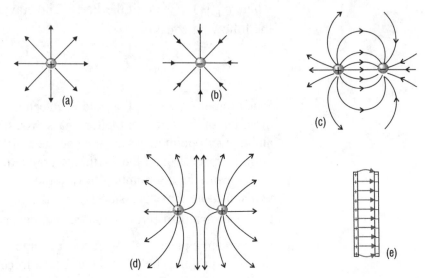

Figure 1.33
Electric field configurations, showing electric field lines for:
(a) a single positive charge, (b) a single negative charge,
(c) a pair of equal, opposite charges,
(d) a pair of equal charges with the same sign, and
(e) two oppositely charged parallel plates

Electric Potential

When you lift a book off a table, you move the book through the Earth's gravitational field. You must exert a force against the force of gravity to move the book a certain distance. We say the book possesses a **potential** at this distance above the table because, if you release the book, it will accelerate and fall back to the tabletop.

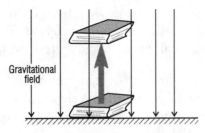 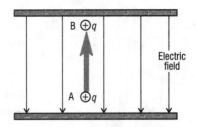

Figure 1.34
A mass has potential if it is moved through a gravitational field.
A charge has potential if it is moved through an electric field.

Similarly, if you move a charge against an electric field, you must exert a force on the charge. Suppose you move a charge a distance d from A to B in a uniform electric field, as shown in Figure 1.34. The charge possesses a potential at B because, if you release it, the charge will accelerate back toward A. We say the field creates an **electric potential difference** between A and B. In a uniform electric field of magnitude E, the electric potential difference ΔV_{AB} between two points A and B, separated by a distance d is the following product

$$\Delta V_{AB} = E \times d$$

The unit of measurement for electric potential difference is the **volt**. Electric potential difference is sometimes simply called **electric potential**, and also **voltage**.

Voltage is the prime mover in electrical systems, like pressure is the prime mover in fluid systems. Consider the simple fluid and electrical systems shown in Figure 1.35. In the fluid system, the water heights in the connected reservoirs are different. The Earth's gravitational field causes a pressure difference, which results in water flow from the left to the right reservoir. The flow will stop when the water levels are equal and there is no longer a pressure difference.

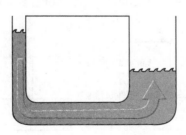 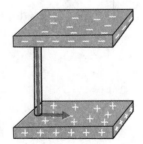

Figure 1.35
Pressure difference is the prime mover in a fluid system.
Potential difference is the prime mover in an electrical system.

In the electrical system, charge has been separated on parallel plates, and the plates are then connected. The electric field causes a potential difference, or voltage, which results in charge flow from the top to the bottom plate. A flow of charge is called an electric **current**. The current will stop when the plates are electrically neutral and there is no longer a potential difference.

In the fluid system, flow can be maintained with a pump. The pump is a source of pressure difference. In the electrical system, current can be maintained with a battery. A battery is a source of potential difference. A source of potential difference is also called a voltage source.

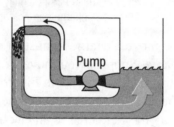 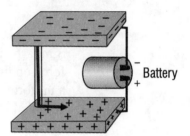

Figure 1.36
A pump is a source of pressure difference.
A battery is a source of potential difference.

Components of Electrical Systems

Electrical systems usually contain four major components:

- at least one voltage source, usually a battery or generator;

- conductors, which can be metal wire or metal connections on printed circuits;

- at least one load; and

- one or more control elements, such as switches.

Figure 1.37 shows how the components are connected in a generalized electrical system.

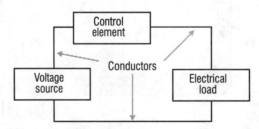

Figure 1.37
Components of a generalized
electrical system

The **load** in an electrical system is usually an appliance or machine, such as an electric motor, water heater, lights, television set, computer, or air conditioner. The purpose of an electrical system like the one shown above is to provide voltage and current to the load. An electrical **conductor** is a material through which charge can easily flow. The **control element** can be a switch that turns the current in the system on or off, or a variable control switch such as the volume control on a stereo.

An **electrical circuit** is a closed path for current flow created by connecting voltage sources, conductors, control elements, and loads.

Direct Current and Alternating Current

There are two types of current used in electrical circuits: **direct current** (DC) and **alternating current** (AC). In DC, the electric charge flows in one direction. In AC, charge flows back and forth, rapidly changing direction many times each second. Whether a circuit uses AC or DC depends on the type of voltage source. For example, batteries produce DC voltage, and alternators produce AC voltage.

Batteries Are Typical DC Voltage Sources

The most common type of DC voltage source is a battery. Batteries are used in portable electric devices, such as cellular phones, flashlights, laptop computers, watches, cars, boats, cameras, and toys. The terms *battery* and *cell* are often used interchangeably, but they have different meanings. A cell is a single unit that houses one or more chemicals. As the chemicals react, electrons are removed from certain molecules, leaving behind positively charged ions. The electrons and ions are separated, and this charge separation creates a voltage. A battery is a bank or collection of two or more cells connected together.

The voltage produced by a cell's chemical reaction depends on the materials used in the reaction. These materials differ among various battery technologies. For example, a standard D cell used for flashlight batteries uses an alkaline reaction and has a cell voltage of 1.5 volts. Most car batteries have six lead-acid cells, each with a cell voltage of 2.0 volts, yielding a 12-volt battery.

The voltage of a cell drops over the course of its life, as the chemical reaction that produces the voltage slows down. When the voltage drops below the requirement for the device it is being used for, the battery is "dead." If it cannot be recharged, a dead battery must be replaced with a new one. *Primary cells* are those designed for one-time use. *Secondary cells* can be recharged. Recharging is usually cheaper and more convenient than replacement. In addition, the chemicals in cells can be toxic to the environment, making rechargeability even more important.

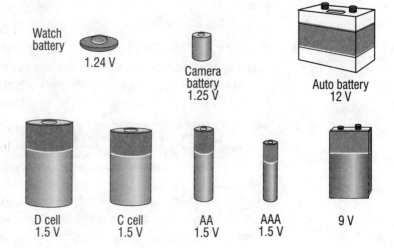

Figure 1.38
Typical voltage sources

In a typical recharging process, current is sent through the battery in a reverse direction. This reverses the direction of the chemical reaction and makes the material available again to produce voltage. Table 1.6 lists the voltage and chemically active materials in typical primary and secondary cells.

Table 1.6 Types of Primary and Secondary Cells for Batteries

Primary (One-Time Use)		Secondary (Rechargeable)	
Cell Voltage	Chemistry	Cell Voltage	Chemistry
1.5	Carbon-Zinc	2.0	Lead-Acid
1.5	Alkaline	1.2	Nickel-Cadmium
1.3	Mercury	1.2	Nickel Metal Hydride
1.6	Silver Oxide	3.6	Lithium Ion
3.0	Lithium	3.0	Lithium Metal
1.4	Zinc-Air		

Connecting Cells to Add Their Voltages

The voltage output of a cell or battery is measured between two terminals that are located on the housing. These terminals are called **electrodes**. Electrodes on car batteries are metal posts on the top or side of the housing. On other batteries, such as those used in flashlights and cellular phones, electrodes are located at opposite ends of the cylindrical housing.

One electrode is marked **positive** (+) and the other **negative** (–). Sometimes they're just color-coded, with red for positive (+) and black for negative (–). When batteries are connected in a circuit, electrons move in the circuit as if they were flowing out of the negative electrode, through the circuit, and into the positive electrode. The negative electrode is called the **cathode**. The positive electrode is called the **anode**.

Most electrical devices require several volts (at least) from the batteries for the devices to operate. This means that two or more cells must be combined so that their voltages add. Cells can be added together in **series** to produce a higher voltage. Adding cells in series means that the positive terminal from one cell is connected to the negative terminal of another cell, as shown in Figure 1.39. When this is done, the electrons from each cell will flow in the same direction. The voltages of the individual cells add together to give a higher total voltage.

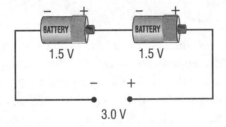

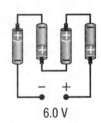

Figure 1.39
Connecting DC voltage sources in series results in the addition of voltages.

A Simple DC Circuit

Figure 1.40 shows a simple circuit. The components are shown in Figure 1.40a: a battery, a switch, three wires, and a lamp. The battery is the voltage source. The light bulb is the load. The wires (and lamp base) are the conductors. Electrons flow from the negative battery terminal (cathode) through wire A into the lamp base. Electrons then flow through the filament of the light bulb and back into the lamp base, through wire B, a switch, and wire C, and into the positive terminal of the battery (anode). Figure 1.40b shows a schematic diagram of this simple circuit. A schematic diagram acts like a road map for you to easily identify the current path and the components of the circuit.

Shorthand symbols are used to indicate the components. In this circuit, four symbols are shown: the battery (⊣|⊢), the light bulb (⬤), the switch (—•—°—), and the conductors (———).

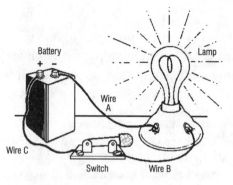
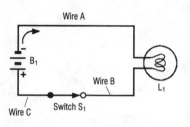

(a) Electrical hookup

(b) Schematic diagram

Figure 1.40
A simple DC circuit

AC Circuits

An AC voltage source reverses the positive and negative terminals many times per second. The current in these circuits flows in one direction, then in the opposite direction, changing in response to the changing voltage source. The overwhelming majority of AC circuits involve voltages and currents that alternate, or cycle, at a rate of 60 times each second. The cycling rate is called the **frequency**. Frequency is measured in cycles per second, or **hertz**.

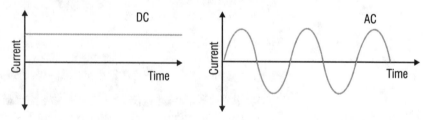

Figure 1.41
The current-time relationships for DC and AC

The main source of 60-hertz current comes from electrical power-generating plants. AC electricity is carried over great distances from power plants to homes and factories in overhead or underground high-voltage lines. The voltage in residential homes that's available at the electrical wall sockets is usually 110 to 120 volts. However, outlets for air-conditioners or clothes dryers may be 220 to 240 volts. These loads require higher voltage and current because they dissipate more power than other household appliances. You will learn about power, and its relationship to voltage and current in Chapter 6.

Summary

- Newton's law of universal gravitation and Coulomb's law are both inverse square laws. The magnitudes of both forces decrease with the square of the distance between the masses and the charges.

- Atoms are composed of protons, neutrons, and electrons. Protons are positively charged, electrons are negatively charged, and neutrons have no charge.

- The flow of electrons in an electrical system is a current.

- Unlike charges attract; like charges repel.

- An electric field is a model of the alteration of space around one or more charges. You can use the field to predict the force exerted on a charge placed in the field.

- The potential difference, or voltage, between two points in a uniform electric field is the product of the field strength and the distance between the points.

- Voltage is the prime mover in electrical systems.

- A battery is a source of DC voltage. It can maintain a current in an electrical circuit.

- Batteries or cells can be connected in series to increase voltage.

Exercises

1. Planets revolve around stars because of gravity. However, gravity is not restricted to acting only between large and small bodies—stars can also revolve around other stars. Two stars revolving around each other form a binary star system. In a binary star system, by how much does the gravitational force between the stars decrease when the distance between them triples? Increases tenfold?

2. Describe two ways in which gravitational forces are like electrical forces.

3. Describe one major difference between gravitational forces and electrical forces.

4. Gravitational and electrical forces act over distances. In other words, two bodies can exert force on each other even if they do not touch. Which force is greater over the distance between the Earth and the sun? Which force is greater over the distance between two oxygen atoms in a water molecule?

5. An astronaut having a mass of 65 kg is standing on the surface of the moon. The mass of the moon is 7.36×10^{22} kg and the radius is 1.74×10^{6} m. What is the gravitational force the astronaut exerts on the moon?

6. When you walk across a carpet, you scuff electrons from your shoes onto the carpet. Are your shoes then positively or negatively charged? Is the carpet positively or negatively charged? What happens when you touch a doorknob?

7. A lamp is connected to an electric circuit between A and B. When the circuit is complete, electrons flow through the lamp. What can you say about the electric potentials at A and B?

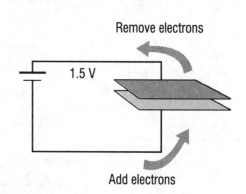

8. Voltage in electric circuits is similar to pressure in fluid circuits. A pressure difference between two points in a complete fluid circuit will make fluids move. A voltage difference between two points in a complete electric circuit will make _____ move.

9. Two metal plates placed parallel to each other with air between them form a device called a capacitor. When the plates are connected in a circuit with a battery as shown, the battery voltage causes some electrons to move away from the top plate and causes some other electrons to move onto the bottom plate.

If 5×10^{12} electrons are removed from the top plate and added to the bottom plate, what is the unbalanced charge, in coulombs, on each plate? (Remember, the elementary charge is 1.60×10^{-19} C.)

10. When the 1.5-volt battery charges the capacitor in Exercise 9, the electric field between the plates of the capacitor is approximately uniform and equal in magnitude to 1800 $\frac{V}{m}$. What is the separation distance between the plates?

11. The distance between the plates of the capacitor in Exercise 9 is 0.1 mm. Find the magnitude of the electric field between the plates.

12. The value of the charge of an electron or proton has been determined to an accuracy of 2.9 parts per million. The result is $1.6021892 \times 10^{-19}$ coulombs. Why would it be impossible for one plate of a capacitor, such as shown in Exercise 9, to have a charge of 4.0856×10^{-18} coulombs?

13. The output voltage of an automobile battery is measured to be 12.4 volts before it is connected in the circuit shown below. After the battery is connected, the alternator has an output voltage of 14.3 volts.

(a) What is the net voltage available to produce current in the circuit?

(b) Which voltage source, the battery or alternator, is forcing current to flow in the circuit?

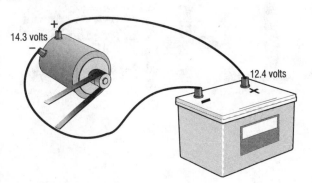

14. When electrical current moves in only one direction through an electrical circuit it is called _____ current.

15. Electrical current that continuously changes direction is called _____ current.

16. What is a common source of direct current? What is a common source of alternating current?

17. When you use such terms as "frequency," "Hertz," or "cycles/second" to describe electrical current you are describing _____ current.

18. Find the unknown voltage in each of these circuits.

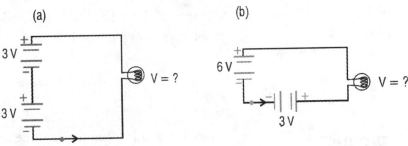

1.4 TEMPERATURE IN THERMAL SYSTEMS

Objectives

- Define thermal energy.

- Name the property of a body that determines its temperature.

- Given Celsius or Fahrenheit temperatures and the formula for conversion, find the equivalent temperatures on the alternate scale.

- Explain the difference between heat and thermal energy.

- Explain the relationship between heat transferred to an object and the change in the object's temperature.

- Use specific heat, heat of fusion, and heat of vaporization to solve problems involving heat transfer.

INTERNET *connection*

To find out more about temperature in thermal systems, follow the links at **www.learningincontext.com**.

In Section 1.1 you learned that a force can move an object from one place to another, or change the object's speed if it is already moving. In the next chapter, you will study work. Work is done on an object when a force moves the object through a distance. Therefore, doing work on an object can change its position or its speed.

For example, when you do work in lifting a hammer, the hammer changes its position in the Earth's gravitational field. By being lifted, the hammer gains the ability to do work on a nail beneath the hammer. The property that enables a body to do work is called **energy**. You increase the energy of the hammer when you lift it. You can also increase the energy of a gas by compressing it with a piston in a cylinder. The added energy comes from the work of a force pushing the piston through a distance. You can increase the energy stored in a battery by charging it. The added energy comes from the work of a force that pushes electrons through a distance in an electric field.

When an object gains energy as a result of changing its position, it has the potential for doing work. This energy is called **potential energy**. An object in motion is also capable of doing work. Energy of motion is called **kinetic energy**. When you lift a hammer, you increase its potential energy. As the hammer falls, it converts potential energy into kinetic energy. The kinetic energy of the hammer is converted into work when it hits the nail.

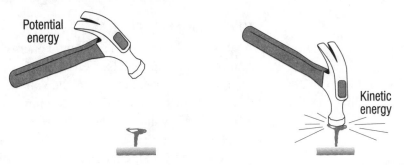

Figure 1.42
Work is done on a hammer to increase its potential energy.
Potential energy is converted into kinetic energy.

You will learn more about work and the different forms of energy in later chapters. In this section, we use the concept of kinetic energy to model the energy of motion of atoms and molecules. These particles are always in motion, vibrating back-and-forth randomly. In fact, the rate of this vibration determines whether an object exists in the solid, liquid, gas, or plasma state. The random motion of vibration of an object's atoms and molecules is called *thermal motion*. The total energy of the thermal motion of all the particles that make up an object is called the **thermal energy** of the object.

Temperature

We use thermal energy every day. When you cook a frozen pot pie you increase its thermal energy in an oven. The total kinetic energy of the molecules of a frozen pie is less than the total kinetic energy of the molecules of a cooked pie. If you touch a frozen pot pie with your hand, thermal energy flows from your hand into the pie. The frozen pie is colder than your hand. If you touch a cooked pot pie, thermal energy flows from the pie into your hand. The cooked pie is hotter than your hand. Whenever two bodies are brought together, thermal energy flows from the hotter body to the colder body.

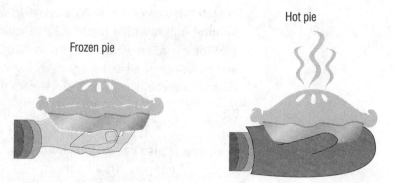

Frozen pie

Hot pie

Figure 1.43
Thermal energy always flows from the hot body to the cold body.

The "hotness" of a body is a property called *temperature*. **Temperature** is determined by the average kinetic energy of the random motion of the atoms and molecules in a body. This average energy is not the same as the thermal energy. The thermal energy is the sum of all the particles' energies, while the average is this sum divided by the number of particles. Notice that the average energy and the temperature of a body do not depend on the total number of particles in the body. The temperature of 1/2, 1/4, or 1/8 of the hot pie is the same as the temperature of the whole pie.

To see why, consider how you would calculate the average age of the students in your class. The sum of all the ages is divided by the number of students to find the average. Notice that the ages of the students are not exactly the same (especially if age is measured in months.) Students have a range of ages from a lowest to a highest value. Now compare the average age of students in your class to the average age of students in 100 eighth-grade science classes. Your average is higher than the eighth-grade average, but the sum of the ages for your class is much lower than the sum of the eighth-grade ages.

In the same way, the thermal energy in a pot of boiling water is lower than the thermal energy of a frozen lake. Water molecules in the boiling water have a range of kinetic energies, and so do the molecules in the lake. The average kinetic energy, or temperature, in the boiling water is higher than the average kinetic energy, or temperature in the lake. But the sum of the energies for the boiling water is much lower than the sum for the lake.

Refer to Appendix F for a career link to this concept.

Measuring Temperature

Thermal energy is measured in joules. Temperature is measured in degrees. Devices for measuring temperature depend on some property of a material that changes when its temperature changes. For example, most materials expand when their temperature increases and shrink when temperature decreases.

A **thermometer** uses expansion and contraction of a liquid, usually colored alcohol or mercury, to measure temperature. The liquid is contained in a glass tube. When the thermometer is placed in contact with an object like hot water, the faster-moving molecules in the water collide with the slower-moving molecules of the glass tube. The collisions transfer energy from the water to the glass. The thermal energy of the glass increases, while the thermal energy of the water decreases. Thermal energy flows between the water and glass, and also between the glass and the liquid inside the glass, until the temperatures are all equal. At this point, the thermometer and water are in **thermal equilibrium**. If you know the temperature of the thermometer, you know the temperature of the water.

Figure 1.44
When the temperature of the thermometer is the same as the temperature of the water, they are in thermal equilibrium.

As the temperature of the thermometer increases, the liquid inside the glass expands and rises. The temperature of the thermometer is read by comparing the height of the liquid to a scale.

The most commonly used temperature scale was devised in 1741 by the Swedish astronomer and physicist Anders Celsius. The **Celsius** scale is based on the properties of water. Zero degrees Celsius (0°C) is defined as the freezing point of pure water at sea level. One hundred degrees Celsius (100°C) is defined as the boiling point.

In some cases in the United States, the **Fahrenheit** scale is still used. Thirty two degrees Fahrenheit (32°F) is the freezing point of water, and 212°F is the boiling point. The Celsius and Fahrenheit scales are compared in Figure 1.45.

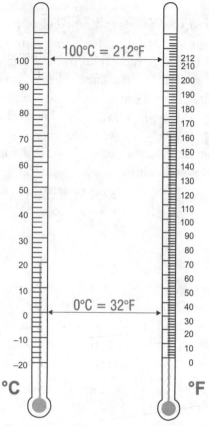

Figure 1.45
The Celsius and Fahrenheit temperature scales

If you know the temperature in degrees Fahrenheit (T_F), you can find the same temperature in degrees Celsius (T_C) by using the following equation:

$$T_C = \frac{5}{9}(T_F - 32)$$

If you know the temperature in degrees Celsius, you can find the same temperature in degrees Fahrenheit by using the following equation:

$$T_F = \frac{9}{5}T_C + 32$$

Example 1.13 Converting °F to °C

A meteorologist forecasts a high temperature of 50°F. What is the predicted high temperature in degrees Celsius?

Solution: Convert 50°F to degrees Celsius.

$$T_C = \frac{5}{9}(T_F - 32)$$

$$= \frac{5}{9}(50 - 32)$$

$$= 10$$

The predicted high temperature of 50°F is the same as 10°C.

A thermostat is set to keep the temperature of a room at 20°C. What is the thermostat setting in degrees Fahrenheit?

Solution:

$$T_F = \frac{9}{5}T_C + 32$$

$$= \frac{9}{5}(20) + 32$$

$$= 68$$

The thermostat setting of 20°C is the same as 68°F.

Heat

When a thermometer is placed in hot water, the temperature of the thermometer increases. This illustrates one way to increase the temperature of any object—place it in contact with a hotter object. Thermal energy flows from the hotter object to the cooler object, as kinetic energy is transferred when particles collide. This process is called **conduction**.

Heat is the energy that flows from one object to another because of a temperature difference. In conduction, heat is the amount of energy that flows from a hotter object to a cooler object after they are placed in contact. Heat never flows from a colder object to a hotter object. Like any measurement of energy or work, heat is measured in joules in the SI system.

Heat is not just another word for thermal energy. A body contains thermal energy, but not heat. Heat is thermal energy in transit. After heat is transferred to a body, it is no longer heat—it becomes thermal energy.

Heat flow depends on a temperature difference, but not necessarily a thermal energy difference. (Remember, temperature is the average kinetic energy of the particles; thermal energy is the total kinetic energy.) For example, when you press a skirt with a hot iron, heat will flow from the iron at a higher temperature to the skirt at a lower temperature. In this case, the thermal energy of the iron is *greater than* the thermal energy of the skirt.

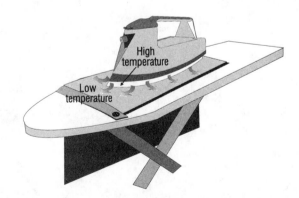

What happens if you take the same hot iron, unplug it, and toss it into a full swimming pool? Heat will still flow from the iron at a higher temperature to the water at a lower temperature. But, in this case, the thermal energy of the iron is *less than* the thermal energy of the water, because there are many more molecules in the swimming pool (with lower average energy) than in the iron (with higher average energy). This is similar to the previous example with average ages.

The amount of heat transferred between two bodies depends on their temperature difference. If there is no temperature difference, there is no heat transfer. As the temperature difference increases, the heat transfer rate increases. Therefore, **temperature difference** is the prime mover in thermal systems. Temperature difference is analogous to the other prime movers:

- In mechanical systems, movement of mass depends on force.

- In fluid systems, movement of fluid depends on pressure difference.

- In electrical systems, movement of charge (current) depends on potential difference (voltage).

- In thermal systems, transfer of heat depends on temperature difference.

In later chapters you will use temperature difference to calculate heat transfer in thermal systems, such as the engine cooling system of an automobile. Actually, the cooling system is a combination of thermal, fluid, and mechanical systems. When the fuel burns, very high levels of heat are transferred to the engine, raising its thermal energy. Heat is transferred from the engine to the coolant (a mixture of water and antifreeze). A pump circulates the coolant through the engine and through the radiator. Heat is transferred from the coolant to the radiator, and then from the radiator to air forced through the radiator by a fan.

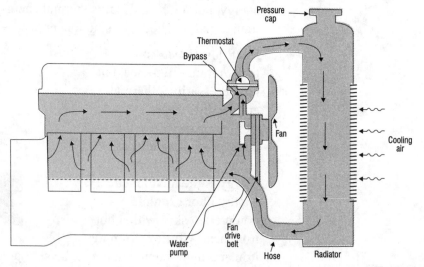

Figure 1.46
The cooling system is a combination of thermal, fluid, and mechanical systems.

Specific Heat

Water is used in the cooling system of an automobile because it has a much higher capacity for storing thermal energy than almost every other substance. A relatively small amount of water can absorb a great deal of heat with a small temperature increase.

In SI, the unit of thermal energy and heat is the joule. Another commonly used unit is the **calorie** (cal). 1 cal = 4.184 J. In some places in the United States, the British thermal unit, or **Btu**, is still used.

> *One calorie is the amount of thermal energy that must be added to water to change the temperature of 1 gram of water by 1 degree Celsius.*

> *One Btu is the amount of thermal energy that must be added to water to change the temperature of 1 pound of water by 1 degree Fahrenheit.*

When heat flows into an object, its thermal energy increases. As long as there is no phase change, the object's temperature increases. The amount of increase depends on the mass of the object, and also on the substance of which the object is made. For example, if you heat a pot of water and an equal mass of iron on the same stove top for two minutes, the temperature of the iron will be much higher than the temperature of the water.

The **specific heat** of a substance is the amount of energy that must be added to raise the temperature of a unit mass of the substance one temperature unit. From the definition above, the specific heat of water is $1\frac{cal}{g\cdot{}^\circ C}$. Specific heats of several substances are shown in Table 1.7.

Table 1.7 Specific Heat of Common Substances

Substance	Specific Heat cal/g·°C	Substance	Specific Heat cal/g·°C
Water	1.00	Stone (average)	0.19
Ice	0.49	Iron	0.16
Wood (average)	0.42	Copper	0.093
Air	0.24	Brass	0.091
Aluminum	0.22	Tin	0.055
Glass	0.21	Lead	0.031

The specific heat of a substance is represented by C. (Don't confuse this C with °C for degrees Celsius.) The amount of heat Q transferred to an object of mass m varies with the object's temperature change ΔT as follows:

$$\text{Heat transferred to an object} = \text{object's mass} \times \text{specific heat} \times \text{temperature change}$$

$$Q = mC\Delta T$$

When an object's temperature changes from an initial value of T_i to a final value of T_f, the change is $\Delta T = T_f - T_i$.

Example 1.15 Heat Transfer in Water

A teakettle holds 0.5 liter of water. How much heat is needed to increase the temperature of the water from 20°C to 100°C?

Solution: Water has a density of 1 g/cm³, and 0.5 L = 500 cm³. The mass m of the water is

$$m = \rho V = 1\frac{g}{cm^3} \times 500 \text{ cm}^3 = 500 \text{ g}$$

The temperature of the water changes from $T_i = 20°C$ to $T_f = 100°C$.

$$\Delta T = T_f - T_i = 100°C - 20°C = 80°C$$
$$Q = mC\Delta T$$
$$= (500 \text{ g})(1\frac{cal}{g \cdot °C})(80°C)$$
$$= 40{,}000 \text{ cal}$$

A heat transfer of 40,000 cal is required to increase the temperature of the water from 20°C to 100°C.

Example 1.16 Heat Transfer to Cool a Ball

A 2.5-kg brass ball at 100°C is placed in an insulated container of water at 10°C. When the ball and water reach thermal equilibrium, their temperature is 30°C.

(a) What amount of heat is transferred between the ball and water?

(b) What is the mass of water in the container?

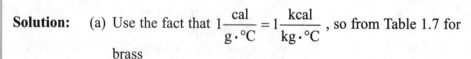

Solution: (a) Use the fact that $1\frac{cal}{g \cdot °C} = 1\frac{kcal}{kg \cdot °C}$, so from Table 1.7 for brass

$$C = 0.091\frac{kcal}{kg \cdot °C}$$

For the brass ball, $T_i = 100°C$ and $T_f = 30°C$, and

$$\Delta T = T_f - T_i = 30°C - 100°C = -70°C$$

The temperature change is negative because the temperature of the ball decreases.

$$Q = mC\Delta T$$

$$= (2.5 \text{ kg})(0.091 \frac{\text{kcal}}{\text{kg} \cdot °C})(-70°C)$$

$$= -15.9 \text{ kcal} \quad \text{or} \quad -15,900 \text{ cal}$$

The heat transfer is negative because the ball loses thermal energy as it cools. 15,900 calories are transferred from the ball to the water.

(b) Since the container is insulated, assume that all the heat lost by the ball is gained by the water. Heat gain is positive. For the water, $\Delta T = 30°C - 10°C = 20°C$. Solve the heat transfer equation for m:

$$m = \frac{Q}{C\Delta T}$$

$$= \frac{15,900 \text{ cal}}{1\frac{\text{cal}}{\text{g} \cdot °C} \cdot 20°C}$$

$$= 795 \text{ g}$$

The mass of water in the container is 795 grams or 0.795 kilogram.

Change of State

The linear relationship between heat transfer and temperature change of a given amount of a substance, $Q = mC\Delta T$, assumes the substance does not change state. If an object is a solid, like the brass ball in Example 1.16, it stays a solid. If it is a liquid, like the water, it stays a liquid. The relationship does not hold if the object changes state—for example, if it changes from a solid to a liquid, or from a liquid to a gas. The reason is that substances change state at *constant temperature*. When heat is added to a substance and $\Delta T = 0$, the heat transfer equation above does not apply.

Figure 1.47 shows what happens when heat is added to a container of ice, with an initial temperature of $-10°C$. At first, the temperature of the ice increases linearly as the ice absorbs thermal energy. When the temperature reaches $0°C$, the ice begins to change state. This temperature is called the

melting point. The temperature does not change as the ice absorbs thermal energy, melts, and changes from solid to liquid.

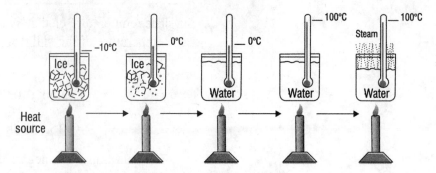

(a) Changes of state and temperatures for ice initially at −10°C.

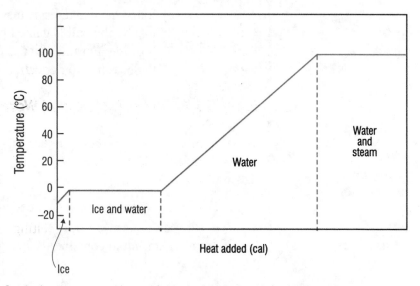

(b) Graph of temperature and heat added for ice initially at −10°C, showing changes of state

Figure 1.47
Q-T relationship for ice, water, and steam

When all the water is in the liquid state, it continues to absorb energy, and its temperature increases linearly to 100°C. When the water reaches 100°C, it starts another change of state to gas (steam). This temperature is called the **boiling point**. Again, the temperature is constant; as heat is absorbed, more water is converted to steam.

The amount of energy required to melt one gram of a solid substance is called the **heat of fusion** of the substance. The amount of energy required to vaporize one gram of a liquid is called the **heat of vaporization**. The values of some heats of fusion (H_f) and vaporization (H_v) are listed in Table 1.8.

Table 1.8 Heat of Fusion and Vaporization of Several Substances

Substance	Heat of Fusion H_f (cal/g)	Heat of Vaporization H_v (cal/g)
Water (Ice)	79.8	540
Iron	63.7	1503
Copper	49.0	1212
Silver	25.0	564
Gold	15.3	392
Lead	5.9	207

The amount of heat Q needed to melt a solid of mass m is

$$Q = mH_f .$$

The amount of heat Q needed to vaporize a liquid of mass m is

$$Q = mH_v .$$

Example 1.17 Melting Ice and Warming Water

A 10-gram ice cube has a temperature of $-5°C$. How much heat is needed to melt the ice cube and warm the resulting water to room temperature ($20°C$)?

Solution: Calculate the heat Q_1 needed to increase the temperature of the ice cube to the melting point, from $-5°C$ to $0°C$. For ice, $C = 0.49$ cal/g·°C.

$$Q_1 = mC\Delta T$$

$$= (10 \text{ g}) (0.49 \frac{\text{cal}}{\text{g} \cdot °\text{C}}) (0°\text{C} - (-5°\text{C}))$$

$$= 24.5 \text{ cal}$$

Calculate the heat Q_2 needed to melt the ice:

$$Q_2 = mH_f$$

$$= (10 \text{ g}) (79.8 \frac{\text{cal}}{\text{g}})$$

$$= 798 \text{ cal}$$

Calculate the heat Q_3 needed to raise the temperature of the water from $0°C$ to $20°C$. For water, $C = 1.00$ cal/g·°C.

$$Q_3 = mC\Delta T$$

$$= (10\ \text{g})\,(1.00\,\frac{\text{cal}}{\text{g}\cdot{}^\circ\text{C}})\,(20^\circ\text{C} - 0^\circ\text{C})$$

$$= 200\ \text{cal}$$

The total heat required is the sum:

$$Q = Q_1 + Q_2 + Q_3$$

$$= 24.5\ \text{cal} + 798\ \text{cal} + 200\ \text{cal}$$

$$= 1022.5\ \text{cal}$$

Summary

- The thermal energy of a body is the total kinetic energy of motion of all the particles that make up the body.

- The temperature of a body is determined by the average kinetic energy of the particles that make up the body.

- A thermometer measures temperature in degrees Celsius or degrees Fahrenheit.

- Heat is the energy that flows from one body to another because of a temperature difference.

- Whenever two bodies are brought together, heat flows from the body with the higher temperature to the body with the lower temperature.

- The amount of heat transferred to an object varies linearly with the object's temperature change, as long as there is no change of state: $Q = mC\Delta T$.

- If heat is transferred to a substance and it changes state, its temperature does not change.

Exercises

1. The thermal energy in an object is the _____ of all the kinetic energy associated with the motion of all the atoms and molecules that make up the object.

2. The temperature of an object is determined by the _____ kinetic energy associated with the motion of all the atoms and molecules that make up the object.

3. A thermometer marked with the Celsius scale is placed in an ice-water mixture and allowed to reach thermal equilibrium with the mixture. The temperature indicated by the thermometer is _____ .

4. The thermometer from Exercise 3 is placed in a pan of boiling water and allowed to reach thermal equilibrium. The temperature indicated by the thermometer is _____ .

5. A television news report includes an item about a medical care crisis in Sao Paulo, Brazil, due to a period of very hot weather. Sao Paulo has 12 consecutive days with temperatures above 41°C. What is the temperature in degrees Fahrenheit?

6. A severe weather warning for the area near Bettles, Alaska, warns that the low temperature tonight is expected to reach –45°F. What is the temperature on the Celsius scale?

7. A heat pump air-conditioning unit has a heat-exchanger coil on the outside of a house. On a summer day the gas flowing through the coil has a temperature of 145°F when the outside air temperature is 95°F. Will heat flow into or out of the gas in the heat-exchanger coil? Explain your answer.

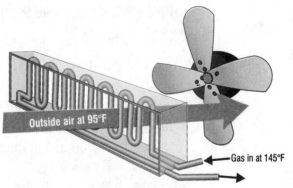

8. On a winter day the gas flowing through the heat-exchanger coil in Exercise 7 has a temperature of 20°F when the air temperature is 35°F. Will heat flow into or out of the gas in the heat-exchanger coil? Explain your answer.

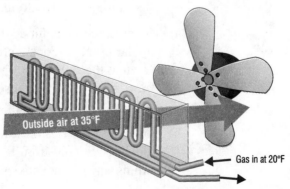

9. The temperature of an ice cube is 0°C. The temperature of liquid oxygen in a container is –183°C. The ice cube is placed in the liquid oxygen. Will heat flow into or out of the ice cube? Explain your answer.

10. Suppose you could measure very accurately the temperature of water at the top and bottom of a waterfall. Would you expect the temperature to be different? Explain your answer.

11. When wax melts, is heat absorbed or released by the wax?

12. When wax freezes, is heat absorbed or released by the wax?

13. Explain the difference between *thermal energy* and *heat*.

14. Explain the difference between *temperature* and *heat*.

15. When you place an ice cube in a glass of warm water, what happens to the temperature of the water in the glass? Use the definitions of heat and temperature to explain why this happens.

16. A thermometer at room temperature is placed in a glass of cold water.

    (a) After the thermometer and water come to thermal equilibrium, how do their temperatures compare?

    (b) Does heat flow into the thermometer or out of the thermometer?

    (c) Does heat flow into the water or out of the water?

17. Suppose the glass from Exercise 16 contains only a few drops of cold water. Why is it impossible to accurately measure the initial temperature of the water with the thermometer?

18. The energy value of food is determined by burning a sample of the food and measuring the heat released. The energy rating assigned to the food is actually a kilocalorie (1000 calories), written as a Calorie (with a capital C). Thus,

    1 Calorie = 1 kilocalorie.

    (a) The nutrition facts for a popular brand of cookie are shown at the right. How many Calories are in one of these cookies?

    (b) How many calories of heat would be released from burning one of the cookies?

Nutrition Facts
Serving Size 3 Cookies (33g)
Servings Per Container About 45

Amount Per Serving

Calories 160   Calories from Fat 60

	% Daily Value*
Total Fat 7g	**11%**
Saturated Fat 1.5g	**7%**
Polyunsaturated Fat 0.5g	
Monounsaturated Fat 3g	
Cholesterol 0mg	**0%**
Sodium 200mg	**9%**
Total Carbohydrate 23g	**8%**
Dietary Fiber 1g	**4%**
Sugars 13g	
Protein 1g	

19. A car's engine block is made of iron and has a mass of 210 kg. How much heat is absorbed by the engine block when its temperature is raised from 20°C to 90°C?

20. You are measuring the specific heat of tungsten. You heat a 215-gram sample of the metal to 100°C and place the sample in 450 grams of water at 20°C. The tungsten and water reach an equilibrium temperature of 21.5°C. What is the specific heat of the tungsten?

21. A 25-gram sample of ice has a temperature of –10°C. How much heat is needed to convert the ice into steam?

CHAPTER ONE SUMMARY

A force is a push or a pull on an object in a direction. In mechanical systems, forces can cause objects to move or change their motion. If a force is exerted on an object at a distance from its axis of rotation, it creates a torque. Torques can cause objects to rotate or change their rotational motion.

In fluids, we think of forces being distributed over areas. Pressure is the force per unit area. Pressure differences in a fluid explain the buoyant force an object feels when it is immersed in the fluid. In fluid systems, a pressure difference can cause fluid to move or change its motion.

When electric charges are separated, each charge feels a force of attraction or repulsion because of the presence of the other charges. The space surrounding the electric charges can be thought of as an electric field. There is a potential difference, or voltage, between two points in an electric field. Voltage causes charge to move in electrical systems.

The temperature of a body is a measure of the average kinetic energy of the random motion of the particles that make up the body. Thermal energy is the total kinetic energy of all the particles. When two bodies with different temperatures are brought together, thermal energy flows from the hotter body to the colder body. The thermal energy transferred is called heat. In thermal systems, a temperature difference causes heat to flow.

The table on the next page summarizes the four energy systems and the prime movers—force, pressure, voltage, and temperature difference.

Energy System	Prime Mover	Units		Quantity Moved
		SI	English	
Mechanical				
Translational	Force	N	lb	Mass moved through a distance
Rotational	Torque	N·m	lb·ft	Mass rotated through an angle
Fluid	Pressure	N/m	lb/in^2	Fluid volume or mass
Electrical	Potential difference	V	V	Charge
Thermal	Temperature difference	°C	°F	Heat

CHAPTER 2

WORK

We say that force is the prime mover in a mechanical system because a net force acting on an object changes the object's motion. If the force acts in the direction of the object's velocity or in the opposite direction, the force does work on the object. For example, when a tennis racket strikes a ball, it exerts a force in the direction opposite the ball's initial velocity. The racket does work on the ball and changes its direction and speed. You can calculate the work done on the tennis ball by using the force applied by the racket and the distance the ball moves while being pushed by the racket.

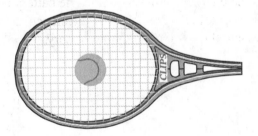

A tennis racket exerts a force on a ball and does work on the ball.

Forces are distributed over areas in fluid systems. The force per unit area is pressure. Pressure (or pressure difference) is the prime mover in fluid systems. If the pressure in a fluid is high enough, it can cause a boundary of the fluid to move, doing work on the boundary. For example, in the power stroke of an internal-combustion engine, an electric spark ignites the fuel-air mixture in a cylinder. The mixture burns rapidly, and the gas pressure inside the cylinder increases by as much as 600 psi. This pressure acting over the surface of the piston forces the piston to move down the cylinder. During the power stroke, the expanding gas does work on the piston. You can use the pressure and the volume to calculate the work done by the gas.

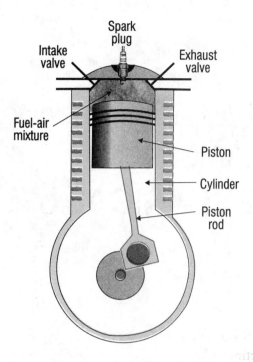

Spark
plug

Intake
valve

Exhaust
valve

Fuel-air
mixture

Piston

Cylinder

Piston
rod

In the power stroke of an
internal-combustion engine,
a fuel-air mixture burns
rapidly in a cylinder. The hot,
high-pressure gas expands
and does work on a piston.

In an electrical system, charges (electrons) move through a circuit because
coulomb forces are exerted on the charges. Coulomb forces are caused by
the presence of other charges. These other charges create an electric field
and a potential difference. Potential difference is the prime mover in
electrical systems. In the circuit below, a current (or flow of charge) drives a
DC motor for a model boat. The source of the potential difference that
moves the charge is a 6-V battery. The battery does work in moving the
charge. You can use the potential difference and the amount of charge moved
to calculate the work done by the battery.

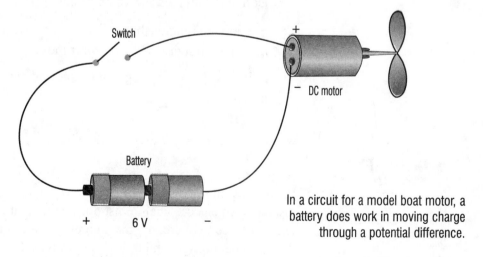

Switch

+

− DC motor

Battery

+   6 V   −

In a circuit for a model boat motor, a
battery does work in moving charge
through a potential difference.

2.1 WORK IN MECHANICAL SYSTEMS

Objectives

- Define work done by a force or torque in a mechanical system.

- Explain the relationship between work, force applied, and the distance an object moves.

- Solve work problems, given force and distance information in English and SI units.

- Explain how efficiency relates to input work and output work for a mechanical system.

- Define radian measure of angles.

- Explain the relationship between work, torque applied, and the angle (in radians) through which an object moves.

- Solve work problems, given torque and angle information in English and SI units.

To find out more about work in mechanical systems, follow the links at **www.learningincontext.com**.

In mechanical systems, work is done when a force moves an object through a distance. An electric chain hoist does work as it raises a beam. The hoist exerts a force to overcome the weight of the beam, and this force acts over the distance through which the beam moves. In meshing gears, one gear drives another—the driving gear does work on the driven gear. You will see in this section that it is easier to use torques than forces when calculating work in rotating systems.

(a) Chain hoist raises a load.

(b) Gear turns a shaft.

Figure 2.1
Mechanical systems do work when forces act through distances.

Work Done by a Force

The **work** W done on an object is defined as the product of the applied force F and the distance d through which the object moves.

$$\text{Work} = \text{force} \times \frac{\text{distance moved in the}}{\text{direction of the force}}$$

$$W = F \times d$$

The units for work come from multiplying a force (in newtons or pounds) by a distance (in meters or feet). Thus, in SI, work is measured in **newton-meters** (N·m) or **joules** (J). 1 N·m = 1 J. In the English system, work is measured in **foot-pounds**. The distance and direction through which an object moves are also called its *displacement*.

The definition of work uses the magnitudes of force and displacement. These quantities are actually vectors, since they also have direction. But we will consider only situations in which force and displacement are in the *same* direction or in *opposite* directions. Thus, work can be positive or negative. If the force on an object and the displacement are in the same direction, the work on the object is *positive*. If the force and the displacement are in opposite directions, the work is *negative*.

Example 2.1 Work Done by a Weight Lifter

Find the amount of work done by a weight lifter in lifting a 200-lb barbell a distance of 5 ft.

Solution: $W = F \times d$

$= (200 \text{ lb}) (5\text{ft})$

$= 1000 \text{ ft·lb}$

The weight lifter does 1000 ft·lb of work.

Now let's take a closer look at the process of lifting a barbell to see exactly what happens (see Figure 2.2).

Suppose you're going to lift the 200-pound barbell. At first, when the barbell is at rest on the floor, the forces on the barbell are balanced. Gravity pulls the barbell down with a force of 200 pounds (its weight) while the floor pushes up with an equal and opposite force of 200 pounds. No motion occurs; therefore, no work is done.

As you begin to lift the barbell, your upward pull is a little stronger than the downward pull of gravity. The barbell begins to move upward. You're now doing work on the barbell. When the barbell is moving, a force of 200 pounds will keep it moving upward *at a constant speed*. This 200-pound upward force does work on the barbell as it moves to its highest position, 5 feet from the floor.

Barbell is not moving.
No work is done.

Work is done while barbell is moving.

Barbell is not moving.
No work is done.

Figure 2.2
A closer look at lifting a barbell

When you've lifted the barbell to five feet, the barbell stops moving. You must still exert a force of 200 pounds to hold it in this position. But this force does no work on the barbell, since the barbell does not move. You will become tired because work is still done by your muscles as they stretch and contract small amounts to keep the barbell in place. These small forces cause small muscular movements, and do work, but this "biological work" is not being done on the barbell.

Example 2.2 Work Done to Stop a Cart

An electric cart is moving to the right. The driver applies the brakes, and stops the cart in 5 meters. A constant braking force of 900 newtons is applied over this distance. What is the direction of the braking force? How much work is done on the cart by this force?

Solution: To slow the cart, the braking force must act in a direction opposing the cart's motion. Therefore, the braking force acts t the left.

While the braking force is applied, the cart moves to the right. Thus, the force and distance moved are in opposite directions and the work is negative:

$$W = F \times d$$

$$= -(900 \text{ N}) (5 \text{ m})$$

$$= -4500 \text{ N·m} \quad \text{or} \quad -4500 \text{ J}$$

The brakes do −4500 J of work on the cart.

In many situations, a force can start an object moving and the object's motion continues after the force is removed. For example, when you throw a ball, your arm applies a force over a small distance. But the ball's motion continues over a much longer distance. In cases like this, it's important to know that work is done only while the force is applied. This means that the distance used to calculate work is the distance the object moves while the force is applied. When you throw a ball, your arm does not apply a force on the ball after it leaves your hand. So, even if the ball keeps moving, you do no work after the ball leaves your hand.

Work Can Change an Object's Potential Energy or Kinetic Energy

Example 2.1 shows that doing work on an object can change its position in the Earth's gravitational field. You learned in Section 1.4 that **potential energy** is the form of energy stored by an object. Potential energy may be due to an elevated position of a body. Thus, when the weight lifter does work on the barbell, she increases its gravitational potential energy. The amount of gravitational potential energy gained by the barbell equals the work done in lifting it. In other words, work equals change in energy.

Example 2.2 shows that doing work on an object can change its speed. You learned in Section 1.4 that **kinetic energy** is energy of motion. When the electric cart's brakes do work on the cart, the speed of the cart and its kinetic energy decrease. The amount of kinetic energy lost by the cart equals the work done on it by the braking force. Once again, work equals change in energy.

Work and Efficiency

Machines are designed to convert energy or work *input* to useful forms of energy or work *output*. In real (nonideal) machines, output work is always less than input work because some input work must be done to overcome undesired but unavoidable losses. For example, whenever two moving parts of a machine are in contact, a force of friction opposes the motion. This force does negative work, and therefore represents work lost by the machine.

When machines do work, they're often rated by efficiency. Efficiency is a ratio of output work to input work. Output is the work done by the machine. Input is work done on the machine to make it operate. In real machines, output work is always less than input work, so efficiency is always less than 1, or 100%.

$$\text{Efficiency} = \frac{\text{output work}}{\text{input work}}$$

$$\text{Percent efficiency} = \frac{\text{output work}}{\text{input work}} \times 100\%$$

A block and tackle is a simple machine consisting of a cord and a system of pulleys used to lift a heavy load. The upper set of pulleys is securely attached at one point. The lower set moves with the load.

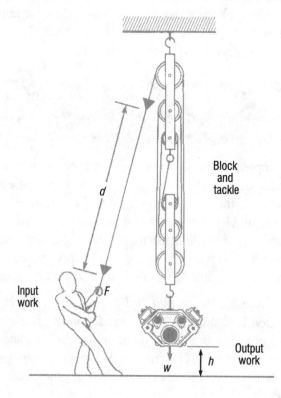

Figure 2.3
With a block and tackle, a force *F* can lift a larger weight *w*.

Block and tackle

d

Input work

F

w

h

Output work

A worker pulls the free end of the cord with force F. This force moves the cord through a distance d. At the same time, a load of weight w is raised through distance h by the action of the block and tackle.

The output work is the work done by the block and tackle to raise the load. The input work is the work done by the force F that causes the block and tackle to operate. Since work is equal to force times distance, the input work is equal to $F \times d$ and the output work is equal to $w \times h$. Friction in the bearings of the pulleys will cause output work to be less than input work.

Example 2.3 Work and Efficiency for a Block and Tackle

The block and tackle shown in Figure 2.3 is used to lift an automobile engine. The engine weighs 600 lb and is raised 0.9 ft. The operator pulls with a force of 100 lb over a distance of 6 ft. Calculate the efficiency of the block and tackle system.

Solution:

$$\text{Input work} = F \times d \qquad\qquad \text{Output work} = w \times h$$
$$= (100\,\text{lb})(6\,\text{ft}) \qquad\qquad\quad = (600\,\text{lb})(0.9\,\text{ft})$$
$$= 600\,\text{ft}\cdot\text{lb} \qquad\qquad\qquad\quad = 540\,\text{ft}\cdot\text{lb}$$

$$\text{Efficiency} = \frac{\text{output work}}{\text{input work}}$$

$$= \frac{540\,\text{ft}\cdot\text{lb}}{600\,\text{ft}\cdot\text{lb}}$$

$$= 0.9 \text{ or } 90\%$$

The block-and-tackle system is 90% efficient.

How much of the 600 ft·lb of input work is lost to friction in the block and tackle?

Measuring Angles in Radians

In Section 1.1, you learned that, when a force is applied to an object at some distance away from an axis of rotation, the resulting torque can cause the object to rotate. If the object rotates, the applied force acts through a distance (in the direction of movement) and does work on the rotating object. Instead of using force and distance, it is easier to use torque and the angle of rotation to calculate work for rotating objects.

First, you need to know how to measure angles in units called **radians**. A radian is defined by placing the vertex of the angle to be measured at the center of a circle. The sides of the angle intersect the circle at two points. Measure the length of the arc of the circle between these points. Arc length is a fraction of the circumference of the circle. The measure of the angle in radians is the arc length divided by the radius of the circle.

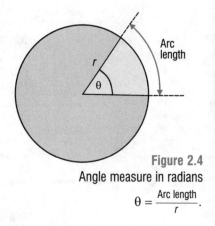

Figure 2.4
Angle measure in radians
$$\theta = \frac{\text{Arc length}}{r}.$$

$$\text{Angle measure in radians} = \frac{\text{arc length}}{\text{radius}}$$

$$\theta = \frac{\text{arc length}}{r}$$

Remember, the circumference of a circle of radius r equals $2\pi r$. When an object completes one revolution (1 rev), it rotates through 360°. This is a whole circle, so the arc length is the whole circumference:

$$1 \text{ rev} = 360° = \frac{\text{arc length}}{r} = \frac{2\pi r}{r} = 2\pi \text{ rad}$$

The abbreviation for radian is *rad*. Since $\pi \approx 3.14$, $360° \approx 6.28$ rad.

A 180° angle is a half circle, so the arc length is half the circumference:

$$180° = \frac{\frac{1}{2}(2\pi r)}{r} = \pi \text{ rad}$$

Can you show how to convert 90° and 45° to radians?

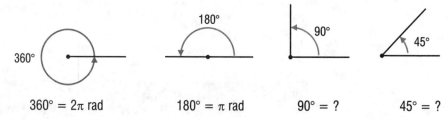

| 360° = 2π rad | 180° = π rad | 90° = ? | 45° = ? |

Figure 2.5
Angles in degrees and radians

The radian is an odd kind of unit. The measure of an angle in radians is a ratio of lengths, and is therefore a pure number with no dimensions. Don't forget, in solving problems mathematically, you must be careful to solve for the correct units—as well as the correct number. We drop the unit *rad* in a calculation unless the result is an angular quantity.

Work Done by a Torque

Figure 2.6 shows a wrench turning a nut. A force F acts on the wrench at a distance r from the axis of rotation. The force produces a torque τ. These quantities are related by

$$\tau = F \times r \quad \text{or} \quad F = \frac{\tau}{r}$$

If the wrench rotates, the force does work. The work equals the force times the distance through which the force moves. Since the movement of the wrench is circular, this distance is the arc length.

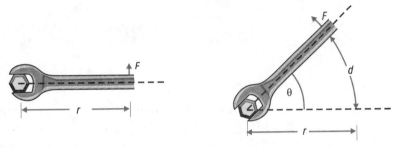

Figure 2.6
A force F produces torque. If the wrench rotates, F does work.

Let θ (the Greek letter *theta*) represent the measure of the angle of rotation. If θ is measured in radians, $\theta = \frac{d}{r}$. What is the relationship between work W and torque τ?

$$W = F \times d$$

$$= \frac{\tau}{r} \times d$$

$$= \tau \times \frac{d}{r}$$

$$= \tau \times \theta$$

The work done when a torque causes a rotation is given by the following form of the work equation:

$$\text{Work} = \text{torque} \times \frac{\text{angle (in radians)}}{\text{moved through}}$$

$$W = \tau \times \theta$$

A *winch* is a reel, a type of axle, with a crank to turn it. A winch is used to wind or unwind rope, wire, or cable. A boat trailer may have a winch. The winch is used to pull the boat out of the water and onto the trailer.

Example 2.4 Work Done to Turn a Crank

A simple mechanical winch has a crank handle of length 1.5 ft. A force of 20 lb is required to turn the crank. How much work is required to turn the crank through five revolutions?

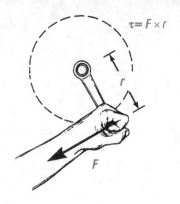

$\tau = F \times r$

Solution: Find the torque:

$$\tau = F \times r$$
$$= (20 \text{ lb})(1.5 \text{ ft})$$
$$= 30 \text{ lb} \cdot \text{ft}$$

Convert the total angle of rotation, 5 revolutions, to radians.

$$\theta = (5 \text{ rev})\left(\frac{2\pi \text{ rad}}{1 \text{ rev}}\right)$$
$$= 10\pi \text{ rad}$$

Find the work done by the torque:

$$W = \tau \times \theta$$
$$= (30 \text{ lb} \cdot \text{ft})(10\pi)$$
$$= 944 \text{ lb} \cdot \text{ft} \quad \text{or} \quad 944 \text{ ft} \cdot \text{lb}$$

A work input of 944 ft·lb is required to turn the crank. Notice that units for work are written as ft·lb. Units for torque are written as lb·ft.

Example 2.5 Work Done to Operate a Pump

An electric motor is used to drive a water pump. The motor provides a torque of 150 N·m. How much work is done when the motor turns through 40 revolutions?

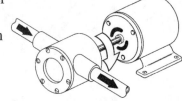

$$\theta = (40 \text{ rev})\left(\frac{2\pi \text{ rad}}{1 \text{ rev}}\right)$$
$$= 80\pi \text{ rad}$$
$$W = \tau \times \theta$$
$$= (150 \text{ N} \cdot \text{m})(80\pi)$$
$$= (150 \text{ N})(80\pi)$$
$$= 37,680 \text{ N} \cdot \text{m} \quad \text{or} \quad 37,680 \text{ J}$$

Therefore, 37,680 joules of work are done by the applied torque.

Summary

- Mechanical systems use force and torque to cause desired movement—and do useful work.

- Work is done when a force or torque moves an object. Work is done only while the force or torque is applied in the direction of movement.

- Work equals force times displacement or torque times angle. Work is measured in ft·lb or N·m (J = N·m). ($W = Fd$; $W = \tau\theta$)

- The displacement used to calculate work is the distance the object moves while the force is applied.

- Efficiency describes how well a machine performs work. Efficiency is the ratio of output work to input work. (Eff = W_{out}/W_{in})

- Angles can be measured in either radians or degrees. The radian is a dimensionless unit and is used in most calculations involving angles.

Exercises

1. Positive mechanical work is done when a force acts on an object and the object _____ in the same direction as the force vector.

2. Positive mechanical work is done when a _____ acts on an object and it rotates in the direction of the _____ .

3. Negative mechanical work is done by a force on an object if the object moves in the direction *opposite* the force vector. For example, Eddy applies an upward force and lifts a 20-lb box to a height of 3 feet. Eddy does positive work of 60 ft·lb on the box. Gravity exerts a force down while the box is moving up. The gravitational force does work, but it is negative work. The gravitational force does –60 ft·lb of work.

   Find the work done in each of the following cases and determine whether it is positive or negative.

   (a) A parachute exerts a force of 5000 newtons on an object that falls 500 meters.

   (b) Larry pushes a cart up a ramp that is 12 meters long. He applies a force of 200 newtons parallel to the ramp.

   (c) A freight elevator carries a 1500-lb box down 300 feet. Find the work done by the elevator on the box.

   (d) The braking system on a car applies a force of 7200 lb and brings the car to a stop in 800 feet.

4. Why do frictional forces reduce the efficiency of machines?

5. When you use an angle measurement in a calculation and the units of the angle are radians, you can drop the rad. Explain why this does not affect the calculation.

6. The work unit of one joule is also equal to one _____.

7. In one or two sentences, explain what mechanical work does to an object.

8. An angle measuring one radian measures _____ degrees.

9. A man who weighs 180 pounds is lifted 200 feet by an elevator. How much work does the elevator do on the man? How much work does the gravitational force do on the man?

10. An automotive technician applies a torque of 120 lb·ft to tighten a cylinder head bolt. The bolt turns $1/8$ of a revolution. How much work is done on the bolt?

11. A gear motor applies a torque of 15 N·m to raise the landing gear of an airplane. The gear motor makes 27.3 revolutions. How much work is done by the gear motor?

12. An electric motor can produce a torque of 51.8 N·m and rotates at a speed of 1728 revolutions per minute. How much work can the motor do in one second?

13. A hydraulic motor rotates 28,000 revolutions to do 9×10^6 joules of work. What is the average torque produced by the motor?

14. A robotic delivery cart carries a part with a mass of 5.4 kg a horizontal distance of 12 meters on a flat floor. The wheels have a diameter of 20 cm and the drive motor applies a torque to the wheels of 5 N·m while the cart is moving.

    (a) How much work does the drive motor do?

    (b) How much work does the gravitational force do?

15. An electric motor on a forklift truck turns at a speed of 600 revolutions per minute (rpm) for 4 seconds. It produces a torque of 20 N·m to turn a hydraulic pump. The hydraulic system lifts a 154-kg box a vertical distance of 2.5 m. What is the efficiency of the system?
    (Hint: θ = angular rate × time)

16. Ricardo uses a chain hoist to lift a 645-pound air compressor 4.5 feet. Ricardo has to pull 54 feet of chain through the chain hoist. If the hoist is 95% efficient, how much force does Ricardo have to apply to the chain?

2.2 WORK IN FLUID SYSTEMS

Objectives

- Describe how open and closed fluid systems are different.

- Explain the relationship between work and pressure in a fluid system, as given in the equation,

$$W = P \times \Delta V$$

- Explain the relationship between work and pressure in a fluid system, as given in the equation,

$$W = -\Delta P \times V$$

- Explain what is meant by positive work and negative work.

- Solve work problems (given pressure and volume information) in English and SI units.

INTERNET *connection*

To find out more about work in fluid systems, follow the links at **www.learningincontext.com**.

In fluid systems, as in mechanical systems, work is done when a force moves an object through a distance. But it is easier to calculate work in a fluid system using the prime mover, pressure (or pressure difference).

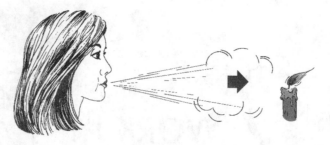

Figure 2.7
Pressure difference causes fluid motion.

A pressure difference can cause a fluid to move. For example, winds are caused by air moving from high-pressure regions to low-pressure regions. You create low- and high-pressure regions when you breathe, and these pressure differences cause air to move into and out of your lungs. When you inhale, you do work to expand your chest cavity and create a region of low pressure inside your lungs. A higher-pressure region outside then forces air into the lungs. When you exhale, you do work to shrink, or decrease, your lung volume. This increases the air pressure in your lungs and forces the air out.

Open and Closed Fluid Systems

We will analyze work in two types of fluid systems—open and closed. A **closed fluid system** retains and recirculates a working fluid. Examples of closed fluid systems are a hydraulic jack, a hydraulic brake system, and the body's circulatory (blood) system. Fluid flows through an **open fluid system** only one time—it is not retained and recirculated. Open fluid systems include city water systems, an irrigation system, and a fire truck water system.

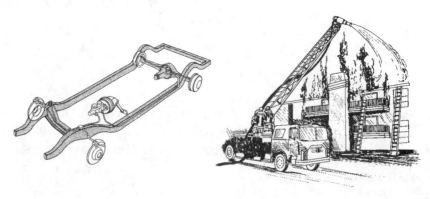

(a) Brake system in car (closed)   (b) Fire truck (open)

Figure 2.8
Open and closed fluid systems

Hydraulic Actuator

Hydraulic actuators are used widely in industry and transportation. They control the movement of airplane landing gears, bulldozer shovels, and forklifts. A basic hydraulic actuator, shown schematically in Figures 2.9 and 2.10, is a closed system. It includes several subsystems, so it can be called a "system of systems." The actuator uses hydraulic fluid to exert pressure on a piston, and work is done when the piston moves a load.

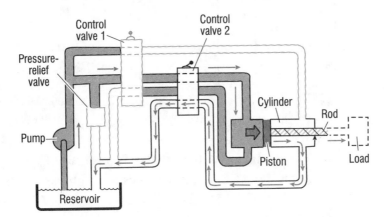

Figure 2.9
A basic hydraulic actuator. The pump moves fluid through control valve 2 into the left side of the cylinder. Control valve 1 is closed and does not allow fluid to flow through it. The piston moves to the right.

The pump draws hydraulic fluid from the reservoir, creates a pressure difference, and forces fluid through the pipes under pressure. The pump is driven by a rotating shaft that's connected to an electric motor. The control valves direct the fluid to the cylinder to either push or pull the load. When valve 1 is closed and valve 2 is open, high-pressure fluid flows to the left side of the cylinder. This creates a force on the piston that causes it to move, extending the rod and pushing the load. This is the arrangement shown in Figure 2.9.

When valve 1 is open and valve 2 is closed, high-pressure fluid flows to the right side of the piston. This causes the rod to retract, pulling the load. This arrangement is shown in Figure 2.10. With control valves in either setting, as the piston in the cylinder moves, fluid is forced out of the cylinder and directed back to the reservoir.

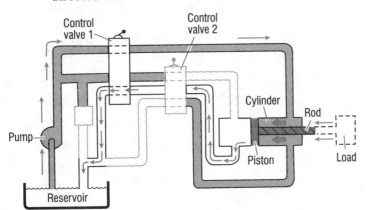

Figure 2.10
A basic hydraulic actuator. Fluid flows through control valve 1 into the right side of the cylinder. Control valve 2 is closed and does not allow fluid to flow through it. The piston moves to the left.

Refer to Appendix F for a career link to this concept.

Work Done in Fluid Systems

Figure 2.11 shows a simple closed fluid system—a cylinder filled with a gas and enclosed by a movable piston. The piston has a fixed weight on top to maintain a constant pressure inside the cylinder.

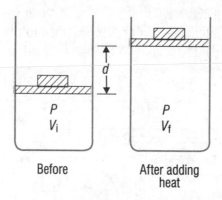

Before

After adding
heat

Figure 2.11
A cylinder and piston make a simple closed fluid system. The piston is one boundary of the system, and this boundary can move.

The volume of the gas in the cylinder is originally V_i. When heat is added to the gas in the cylinder, the gas expands to a volume V_f. The change in volume is $\Delta V = V_f - V_i$. The piston rises a distance d from its original position. The cross-sectional area A of the cylinder does not change, so the volume change ΔV is

$$\Delta V = A \times d$$

The work W done by the fluid in lifting the piston is the force times the distance moved in the direction of the force. The force F is the pressure P times the area A. The pressure does not change because the weight supported by the piston does not change.

$$F = P \times A$$
$$W = F \times d$$
$$= (P \times A) \times d$$
$$= P \times (A \times d)$$
$$= P \times \Delta V$$

This is the equation for calculating work done by a fluid on the moving boundary of a closed system when the pressure is constant and the volume changes.

$$\text{Work} = \frac{\text{constant}}{\text{pressure}} \times \frac{\text{fluid volume}}{\text{change}}$$

$$W = P \times \Delta V$$

Notice that ΔV can be positive or negative. (P is always positive.)

- If the fluid volume increases, ΔV is positive and W is positive. Positive work means *the fluid does work*, as when a gas expands in a cylinder, lifting a load.

- If the fluid volume decreases, ΔV is negative and W is negative. A negative value for work means that *work is done on the fluid*. For example, a weight or force applied to the piston compresses the gas in a cylinder. This applied force does work on the gas.

Figure 2.12 shows a simple open fluid system—a water pump. Water enters the pump at pressure P_i. The pump does work on the water and increases its pressure to P_f. In a given time interval, the same amount of water must enter and leave the pump. (There is no source of extra water, and there is no place to store water inside the pump.) This is called a *steady-flow* process. If 1 kg of water per second enters the pump, 1 kg per second must leave the pump.

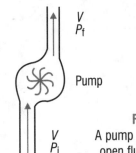

Figure 2.12
A pump is a simple open fluid system.

In one second, the pump will do work on 1 kg of water. If the density is constant, the volume moved is $V = m/\rho = \dfrac{1\ \text{kg}}{10^3\ \text{kg/m}^3} = 10^{-3}\ \text{m}^3$.

The following equation is used for calculating work done by a fluid in a steady-flow process when the density is constant and the pressure changes.

$$\text{Work} = \begin{array}{c}\text{pressure} \\ \text{difference}\end{array} \times \begin{array}{c}\text{volume} \\ \text{moved}\end{array}$$

$$W = -\Delta P \times V$$

The negative sign in the equation is important. The pressure difference ΔP can be positive or negative. (V is always positive.)

- If the pressure increases, ΔP is positive and W is negative. As before, a negative value for work means that *work is done on the fluid*. A pump is a typical source of work done on a fluid.

- If the pressure decreases, ΔP is negative and W is positive. Positive work means *the fluid does work*. In a hydroelectric dam, water flows from a high-pressure region behind the dam to a low-pressure region, turns a turbine, and does work.

Example 2.6 Work Done by a Hydraulic Cylinder

An industrial robot moves objects with hydraulic cylinders. Each cylinder contains a piston and a working fluid (oil). The oil is forced into the cylinder under high pressure on one side of the piston. The oil pushes against the piston. This causes the piston to move. The other end of the piston is connected to a load. As the piston moves, it moves the load.

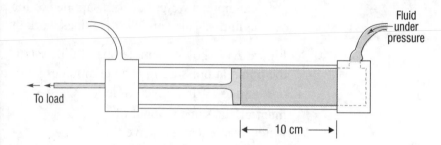

The fluid is injected into the cylinder at a constant pressure of 80 kPa. The cross-sectional area of the cylinder is 12 cm². Find the work done by the hydraulic fluid while moving the piston and load 10 cm.

Solution: The pressure on the piston is constant, and the volume of oil in the cylinder changes.

$$\text{Work} = \begin{array}{c}\text{constant} \\ \text{pressure}\end{array} \times \begin{array}{c}\text{fluid volume} \\ \text{change}\end{array}$$

$$W = P \times \Delta V$$

No oil is in the cylinder initially. Therefore, $V_i = 0$ cm³. The volume of oil that enters the cylinder and moves the piston is the same as the volume of a cylinder of cross-sectional area 12 cm² and length 10 cm.

$$V_f = 12 \text{ cm}^2 \times 10 \text{ cm} = 120 \text{ cm}^3$$

The change in volume is $\Delta V = V_f - V_i = 120$ cm³.

Convert to m³:

$$\Delta V = 120 \text{ cm}^3 \times \frac{1 \text{ m}^3}{10^6 \text{ cm}^3} = 1.2 \times 10^{-4} \text{ m}^3$$

$$W = P \times \Delta V$$

$$= 80 \text{ kPa} \times (1.2 \times 10^{-4} \text{ m}^3)$$

$$= (8.0 \times 10^4 \text{ N/m}^2) \times (1.2 \times 10^{-4} \text{ m}^3) \qquad \left[\text{Pa} = \text{N/m}^2 \right]$$

$$= 9.6 \text{ N·m} \quad \text{or} \quad 9.6 \text{ J}$$

The hydraulic fluid does 9.6 J of work while moving the load attached to the piston a distance of 10 cm.

Example 2.7 Work Done by a Pump to Fill a Tank

A community's water supply is stored in an elevated tank to maintain water pressure. The tank is filled by water pumped from a reservoir 150 feet below the inlet to the tank. The tank has a volume of 5000 ft³. If the tank is empty, what minimum work must be done by the pump to fill it?

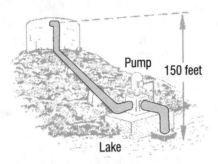

Solution: The volume of water moved by the pump is 5000 ft³. The pump increases the water pressure. The minimum work done by the pump is that required to push the water up the 150-ft height.

$$\text{Work} = \frac{\text{pressure}}{\text{difference}} \times \frac{\text{volume}}{\text{moved}}$$

$$W = -\Delta P \times V$$

Find the pressure difference for this situation. On the low-pressure side of the pump (the lake side), the water pressure P_i equals atmospheric pressure P_{atm}. On the high-pressure side of the pump (the tank side), the water pressure P_f equals P_{atm} plus the pressure of a column of water 150 feet high. The weight density ρ_w of water is 62.4 lb/ft³.

$$P_i = P_{atm} \qquad\qquad P_f = P_{atm} + \rho_w h$$

$$= P_{atm} + 62.4\frac{\text{lb}}{\text{ft}^3} \times 150 \text{ ft}$$

$$= P_{atm} + 9360 \text{ lb/ft}^2$$

$$\Delta P = P_f - P_i$$

$$= (P_{atm} + 9360 \text{ lb/ft}^2) - P_{atm}$$

$$= 9360 \text{ lb/ft}^2$$

$$W = -\Delta P \times V$$

$$= -9360 \text{ lb/ft}^2 \times 5000 \text{ ft}^3$$

$$= -4.68 \times 10^7 \text{ ft} \cdot \text{lb}$$

The negative sign means that work is done on the fluid. The pump must do at least 4.68×10^7 ft·lb of work to fill the tank.

Other Examples of Work in Fluid Systems

You've studied work done in a closed fluid system (hydraulic cylinder) and an open fluid system (pumping water to fill a tank). You found fluid work to be positive when the fluid does work and negative when work is done on the fluid.

Other fluid systems that do work include the following:

- Burning fuel-air mixture in a cylinder of an internal-combustion engine (*Positive work* is done by the expanding gas.)

- A heart pumping blood (The blood does *negative work*—the heart does work on the blood.)

- A refrigerator compressor using a piston and cylinder to increase the temperature and pressure of the working fluid (The fluid does *negative work*—the piston does work on the fluid.)

- Burning fuel expanding through a nozzle to lift a rocket (*Positive work* is done by the fuel.)

- Pushing down on the input cylinder of a hydraulic jack (The hydraulic fluid does *negative work*—work is done on the fluid.) and the output cylinder lifting a heavy load (*Positive work* is done by the fluid.)

If you look back at the basic hydraulic actuator shown in Figures 2.9 and 2.10, you can see that three different forms of work are involved in the operation of the "system of systems." Electrical work is done on a motor (not shown) operating the pump. The pump does mechanical (rotational) work to create a pressure difference for the fluid. The fluid, under pressure, does work on the piston and load. It's often true, as shown in this system, that work is being done at several places at the same time. That's why understanding work in mechanical, fluid, and electrical systems is important.

You can now calculate work in mechanical and fluid systems. Notice the similarity in the equations. Work equals the prime mover times another quantity:

In mechanical systems: $\text{Work} = F \times d$ or $\text{Work} = \tau \times \theta$

In fluid systems: $\text{Work} = P \times \Delta V$ or $\text{Work} = -\Delta P \times V$

Summary

- Fluids flow from regions of high pressure to regions of low pressure.

- Closed fluid systems retain and recirculate fluids.

- Open fluid systems move fluids into and out of the systems. They don't retain or recirculate fluids.

- A fluid does work in a closed system when a boundary moves. The pressure is constant and the volume changes, $W = P \times \Delta V$.

- A fluid does work in a steady-flow, constant-density process when a fixed volume moves through a pressure difference. $W = -\Delta P \times V$.

- Fluid work can be positive or negative.

Exercises

1. When a fluid does positive work in a closed system and the pressure is constant, does the volume of the fluid increase or decrease?

2. When a fluid does positive work in a steady-flow process and the volume is constant, does the pressure of the fluid increase or decrease?

3. Why is a pump an *open* fluid system?

4. Why do a cylinder and piston form a *closed* fluid system?

5. For each of the following situations, tell if the air does positive or negative work.

   (a) A sailboat moves forward in the wind.

   (b) You move air out of your lungs when you exhale.

   (c) A fan draws air through a car's radiator.

   (d) A balloon flies around the room as it deflates.

6. Tell whether each of the following is true or false. If a statement is false, explain why.

   (a) In a closed fluid system, work is always positive.

   (b) If the pressure and volume of a fluid are both constant, the fluid does no work.

   (c) If fluid work is negative, work is done on the fluid.

   (d) In a steady-flow process, the final pressure is always greater than the initial pressure.

A pump is used to maintain the water level in a tank at 105 feet above the pump, as shown at the right. Use this information to answer Exercises 7–9.

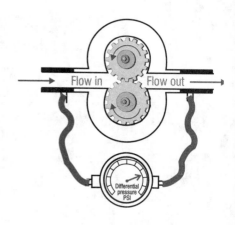

105 ft

Output pipe

7. When the pump is not running, what is the water pressure at the output pipe of the pump?

8. To move water, the pump must overcome friction between the water and the pipe. If the pressure required to overcome friction is 5 psi, how much pressure, in psi, must the pump supply to pump water into the tank?

9. How much work must the pump do to put 120 ft³ of water in the tank?

10. A hydraulic motor has a *displacement* of 2.5 in³. This means that, each time the shaft makes one revolution, 2.5 in³ of hydraulic fluid go through the motor. Louis measures a pressure drop of 75 psi across the motor while it is in use. He measures the motor speed to be 120 rpm. How much work, in ft·lb, does the fluid do in one minute? How much work, in ft·lb, does the fluid do in one second?

11. The amount of work done by a motor in one second is called the **power** of the motor. In English units, power can be expressed in foot-pounds/second or in **horsepower**.

$$1 \text{ horsepower} = 550 \text{ ft·lb/s}$$

What is the power produced by the hydraulic motor in Exercise 10, expressed in horsepower?

12. A robot arm is actuated by hydraulic cylinders. The arm is used to lift a 53.8-pound truck door 4.2 feet and hold it in place while the hinge bolts are installed. A volume of 28 in³ of hydraulic fluid is pumped into a hydraulic cylinder while it lifts the door.

    (a) What work must be done to lift the door?

    (b) What is the pressure of the fluid pumped into the cylinder?

13. The diameter of an uninflated, spherical balloon is 3.0 cm. To inflate the balloon, your lungs provide a constant pressure with each breath, equal to 1.2 kPa over atmospheric pressure. The diameter of the inflated balloon is 30 cm. Calculate the work done by your lungs to inflate the balloon. (The volume of a sphere of radius r is $\frac{4}{3}\pi r^3$.)

14. A small hydroelectric plant has an input water pressure of 85 psi and an output pressure of 3 psi. Note that the direction of the water flow is against the pressure drop when the water is causing the turbine to turn. How much work is done by the water when 8500 gallons flow through the turbine? (1 gal = 231 in³)

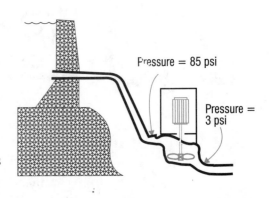

Pressure = 85 psi

Pressure = 3 psi

15. The air-conditioning unit in the Lake Air High School auditorium is being replaced. The building code requires that the system be capable of moving enough air to change the air in the auditorium 6 times per hour. The dimensions of the auditorium are 75 ft by 110 ft by 16 ft. A fan produces the pressure difference required to move the air through the filters and ductwork. The required pressure difference is 0.1 psi.

(a) Convert the pressure difference to lb/ft².

(b) How much work, in ft·lb, is done by the fan on the air in one hour?

(c) How much work is done by the fan in one second?

(d) What is the power absorbed by the air-circulation system expressed in horsepower? (See Exercise 11.)

2.3 WORK IN ELECTRICAL SYSTEMS

Objectives

- Explain the relationship between work done in electrical systems, charge moved, and the potential difference.

- Calculate the amount of electrical charge in coulombs moving past a point in a circuit.

- Define the units of electric current.

- Solve electrical work problems, given voltage and charge information.

- Identify the effects of work done in electrical systems.

- Explain how efficiency relates to input work and output work in an electrical system.

INTERNET *connection*

To find out more about work in electrical systems, follow the links at **www.learningincontext.com.**

A force does work on an object when it moves the object. In an electrical system, forces are applied to charged objects by electric fields. Electric fields are created by *other charges*.

You learned in Section 1.3 that a collection of charges creates an electric field. When there is an electric potential (or voltage) difference between two points within the field, a force is exerted on a charge placed at one of the points. If you connect the two points with a conductor (a piece of metal or a wire), the force causes charge to move from one point toward the other through the conductor. For this reason, we say that potential difference is the prime mover in electrical systems. Just as the presence of a pressure difference can result in a fluid moving and doing work in a fluid system, the presence of a potential difference can result in charge moving and doing work in an electrical system.

Examples of electrical systems are shown in Figure 2.13. Notice that, in each example, you can't see the electrical work being done. You can see (or hear or feel) only the *results* of electrical work—rotation, light, sound, heat—as electrical work is converted into other forms of energy.

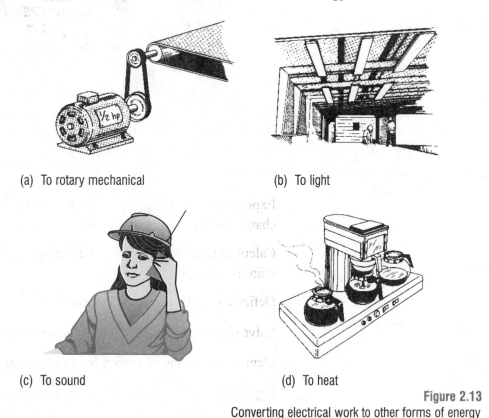

(a) To rotary mechanical

(b) To light

(c) To sound

(d) To heat

Figure 2.13
Converting electrical work to other forms of energy

How Big Is a Coulomb?

Batteries are sources of potential difference. In Figure 2.14 a battery is connected to a parallel-plate capacitor. The battery's potential difference results in electrons moving from the top plate, into the battery, and onto the bottom plate. The bottom plate now has an excess of electrons stored on it and is negatively charged. The top plate has a deficiency of electrons and is positively charged.

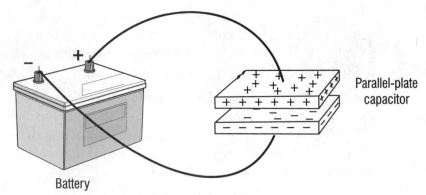

Figure 2.14
A battery moves charge off one plate and onto the other.

Electric charge is measured in coulombs (C). In Section 1.3, you learned that the elementary charge, or the charge of a single electron or proton, is 1.6×10^{-19} C. (An electron's charge is negative and a proton's is positive.) How many electrons are needed if one coulomb is deposited on the bottom plate?

$$\frac{1 \text{ electron}}{1.6 \times 10^{-19} \text{ C}} = \frac{N \text{ electrons}}{1 \text{ C}}$$

$$N = \frac{1}{1.6 \times 10^{-19}} = 6.25 \times 10^{18} \text{ electrons}$$

One coulomb is equal to the charge of 6.25×10^{18} electrons. This is 6.25 *billion billion* electrons.

1 C = charge of 6,250,000,000,000,000,000 electrons

Thus, a *net* charge of one coulomb represents 6,250,000,000,000,000,000 *more* electrons on the bottom plate of the capacitor than on the top plate. That's such a large number that most of us can't grasp its size. But we can develop an appreciation for this number by going through the following *thought exercise.*

> Think of an electron as a single grain of sand, approximately in the shape of a cube, 0.05 mm on a side. It would then take about 20,000 rooms, each 12 ft × 12 ft × 10 ft, filled with sand, to equal 6.25×10^{18} grains. That's the same as the number of electrons that provide the charge equal to one coulomb.

Refer to Appendix F for a career link to this concept.

Work in Electrical Systems

In Section 1.3, you learned that, when a charge q is placed in an electric field **E**, a force $\mathbf{F_E}$ is exerted on the charge. The relationship between these values is

$$\mathbf{E} = \frac{\mathbf{F_E}}{q}$$

For a positive charge, the direction of the force is the same as the direction of the electric field. You can solve this equation for force. The magnitude of the force can be found from the following equation:

$$F_E = E \times q$$

Figure 2.15

When a charge is moved in an electric field, work is done.

Also from Section 1.3, the potential difference, or voltage difference ΔV, between two points A and B in a uniform electric field depends on the distance d between the points and the magnitude of the electric field. The relationship is

$$\Delta V = E \times d$$

The subscript used in Section 1.3 has been dropped. When the charge is moved from A to B, as in Figure 2.15, an outside force is applied, equal in magnitude but opposite in direction to $\mathbf{F_E}$. This force is applied over a distance d. Therefore, work W is done on the charge equal to the force times the distance.

$$W = F_E \times d$$
$$= (E \times q) \times d$$
$$= (E \times d) \times q$$
$$= \Delta V \times q$$

Electrical work is the product of potential difference and charge moved.

$$\boxed{\text{Work} = \frac{\text{potential}}{\text{difference}} \times \frac{\text{charge}}{\text{moved}}}$$

$$W = \Delta V \times q$$

As in mechanical and fluid systems, work in electrical systems is measured in newton-meters (N·m), or joules (J). Since potential difference is measured in volts (V) and charge is measured in coulombs (C), the equation above shows that one joule equals one volt·coulomb.

$$1\,\text{J} = 1\,\text{V}\cdot\text{C}$$

We can solve the work equation for the potential difference:

$$\Delta V = \frac{W}{q}$$

This equation shows a new meaning for voltage. If 1 J of work is required to move a charge of 1 C between two points in an electric field, the potential difference between the points is 1 V.

$$1\,\text{V} = 1\frac{\text{J}}{\text{C}}$$

The derivation of the work equation used a positive charge being moved through a positive potential difference and resulting in positive work done on the charge. In general, charge can be either positive or negative; so can potential difference and, therefore, so can work.

Remember, electric fields and potential differences are created when there is a separation of charge. By convention in science and engineering, electric field vectors always point in a direction *away from* the positive charge and *toward* the negative charge. This is illustrated in Figure 2.16 for the simple case of charged parallel plates with a uniform electric field between them. In the diagrams, point B is at a *higher potential* than point A. To see why, imagine placing a positive test charge at B. The charge will feel a force acting in the direction of the electric field. If the charge is released, it will accelerate toward A. Therefore, if a charge is moved from A to B, the change in potential, or potential difference, is positive. If the charge is moved from B to A, the potential difference is negative.

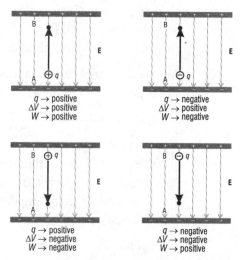

$q \rightarrow$ positive
$\Delta V \rightarrow$ positive
$W \rightarrow$ positive

$q \rightarrow$ negative
$\Delta V \rightarrow$ positive
$W \rightarrow$ negative

$q \rightarrow$ positive
$\Delta V \rightarrow$ negative
$W \rightarrow$ negative

$q \rightarrow$ negative
$\Delta V \rightarrow$ negative
$W \rightarrow$ positive

Figure 2.16
When a charge is moved in an electric field, $W = q\Delta V$.
Work can be positive or negative.

The diagrams show all four possible combinations of the signs of charge and potential difference. Since work is the product of charge and potential difference, two of the products result in positive work and two result in negative work.

Example 2.8 Work Done to Charge a Battery

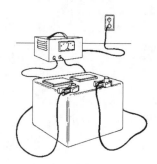

An automobile battery is being charged. During the first 15 minutes of charging, 800 C of charge are deposited in the battery by an average potential difference of 8 V. How much electrical work is done by the charger during the first 15 minutes?

Solution:
$$W = \Delta V \times q$$
$$= (8 \text{ V}) (800 \text{ C})$$
$$= 6400 \text{ V} \cdot \text{C} \quad \text{or} \quad 6400 \text{ J}$$

Therefore, 6400 J or 6.4 kilojoules (kJ) are required to recharge the battery during the first 15 minutes.

Electric Charge and Current

The amount of electric charge moved in a circuit can't be measured easily in coulombs. It's more practical to measure the *rate* at which charge flows, or *electric current.* Current is measured in coulombs per second. A flow of one coulomb per second (C/s) is called an **ampere** (A). 1 A = 1 C/s. A device for measuring current is called an ammeter.

We use the variable I to represent current. If an amount of charge q flows past a point in a circuit in a time interval Δt, the current is

$$I = \frac{q}{\Delta t}$$

In Example 2.8, the charge deposited in a battery was given as 800 coulombs. Batteries are normally rated in units of ampere-hours rather than coulombs. But an ampere-hour is really a unit of charge, and can be converted to coulombs. Let's see how.

$$I = \frac{q}{\Delta t} \qquad\qquad 1 \text{ ampere} = \frac{1 \text{ coulomb}}{1 \text{ second}}$$

$$q = I \times \Delta t \qquad\qquad 1 \text{ coulomb} = 1 \text{ ampere} \times 1 \text{ second}$$

$$1 \text{ coulomb} = 1 \text{ ampere} \cdot \text{second}$$

$$1 \text{ C} = 1 \text{ A} \cdot \text{s}$$

So one coulomb equals one ampere·second. If one ampere of current flows for one second, one coulomb of charge is moved past a point in a circuit. What if the current flows for one hour? One hour equals 3600 seconds. There would be 3600 times as many coulombs moved. Thus:

$$1 \text{ ampere} \cdot \text{hour} = 3600 \text{ ampere} \cdot \text{seconds} = 3600 \text{ coulombs}$$

So ampere-hours are really units of charge. Suppose the battery in Example 2.8 is rated at 2.5 ampere-hours. How many coulombs of charge can the battery hold?

$$2.5 \text{ ampere} \cdot \text{hours} \times \frac{3600 \text{ coulombs}}{1 \text{ ampere} \cdot \text{hour}} = 9000 \text{ coulombs}$$

What current will completely drain this battery in 6 hours?

$$I = \frac{q}{\Delta t}$$

$$= \frac{9000 \text{ C}}{6 \text{ h}} \cdot \frac{1 \text{ h}}{3600 \text{ s}}$$

$$= 0.42 \, \frac{\text{C}}{\text{s}} \quad \text{or} \quad 0.42 \text{ A}$$

Example 2.9 Work Done on an Electric Motor

A 12-volt DC electric motor uses a current of 4 amperes. Find the electrical work done to operate this motor for two minutes.

Solution: First, find the charge moved in the circuit:

$$q = I \times \Delta t$$
$$= (4 \text{ A}) (120 \text{ s})$$
$$= 480 \text{ A·s} \quad \text{or} \quad 480 \text{ C}$$
$$W = \Delta V \times q$$
$$= (12 \text{ V}) (480 \text{ C})$$
$$= 5760 \text{ V·C} \quad \text{or} \quad 5760 \text{ J}$$

The electrical work done to run the motor for 2 minutes is **5760 J**.

Example 2.10 Work Done on a Solenoid

A solenoid on an automobile's starter draws a current of 15 **amperes** at a voltage of 12 volts. Find the amount of time the solenoid is **active if 216 J** of electrical work are done on the solenoid.

$$W = \Delta V \times q \rightarrow q = \frac{W}{\Delta V} = \frac{216 \text{ J}}{12 \text{ V}} = 18 \text{ J/V} \quad \text{or} \quad 18 \text{ C}$$

$$I = \frac{q}{\Delta t} \rightarrow \Delta t = \frac{q}{I} = \frac{18 \text{ C}}{15 \text{ A}} = 1.2 \text{ C/A} \quad \text{or} \quad 1.2 \text{ s}$$

The solenoid is active for 1.2 seconds.

Effects of Electrical Work

Electrical work is done when a voltage results in charge movement. Electrical work produces movement, thermal energy, light, and sound. In your daily life, you're exposed to the effects of electrical work whether you're at home, in school, in a business office, or in a manufacturing plant.

Electric motors move fluids by driving pumps and fans. Electric relays and solenoids open or close switches and valves. Electric motors also turn wood- and metal-working machines, conveyor belts, and computer hard drives.

Another effect of charge movement resulting from a voltage can be the production of thermal energy. The resulting heat transfer may be desired, such as in electric heaters, clothes dryers, furnaces, or ovens. Or heat may be simply an unwelcome by-product, such as that produced in electric motors or incandescent light bulbs.

Light—whether from an incandescent bulb, a fluorescent tube, a light-emitting diode, or a laser—can be produced when electrical work is done. Radio waves, TV signals, and microwaves are related to light (they are all electromagnetic radiation). These also are produced when a charge moves as a result of potential difference.

Sound from the speakers of electronic devices such as radios, TVs, and CD players is also a result of converting electrical work into mechanical work.

Efficiency of Electrical Devices

In an electrical device, such as a motor, not all electrical work is converted to mechanical work. Instead, some of the electrical work is converted into thermal energy, thereby raising the temperature of the motor.

If the electrical device is designed to produce mechanical work, the undesired thermal energy represents a loss of useful electrical work. This loss lowers the electrical efficiency of the system.

The efficiency of any device is defined by the ratio of output work to input work.

$$\text{Efficiency} = \frac{\text{output work}}{\text{input work}}$$

$$\text{Percent efficiency} = \frac{W_{\text{out}}}{W_{\text{in}}} \times 100\%$$

If *output work* were the same as *input work*, the ratio $W_{\text{out}}/W_{\text{in}}$ would be equal to one. In that case, the efficiency of the device would be 100%. However, in actual devices, *output work* is always less than *input work*. All devices are less than 100% efficient.

Example 2.11 Efficiency of an Electric Motor

In Example 2.9, the input work to an electric motor was shown to be 5760 joules. Suppose the motor provides the lifting capacity for an overhead crane. Find the work done by the motor and the efficiency of the motor if the crane lifts an I-beam weighing 2000 newtons to a height of 2.5 meters.

Solution: The input work was calculated in Example 2.9 as 5760 J. The output work done by the motor is the lifting force times the distance the beam moves.

$$W_{out} = \text{force} \times \text{distance}$$
$$= (2000\ N)\,(2.5\ m)$$
$$= 5000\ N{\cdot}m \quad \text{or} \quad 5000\ J$$
$$\text{Efficiency} = \frac{W_{out}}{W_{in}} \times 100\%$$
$$= \frac{5000\ J}{5760\ J} \times 100\%$$
$$= 86.8\%$$

The motor does 5000 J of work. The efficiency of the motor is 86.8%.

Why Use Electricity to Do Work?

Most electricity is produced at electrical generating stations by the following process:

- Coal, gas, or oil is burned to produce thermal energy.

- Thermal energy is used to convert water into high-pressure steam.

- Steam pressure is used to drive (rotate) turbines.

- Turbines drive electrical generators to produce electricity.

At the using end, electricity is converted back to useful forms of fluid, mechanical, and electrical work. In each step of the process, heat is created as a loss of work and energy. The overall efficiency of this conversion process is less than 60%. Why go through this long process to produce electricity when we must reverse the process to use it?

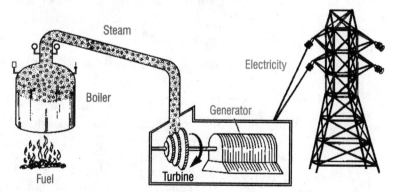

Fig. 2.17
Generating electricity

There are several good reasons for using electricity:

- Electricity is an affordable way to transport energy to offices, homes, and factories.

- Electricity can move over long distances through overhead or underground wires.

- Electrical energy can be transformed into other forms of energy and work.

- Electricity is convenient and easy to use, and provides a ready source of energy "at the wall plug."

Summary

- Electrical work is done when charge moves through a potential difference. ($W = q\Delta V$)

- One joule of electrical work is done when one coulomb of charge is moved through a potential difference of one volt. (J = V/C)

- The rate of movement of electrical charge is current. Current is measured in amperes. One ampere is a rate of one coulomb per second. ($I = q/\Delta t$; A = C/s)

- The efficiency of an electrical device is the ratio of work output to work input. The efficiency is always less than 100%. (Eff = W_{out}/W_{in})

Exercises

1. Is it possible to do work on a single, isolated electron using no other charge? Explain your answer.

2. Batteries have positive and negative terminals. Using the convention for the direction of the electric field (see Figure 2.16), which terminal on a battery has a higher potential?

3. A 1.5-V battery delivers 0.4 C of charge. How much work is done by the battery?

4. A current of 15 mA (milliamperes) flows in an electronic circuit. How much charge flows past a point in the circuit in 5 seconds? How many electrons does this charge represent?

5. An electric pump lifts 800 N of water from a well 50 m deep in 90 seconds. The potential difference across the pump is 48.5 V, and a current of 10.3 A flows through the pump.

   (a) How much work is done by the pump in lifting the water?

   (b) How much work is done on the pump by the electrical current during the time interval?

   (c) What is the efficiency of the pump?

6. An electric motor turning a fan has a voltage drop across it of 12.6 volts and a current through it of 5.6 amperes. The fan produces a pressure difference of 1.38 kPa and moves 0.048 m³ of air in one second.

   (a) How much work, in joules, is done on the motor by the electrical current in one second?

   (b) How much work, in joules, is done to the air in one second?

   (c) What is the efficiency of the motor-fan system?

7. A charge of 25 nanocoulombs is removed from one plate of a capacitor, and the same amount is added to the other. The initial voltage across the capacitor is 1.2 volts, and the final voltage is 3.1 volts.

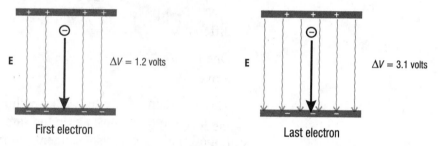

First electron   Last electron

   (a) How much work is done removing the first electron from one plate and adding one electron to the other?

   (b) How much work is done removing the last electron from one plate and adding the last electron to the other?

8. A metal-plating shop uses an electrolytic process to plate copper onto steel parts. A charge of 1.929×10^5 C must flow through the plating solution to deposit 63.54 grams of copper onto the steel parts. The voltage across the plating cell is 4.85 V. How much work is done by the electrical current to plate 100 grams of copper onto the steel parts?

9. A hydroelectric power plant has an output of 25,000 amperes at 12,500 volts.

   (a) How much work, in joules, is done in one second to produce the electric power?

   (b) Suppose the efficiency of the energy conversion process is 80%. How much work is done by the water flowing through the turbine in one second?

10. A battery used to start aircraft engines has an output voltage of 12.6 V over its useful discharge range. The battery has a rating of 825 ampere-hours over the useful range. How much work can the battery do?

11. In a particle accelerator, a proton is accelerated across a voltage difference of 2.5 million volts. How much work, in joules, is done on the proton?

CHAPTER TWO
SUMMARY

Work is done when a force moves something through a distance. To do work on the object, the force must act in the same direction as, or opposite the direction of, the object's displacement. Work can be positive or negative. In each energy system where work is done, you can think of work as the product of the prime mover and another quantity.

In mechanical systems, force is the prime mover. Work done on an object is the product of the applied force and the distance the object moves while the force is applied. If the system rotates, the applied force creates a torque. The work done on a rotating object is the product of the torque and the angle in radians through which the object rotates while the torque is applied. When the force is in the same direction as the object's displacement, work is positive. When force is opposite the direction of displacement, work is negative.

In fluid systems, pressure (or pressure difference) is the prime mover. A fluid can do work under constant pressure when the volume of fluid changes. In this case, work done by the fluid is the product of the pressure and the volume change. A fluid can also do work in steady flow. When the fluid density is constant, work done is the product of the pressure drop and the volume. When the fluid does work, work is positive. When work is done on the fluid, work is negative.

In electrical systems, potential difference is the prime mover. Work is done on charge (electrons in electrical circuits) to move the charge through a potential difference. Work done is the product of potential difference and charge move

The table below summarizes the work equations in the three energy systems. Work is not done in thermal systems.

Energy System	Prime Mover	Work Equation	Units	
			SI	**English**
Mechanical				
Translational	Force	$W = F \times d$	$1\,\text{J} = 1\,\text{N} \cdot 1\,\text{m}$	$1\,\text{ft} \cdot \text{lb} = 1\,\text{ft} \cdot 1\,\text{lb}$
Rotational	Torque	$W = \tau \times \theta$	$= 1\,\text{N} \cdot \text{m}$	
Fluid	Pressure	$W = P \times \Delta V$	$1\,\text{J} = 1\,\dfrac{\text{N}}{\text{m}^2} \cdot 1\,\text{m}^3$	$1\,\text{ft} = 1\,\dfrac{\text{lb}}{\text{ft}^2} \cdot 1\,\text{ft}^3$
	or	or		
	Pressure Difference	$W = -\Delta P \times V$	$= 1\,\text{N} \cdot \text{m}$	
Electrical	Potential Difference	$W = \Delta V \times q$	$1\,\text{J} = 1\,\text{V} \cdot 1\,\text{C}$ $= 1\,\text{V} \cdot \text{C}$	

RATE

Rate is a quantity that describes how fast or slowly something happens. For example, your reading rate is the number of words per minute that you can read. You can measure reading rate by using a watch to measure the time interval it takes to read a page from a book. Then count the number of words on the page. Divide the number of words by the time interval, and convert the result to a unit rate. (A unit rate is an equivalent ratio with a denominator of one). As an example, suppose you read 450 words in 1.8 minutes. Your reading rate is:

$$\frac{450 \text{ words}}{1.8 \text{ minutes}} = \frac{250 \text{ words}}{1 \text{ minute}} \quad \text{or} \quad 250 \text{ words per minute}$$

The data-transfer rate of a computer modem is the number of bits of data per second that the modem transmits or receives. If a modem's data-transfer rate is 50,000 bits per second, how many bits can be transmitted in 10 seconds?

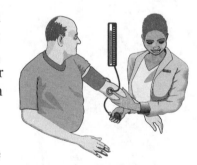

Your heart rate is the number of times per minute that your heart beats. If you measure 15 beats in 15 seconds, what is your heart rate?

Heart rate is number of beats per unit time.

Rate is a ratio of a measured quantity to a time interval. The measured quantities in the examples above are words, data bits, and heartbeats. Can you name another rate? What is the measured quantity?

$$\text{Rate} = \frac{\text{measured quantity}}{\text{time interval}}$$

In this chapter, you will study rates in the four energy systems. The measured quantities and rates are different in each system.

In mechanical systems, the *distance traveled* by an object is a measured quantity. This quantity is also called the change in the object's position. You can calculate your jogging rate by dividing the distance traveled, or your change in position, by the time interval. This rate is your *speed*. Speed is a measure of how fast an object's position changes. If you speed up or slow down your jogging rate, you can use the change in speed as a measured quantity. In this case, acceleration is the rate calculated by dividing the change in speed by the time interval. For an object moving in a straight line, *acceleration* is a measure of how fast the object's speed changes. Typical units for speed are meters per second and miles per hour. Typical units for acceleration are meters per second per second and miles per hour per minute.

Speed is distance traveled per unit time.
Acceleration is change in speed per unit time.

Fluid quantities can be measured using *mass* or *volume*. An IV fluid flows from a bag, through a tube, and into a patient's arm. The mass and volume of IV fluid in the bag change. The *mass flow rate* through the tube is the change in mass divided by the time interval. The *volume flow rate* is the change in volume divided by the time interval. Typical units for mass flow rate are grams per second and kilograms per hour. Typical units for volume flow rate are cubic centimeters per second, gallons per minute, and liters per hour.

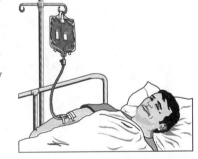

In electrical systems, the measured quantity is *charge*. In a wire or circuit, the amount of charge flowing past a point divided by the time interval is called the *current*. Thus, current is a measure of the amount of charge flowing per unit time. Current is measured in units of coulombs per second. One ampere is defined as one coulomb per second.

Thermal energy or *heat* is the measured quantity in thermal systems. Heat is the thermal energy that flows from regions of higher temperature to regions of lower temperature. *Heat flow rate* is a measure of how fast heat flows. This rate is the ratio of the heat transferred to the time interval. Typical units for heat flow rate are joules per second, calories per minute, and Btu per hour.

3.1 RATE IN MECHANICAL SYSTEMS

Objectives

- Define speed, velocity, and acceleration.

- Explain the difference between speed and velocity.

- Explain the difference between velocity and acceleration.

- Use speed, velocity, and acceleration to solve problems involving linear motion.

- Define angular speed and angular acceleration.

- Use angular speed and angular acceleration to solve problems involving rotational motion.

In mechanical systems, rates describe how quickly something changes. Speed or velocity describes how quickly the position of an object changes. Acceleration describes how quickly velocity changes. You can use speed, velocity, and acceleration to analyze the motion of objects moving in a straight line, a circle, a curved path, or back-and-forth vibration.

INTERNET *connection*

To find out more about rate in mechanical systems, follow the links at **www.learningincontext.com**.

Speed

If an object is in motion, it travels some distance in a given time interval. The **speed** of the object is the ratio of the distance traveled to the time interval. You can measure speed with a tape measure and stopwatch.

For example, to determine the speed of an automobile, you use a tape measure and stopwatch to find the distance traveled in some interval of time. Suppose you observe the automobile to travel 5 meters in 1 second, 10 meters in 2 seconds, 15 meters in 3 seconds, and so on for five seconds. The observed times t and distances d are shown in Table 3.1. The data are plotted on a coordinate plane in Figure 3.1.

Table 3.1
Time and Distance Data

Time, t	Distance, d
1 s	5 m
2 s	10 m
3 s	15 m
4 s	20 m
5 s	25 m

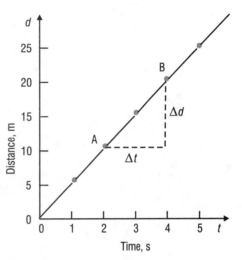

Figure 3.1
Time and distance plot for a car traveling at constant speed

Notice the data fall on a straight line. The **slope** of the line, the ratio of the *rise* to the *run*, is constant—it is the same everywhere on the line. If you locate any two points A and B on the line, the rise is the distance Δd traveled between the points and the run is the time interval Δt. Therefore, the speed equals the slope:

$$\text{Speed} = \frac{\text{distance traveled}}{\text{time interval}} = \frac{\Delta d}{\Delta t}$$

For points A and B in Figure 3.1, let the (t, d) coordinates be A (t_1, d_1) and B (t_2, d_2). The speed is calculated as follows:

$$\text{Speed} = \frac{\Delta d}{\Delta t} = \frac{d_2 - d_1}{t_2 - d_1} = \frac{20 \text{ m} - 10 \text{ m}}{4 \text{ s} - 2 \text{ s}}$$

$$\text{Speed} = \frac{10 \text{ m}}{2 \text{ s}}$$

$$= 5 \text{ m/s} \quad \text{or} \quad 5 \text{ meters per second}$$

Select any two points (t_1, d_1) and (t_2, d_2) from Table 3.1. Calculate the speed between these points. Is the speed 5 m/s?

Now suppose the measured time and distance data at A and B are the same, but the speed of the automobile between A and B varies. Sample measurements of time and distance between A and B are plotted in Figure 3.2.

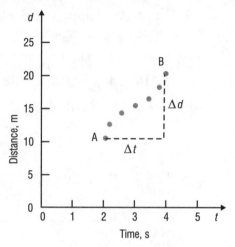

Figure 3.2
Time and distance plot for a car traveling at a varying speed

You can still calculate the speed between A and B as $\Delta d/\Delta t$, but this ratio is now more precisely called the **average speed** of the automobile between A and B. We use the symbol v for speed and v_{ave} for average speed.

$$\text{Average speed} = \frac{\text{distance traveled}}{\text{time interval}}$$

$$v_{ave} = \frac{\Delta d}{\Delta t}$$

The speed v at any one instant is called the **instantaneous speed**. This is the speed indicated by the automobile's speedometer. As shown in Figure 3.1, if the instantaneous speed is constant, $v = v_{ave}$. But, as shown in Figure 3.2, the instantaneous speed is often quite different from the average speed.

You can calculate the average speed between A and B as follows: Let the (t, d) coordinates of A and B be $A(t_1, d_1)$ and $B(t_2, d_2)$.

$$v_{ave} = \frac{\Delta d}{\Delta t} = \frac{d_2 - d_1}{t_2 - t_1}$$

$$= \frac{20 \text{ m} - 10 \text{ m}}{4 \text{ s} - 2 \text{ s}}$$

$$= \frac{10 \text{ m}}{2 \text{ s}}$$

$$= 5 \text{ m/s}$$

Example 3.1 Average Speeds in a Round Trip

You leave home to visit a friend and drive 100 miles east. The trip takes two hours. On the return trip home, you drive through a rainstorm, and take three hours, driving 100 miles west, to return. Calculate (a) the average speed driving east to your friend's home, (b) the average speed driving west to your home, and (c) the average speed for the total round trip.

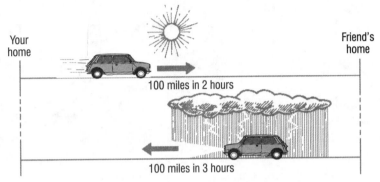

100 miles in 2 hours

100 miles in 3 hours

Solution: (a) Driving east to your friend's home:

$$v_{ave} = \frac{\Delta d}{\Delta t} = \frac{100 \text{ mi}}{2 \text{ h}} = 50 \text{ mi/h} \quad \text{or} \quad 50 \text{ mph}$$

(b) Driving west to your home:

$$v_{ave} = \frac{\Delta d}{\Delta t} = \frac{100 \text{ mi}}{3 \text{ h}} = 33.3 \text{ mi/h} \quad \text{or} \quad 33.3 \text{ mph}$$

(c) Driving the round trip:

$$v_{ave} = \frac{\Delta d}{\Delta t} = \frac{200 \text{ mi}}{5 \text{ h}} = 40 \text{ mi/h} \quad \text{or} \quad 40 \text{ mph}$$

During the trip to your friend's home, your average speed is 50 mph. On the return trip, you average 33.3 mph. For the total round trip, your average speed is 40 mph. Notice that the average for the round trip does not equal the average of the eastbound and westbound averages. Can you explain why?

Velocity

In Example 3.1, the speed and direction of two trips were important—50 mph east and 33.3 mph west. When we state the speed and direction of an object's motion, we are stating the object's **velocity**. Velocity **v** is a vector quantity. (Remember, we use boldface to represent vector quantities.) Speed v is the magnitude of the object's velocity. Speed is a scalar quantity.

If an object moves with a constant velocity, it moves with constant speed along a straight-line path. But constant speed and constant velocity are not the same thing. A race car can travel around a circular race track at constant speed, but its velocity is continuously changing because its direction is continuously changing.

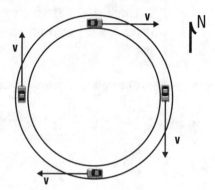

Figure 3.3
On a circular race track, a car's speed can be constant, but its velocity changes continuously.

You can calculate velocity, a vector, as a ratio. But instead of a scalar value for distance traveled, you need to use *displacement*.

Thus,

$$\text{Speed} = \frac{\text{distance}}{\text{time}}$$

$$\text{Velocity} = \frac{\text{displacement}}{\text{time}}$$

Displacement is a vector that defines the distance and direction between two positions. For example, Cincinnati is 145 km northeast of Louisville. If you fly from Louisville to Cincinnati, your displacement is 145 km northeast. The magnitude of the displacement vector is 145 km—the distance traveled. The direction is northeast. We use the symbol Δ**d** for displacement.

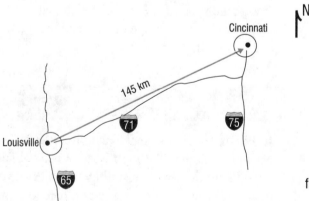

Figure 3.4
The displacement vector from Louisville to Cincinnati is 145 km northeast.

$$\boxed{\begin{array}{c} \text{Average velocity} = \dfrac{\text{displacement}}{\text{time interval}} \\[2mm] \mathbf{v}_{ave} = \dfrac{\Delta \mathbf{d}}{\Delta t} \end{array}}$$

What is your average velocity if your flight from Louisville to Cincinnati takes 0.8 hour?

Example 3.2 Average Velocity is Not Average Speed

A bicyclist travels east for 3 kilometers in 5 minutes, then turns north and travels 4 kilometers in 5 minutes. Is the magnitude of the average velocity the same as the average speed for each leg of the trip? For the total trip?

Solution: The bicycle trip has two legs: One has a displacement of 3 km east, and one has a displacement of 4 km north. The net displacement is the vector sum. Since the two legs are perpendicular, the three vectors form a right triangle. The magnitude of the net displacement can be found using the Pythagorean theorem:

$$c^2 = 3^2 + 4^2$$
$$= 9 + 16$$
$$= 25$$
$$c = 5 \text{ km}$$

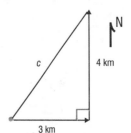

For the eastbound leg, the displacement is 3 km east:

$$v_{ave} = \frac{\Delta d}{\Delta t} = \frac{3 \text{ km}}{5 \text{ min}} \cdot 60 \frac{\text{min}}{\text{h}} = 36 \text{ km/h}$$

$$\mathbf{v}_{ave} = \frac{\Delta \mathbf{d}}{\Delta t} = \frac{3 \text{ km east}}{5 \text{ min}} \cdot 60 \frac{\text{min}}{\text{h}} = 36 \text{ km/h east}$$

$$v_{ave} = \text{magnitude of } \mathbf{v}_{ave} \text{ for the eastbound leg}$$

For the northbound leg, the displacement is 4 km north:

$$v_{ave} = \frac{\Delta d}{\Delta t} = \frac{4 \text{ km}}{5 \text{ min}} \cdot 60 \frac{\text{min}}{\text{h}} = 48 \text{ km/h}$$

$$\mathbf{v}_{ave} = \frac{\Delta \mathbf{d}}{\Delta t} = \frac{4 \text{ km north}}{5 \text{ min}} \cdot 60 \frac{\text{min}}{\text{h}} = 48 \text{ km/h north}$$

$$v_{ave} = \text{magnitude of } \mathbf{v}_{ave} \text{ for the northbound leg}$$

For the total trip, the distance traveled is 3 km + 4 km = 7 km, and the time interval is 5 min + 5 min = 10 min. The displacement is 5 km northeast:

$$v_{ave} = \frac{\Delta d}{\Delta t} = \frac{7 \text{ km}}{10 \text{ min}} \cdot 60 \frac{\text{min}}{\text{h}} = 42 \text{ km/h}$$

$$\mathbf{v}_{ave} = \frac{\Delta \mathbf{d}}{\Delta t} = \frac{5 \text{ km northeast}}{10 \text{ min}} \cdot 60 \frac{\text{min}}{\text{h}} = 30 \text{ km/h northeast}$$

$v_{ave} \neq$ magnitude of $\mathbf{v}_{ave}$ for the total trip.

Example 3.2 illustrates a general property of speed and velocity: When an object travels from one point to another, the average speed depends on the path traveled but the average velocity does not. This is because you use the actual distance traveled to calculate average speed but you use the displacement vector to calculate average velocity. The displacement vector depends on only the object's initial and final locations, not the path traveled.

Acceleration

Velocity describes the motion of an object as the rate of change of its position. **Acceleration** describes the rate of change of an object's velocity. Acceleration is a vector. We use the symbol **a** to represent acceleration, and a to represent the magnitude.

You can accelerate an object by changing its speed, its direction of motion, or both its speed and direction. When you accelerate your car in a straight line from a stoplight, you are changing your speed. For example, suppose you are stopped, so that at time $t = 0$ seconds, your speed $v = 0$ km per hour; and in 6 seconds you increase your speed to 20 km per hour. These two data points are plotted on a (t, v) coordinate plane in Figures 3.5 and 3.6.

Table 3.2

Time, t	Speed, v
0 s	0 km/h
6 s	20 km/h

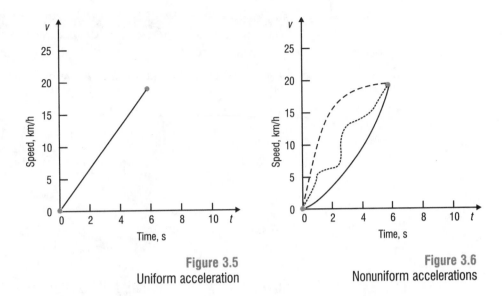

Figure 3.5
Uniform acceleration

Figure 3.6
Nonuniform accelerations

In Figure 3.5, we have drawn the speed change as a constant. This is constant, or uniform, acceleration. Three other possible ways of changing speed are shown in Figure 3.6. These are nonuniform accelerations. Regardless of how the speed changes from 0 s to 6 s, the two values of speed (0 km/h and 20 km/h) can be used to calculate acceleration. But the ratio is the **average acceleration** between these times.

$$\text{Average acceleration} = \frac{\text{velocity change}}{\text{time interval}}$$

$$\mathbf{a}_{ave} = \frac{\Delta \mathbf{v}}{\Delta t}$$

For the data in Table 3.2, we can use magnitudes since the direction of the car's motion does not change. In this case, the acceleration is in the same direction as velocity.

$$a_{ave} = \frac{\Delta v}{\Delta t} = \frac{v_2 - v_1}{t_2 - t_1}$$

$$= \frac{20 \text{ km/h} - 0 \text{ km/h}}{6 \text{ s} - 0 \text{ s}}$$

$$= \frac{20 \text{ km/h}}{6 \text{ s}}$$

$$= 3.33 \text{ km/h per s}$$

On average, during the six seconds of acceleration, the car's speed changes by 3.33 km/h each second.

Example 3.3 Acceleration of an Airliner

A pilot increases the takeoff speed of an airliner from 20 ft/s to 200 ft/s in 30 seconds. Find the magnitude of the average acceleration of the airliner.

Solution:
$$a_{ave} = \frac{\Delta v}{\Delta t} = \frac{200 \text{ ft/s} - 20 \text{ ft/s}}{30 \text{ s}}$$

$$= \frac{180 \text{ ft/s}}{30 \text{ s}}$$

$$= 6.0 \text{ ft/s /s} \quad \text{or} \quad 6.0 \text{ ft/s}^2$$

During the takeoff acceleration, the airliner's speed increases an average of 6.0 ft/s each second.

If the speed of an object is decreasing, Δv is negative and a is negative. In this case, negative acceleration means the object is slowing down. We call this *deceleration*.

Figure 3.7 shows the graph of speed versus time for a motorcycle as it moves from one stoplight to another. Section A of the graph shows the motorcycle's acceleration as it starts from rest and increases its speed in first gear. Section B shows deceleration as the gears are shifted from first to second. Sections C and D show acceleration and deceleration for second gear. For which gear is acceleration greater, first or second? How do you know?

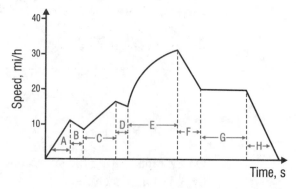

Figure 3.7
Speed versus time for a motorcycle

Section E shows acceleration in third gear. What is different about Section E compared to A and C? Section F shows deceleration as the motorcycle's brakes are applied.

What happens to the speed during Section G? What is the acceleration during this time?

Describe what is shown in Section H.

Angular Speed

Speed and velocity are rates of linear motion. *Angular speed* is a rate of rotational motion. An object such as a bicycle is in linear motion when it moves from one point to another along a straight line. The wheel of the bicycle also is in rotational motion. If you ride along on the bicycle, you will see the front wheel rotate. A point on the wheel's rim moves through an angle as the wheel rotates about its axis.

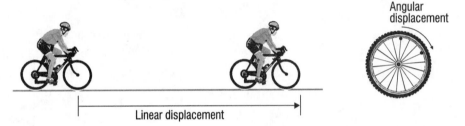

Linear displacement

Figure 3.8
A moving bicycle is in linear motion.
To the rider, the front wheel is in rotational motion.

Linear displacement is the distance the bicycle moves to the right. Angular displacement is the angle through which the wheel rotates. In Figure 3.8, the wheel rotates clockwise. In this book, we will describe rotational motion as clockwise or counterclockwise. But we will not use vectors to describe rotational motion.

The bicycle's speed is the magnitude of linear displacement divided by the time interval. The wheel's **angular speed** ω is the angular displacement $\Delta\theta$ divided by the time interval Δt.

$$\text{Angular speed} = \frac{\text{angular displacement}}{\text{time interval}}$$

$$\omega = \frac{\Delta\theta}{\Delta t}$$

The symbol for angular speed ω is the Greek letter *omega*. The most common unit for angular speed is radians per second, where angular displacement $\Delta\theta$ is measured in radians. Recall from Section 2.1 that

$$1 \text{ revolution} = 360° = 2\pi \text{ radians}$$

Example 3.4 Angular Speed of a Second Hand

Calculate the angular speed of the second hand of a clock in radians per second.

Solution: The second hand makes one revolution in one minute. Therefore its angular speed is 1 revolution/min or 1 rpm.

$$\omega = 1 \text{ rpm}$$

$$= 1\frac{\text{rev}}{\text{min}} \cdot \frac{2\pi \text{ rad}}{\text{rev}} \cdot \frac{1 \text{ min}}{60 \text{ s}} = 0.105 \text{ rad/s}$$

The angular speed of the second hand of a clock is 0.105 radian per second.

Suppose the second hand of the clock in Example 3.4 is 10 cm long. What is the speed, in cm/s, of the tip of the second hand?

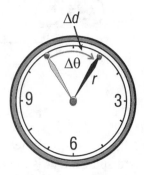

Figure 3.9

In an interval of time Δt, the second hand sweeps through an angular displacement $\Delta\theta$. Let Δd represent the distance traveled by the tip of the second hand. Notice that Δd is a fraction of a circle's circumference. Remember that angular displacement measured in radians is

$$\Delta\theta = \frac{\Delta d}{r} \quad \text{and therefore} \quad \Delta d = r\Delta\theta$$

The speed is the ratio of distance traveled to the time interval.

$$v = \frac{\Delta d}{\Delta t} = \frac{r\Delta\theta}{\Delta t} = r\omega$$

The length of the second hand is the radius r.

$$v = r\omega = (10 \text{ cm})(0.105 \text{ rad/s}) = 1.05 \text{ cm/s}$$

The speed of the second hand demonstrates a general relationship between speed v and angular speed ω:

> For any point on a rotating body, if the distance from the center of rotation to the point is r and the angular speed of rotation is ω, the speed v of the point is

$$v = r\omega.$$

Example 3.5 Speed of a Vacuum Cleaner Belt

A vacuum cleaner motor shaft is 1.5 inches in diameter and turns at an angular speed of 1728 rpm. As the shaft turns, it moves a belt, which turns a brush. The brush is 4 inches in diameter.

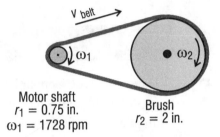

Motor shaft
$r_1 = 0.75$ in.
$\omega_1 = 1728$ rpm

Brush
$r_2 = 2$ in.

A vacuum cleaner motor, belt, and brush assembly

What is the belt speed in inches per second? What is the angular speed of the brush, in revolutions per minute?

Solution: Let r_1 and ω_1 represent the radius and angular speed of the motor shaft. Convert units of ω_1 from rpm to radians per second:

$$\omega_1 = 1728 \frac{\text{rev}}{\text{min}} \cdot \frac{2\pi \text{ rad}}{\text{rev}} \cdot \frac{1 \text{ min}}{60 \text{ s}} = 181 \text{ rad/s}$$

The belt moves with the same speed as a point on the outside circumference of the motor shaft. Let v_{belt} represent the speed of the belt.

$$v_{\text{belt}} = r_1\omega_1 = (0.75 \text{ in})(181\tfrac{\text{rad}}{\text{s}}) = 136 \text{ in/s}$$

The belt also moves with the same speed as a point on the outside circumference of the brush. Let r_2 and ω_2 represent the radius and angular speed of the brush.

$$v_{belt} = 136 \text{ in/s} = r_2 \omega_2$$

$$= (2 \text{ in}) \omega_2$$

$$\omega_2 = \frac{136 \dfrac{\text{in}}{\text{s}}}{2 \text{ in}} = 68 \text{ rad/s}$$

Convert units to rpm:

$$\omega_2 = 68 \ \frac{\text{rad}}{\text{s}} \cdot \frac{1 \text{ rev}}{2\pi \text{ rad}} \cdot \frac{60 \text{ s}}{1 \text{ min}} = 649 \text{ rev/min}$$

The speed of the belt is 136 in/s. The angular speed of the brush is 649 rpm.

Angular Acceleration

Have you ever seen an ice skater spin? He starts with his arms extended with an initial angular speed ω_1. As he brings his arms in closer to his chest, his angular speed increases, and reaches a final value ω_2. The change in angular speed is

$$\Delta\omega = \omega_2 - \omega_1.$$

Figure 3.10
A skater increases his angular speed by bringing his arms in closer to his chest.

This change in angular speed occurs over a time interval Δt. The skater's **angular acceleration** α (the Greek letter *alpha*) is the ratio of the change in angular speed to the time interval. We will not use vectors to describe angular acceleration. In this book, angular acceleration will be treated as a scalar quantity.

$$\text{Angular acceleration} = \frac{\text{change in angular speed}}{\text{time interval}}$$

$$\alpha = \frac{\Delta\omega}{\Delta t}$$

Example 3.6 Angular Acceleration of a Wheel

A car's brake is applied to a wheel for 5 seconds, reducing the wheel's angular speed from 220 rad/s to 180 rad/s. What is the angular acceleration?

Solution: The initial angular speed ω_1 is 220 rad/s, and the final angular speed ω_2 is 180 rad/s.

$$\alpha = \frac{\Delta\omega}{\Delta t} = \frac{\omega_2 - \omega_1}{\Delta t} = \frac{180 \text{ rad/s} - 220 \text{ rad/s}}{5 \text{ s}}$$

$$\alpha = \frac{40 \text{ rad/s}}{5 \text{ s}} = 8 \text{ rad/s}^2$$

The negative value of acceleration indicates that the wheel is slowing down—it is being decelerated. The wheel decelerates at a rate of 8 rad/s².

Summary

- Speed is a measure of the rate of motion of an object. It is the ratio of distance traveled to the time interval. Speed is a scalar quantity.

- Velocity is the ratio of displacement to the time interval. Velocity and displacement are vector quantities. Speed is the magnitude of velocity.

- Acceleration is a measure of the rate of change of an object's velocity. It is the ratio of change in velocity to the time interval.

- Angular speed is a measure of the rate of rotational motion of an object. It is the ratio of angular displacement to time interval.

- Angular acceleration is a measure of the rate of change of an object's angular speed. It is the ratio of change in angular speed to the time interval.

Exercises

1. What are the SI units for speed? Acceleration? Angular speed? Angular acceleration?

2. Explain the difference between speed and velocity.

3. Explain the difference between velocity and acceleration.

4. In qualifying for a race, a car completes one lap around a 1.5-mile track in 34.662 seconds.

   (a) What is the car's average speed in miles per hour?

   (b) What is the car's average velocity? Explain your answer.

5. An airplane's propeller completes one revolution in 65 ms. (ms = 10^{-3} s)

   (a) What is the angular speed in rpm? In rad/s?

   (b) The angular speed increases from the initial value (in part a) with an average acceleration of 7.3 rad/s^2 for 4.0 seconds. What is the propeller's final angular speed?

6. A printer head moves 15.6 cm from the left margin of the paper to the location where a line starts. The time required for the move is 0.030 second. What is the average speed of the printer head?

7. The Elco Voltmeter Company has a robot part-delivery system that moves at a speed of 3 ft/s. The path that the robot follows from the stock room through the assembly area is 570 feet in length. How much time is required for the robot to travel this path?

8. Speedlite Air Charter sends one of its airplanes from San Antonio to New Orleans to pick up Juanita and take her to Memphis, Tennessee, to a repair job. The plane flies 500 miles east to New Orleans in 1.81 hours. After picking up Juanita, the plane flies 370 miles north to Memphis in 1.41 hours.

   (a) What is the speed of the plane from San Antonio to New Orleans?

   (b) What is the speed of the plane from New Orleans to Memphis?

   (c) What is the speed of the plane for the combined flying time? Ignore any time on the ground in New Orleans.

   (d) What is the velocity of the plane for the complete trip? Ignore any time on the ground in New Orleans.

   (e) What is the magnitude of the velocity of the plane for the complete trip?

9. A motor turns 21.6 revolutions in 0.75 second. What is the angular speed of the motor in rpm? In radians per second?

10. A winch has a drum diameter of 2 feet. It turns at a rate of 3 rpm. How much cable will it pull in 5 minutes?

11. B.U.S. Chemical Company has a large compressor to compress hydrogen gas that is a by-product of its chlorine production. The compressor turns at 445 rpm.

    (a) What is the angular speed of the compressor in rev/s?

    (b) What is the angular speed of the compressor in rad/s?

12. The torque applied to the input shaft of the compressor in Exercise 11 is 2×10^4 N·m. How much work is done on the compressor in one second?

13. A Navy air-to-air missile is launched from an airplane with a speed of 1100 ft/s. Five seconds after launch the missile has a speed of 2460 ft/s. What is the average acceleration during the first five seconds of flight?

14. A semi-trailer truck has a speed of 60 mph and an engine speed of 1850 rpm. The driver accelerates to 65 mph in 26 seconds while the engine speed increases to 2005 rpm.

    (a) What is the linear acceleration of the truck in ft/s?

    (b) What is the angular acceleration of the engine in rpm/s?

    (c) What is the angular acceleration of the engine in rad/s²?

15. The instantaneous linear speed of an object moving in a circle can be found from its angular speed and the radius of the circle, <u>if the angular speed is expressed in units of rad/s</u>.

    linear speed = (radius)(angular speed)

    A fan blade is turning at 345 rpm. The radius of the fan blade is 1.4 m. What is the linear speed of the tip of the fan blade?

16. A 150-ft-diameter Ferris wheel completes one revolution in 45 seconds.

    (a) How far does a chair on the Ferris wheel travel in one revolution?

    (b) What is the linear speed of the chair in ft/s?

    (c) What is the angular speed of the chair in rad/s?

3.2 RATE IN FLUID SYSTEMS

Objectives

- Define volume flow rate.

- Solve problems using the volume flow rate equation.

- Define mass flow rate.

- Solve problems using the mass flow rate equation.

- Explain how volume and mass flow rates can be measured.

Rates in fluid systems describe the motion of liquids and gases. Fluids in motion have speed and acceleration. However, we use two different rates to describe how quickly fluids flow—*volume flow rate* and *mass flow rate*.

For example, fans move air to control temperatures inside buildings, to cool electronic components in computer systems, and to force air into combustion chambers in jet engines. In all of these fluid systems, the amount of air moved by the fan over a period of time can be specified as a fluid flow rate.

To find out more about rate in fluid systems, follow the links at www.learningincontext.com.

Volume Flow Rate

Let V represent the volume of fluid in a container. Suppose fluid flows out of the container, so that V changes in an interval of time. We use ΔV to represent the change in volume, or the volume of fluid moved in a time interval Δt. The **volume flow rate** is the change in volume per unit time, or the ratio $\dfrac{\Delta V}{\Delta t}$. We use a dot over the variable to represent *rate of change*.

Thus, $\dot{V}$ represents volume flow rate.

$$\text{Volume flow rate} = \frac{\text{change in volume}}{\text{time interval}}$$

$$\dot{V} = \frac{\Delta V}{\Delta t}$$

Volume can be measured in many units, for example m^3, cm^3, ft^3, in^3, liters, or gallons. Thus, volume flow rate can be measured in m^3/s, ft^3/min, liters/h, etc.

Example 3.7 Volume Flow Rate of Liquid Oxygen

The space shuttle's main engine burns a mixture of hydrogen and oxygen as its fuel. The shuttle's external fuel tank stores liquid hydrogen and liquid oxygen in separate tanks. The liquid oxygen tank holds 143,000 gallons. During liftoff, the flow rate of liquid oxygen to the shuttle's main engine is 16,800 gallons per minute. At this rate, how long can liquid oxygen be supplied to the main engine?

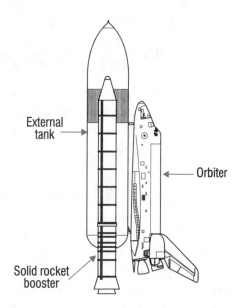

External tank

Orbiter

Solid rocket booster

The space shuttle external tank contains a liquid oxygen tank and a liquid hydrogen tank.

Solution: The volume of fluid moved is 143,000 gal, and the flow rate is 16,800 gal/min. Solve the volume flow rate equation for the time interval.

$$\dot{V} = \frac{\Delta V}{\Delta t}$$

$$\Delta t = \frac{\Delta V}{\dot{V}} = \frac{143,000 \text{ gal}}{16,800 \, \frac{\text{gal}}{\text{min}}} = 8.51 \text{ min}$$

Liquid oxygen can be supplied to the main engine for 8.51 minutes.

Mass Flow Rate

The **mass flow rate** is the mass of fluid moved per unit time. We use the symbol m to represent mass and $\dot{m}$ to represent mass flow rate. If Δm is the change in mass, or the mass of fluid moved in a time interval Δt, the mass flow rate is

$$\text{Mass flow rate} = \frac{\text{change in mass}}{\text{time interval}}$$

$$\dot{m} = \frac{\Delta m}{\Delta t}$$

Example 3.8 Mass Flow Rate of Liquid Oxygen

The space shuttle's external fuel tank holds 226,000 pounds of liquid hydrogen. If all the fuel in the external tank is consumed during the first 8.5 minutes of flight, what is the mass flow rate of liquid hydrogen, in slugs per second?

Solution: A mass of 1 slug weighs 32.2 pounds. Convert the weight to mass:

$$\Delta m = 226,000 \text{ lb} \cdot \frac{1 \text{ slug}}{32.2 \text{ lb}} = 7019 \text{ slugs}$$

$$\dot{m} = \frac{\Delta m}{\Delta t} = \frac{7019 \text{ slugs}}{8.5 \text{ min}} \cdot \frac{1 \text{ min}}{60 \text{ s}} = 13.8 \text{ slugs/s}$$

The mass flow rate of liquid hydrogen is 13.8 slugs/s.

Refer to Appendix F
for a career link
to this concept.

Measuring Fluid Rates

Methods for measuring volume and mass flow rates vary, depending on the situation. The simplest, most direct method to find average flow rate is to collect fluid and measure the amount of fluid collected over a time interval. The volume or mass of fluid collected divided by the time interval is the average flow rate. *Flowmeters* use indirect methods that do not significantly interrupt the flow. These instruments typically measure fluid properties such as pressure and velocity. From these values, the instruments can calculate volume or mass flow rate.

For example, suppose an instrument measures the speed of a fluid flowing through a pipe. The measurement is taken over a time interval Δt. This interval is small enough that the fluid speed does not change during the measurement. Now imagine a particle suspended in the fluid, and moving with the fluid at the fluid speed. How far does this particle move in the time interval Δt? As shown in Figure 3.11, if the fluid speed is v, it moves a distance $L = v\Delta t$.

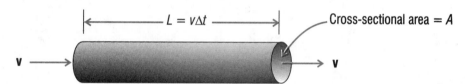

Figure 3.11
A particle moving at constant speed v
moves a distance $v\Delta t$ in a time interval Δt.

What volume of fluid enters this section of pipe from the left during the time interval Δt? As long as this fluid completely fills the pipe, the volume of the entering fluid must equal the volume of the section of pipe shown. Let A represent the cross-sectional area of the pipe. The volume of the pipe section is the product of the length L and cross-sectional area A. Thus, the volume of fluid ΔV moving through the pipe section in time interval Δt is:

$$\Delta V = AL$$

$$= Av\Delta t$$

Divide both sides of this equation by Δt:

$$\frac{\Delta V}{\Delta t} = \frac{Av\Delta t}{\Delta t} = Av$$

The ratio $\frac{\Delta V}{\Delta t}$ is the volume flow rate $\dot{V}$. We have shown that, if an instrument measures a fluid's speed, it can calculate the volume flow rate by multiplying the speed by the cross-sectional area of the flow.

$$\begin{array}{c c c} \text{Volume flow} \\ \text{rate} \end{array} = \begin{array}{c} \text{cross-sectional} \\ \text{area} \end{array} \times \begin{array}{c} \text{fluid} \\ \text{speed} \end{array}$$

$$\dot{V} = Av$$

To find the mass flow rate, you can use this equation and the density of the fluid. Density is the ratio of mass to volume. If the density ρ of the fluid does not change as it flows through the section of pipe,

$$\text{Density} = \frac{\text{mass moved}}{\text{volume moved}}$$

$$\rho = \frac{\Delta m}{\Delta V}$$

Solve for Δm:

$$\Delta m = \rho \Delta V$$

Divide both sides of this equation by the time interval Δt:

$$\frac{\Delta m}{\Delta t} = \rho \frac{\Delta V}{\Delta t}$$

$$\dot{m} = \rho \dot{V}$$

Since $\dot{V} = Av$, substitute:

$$\dot{m} = \rho Av$$

If an instrument measures a fluid's speed, it can calculate the mass flow rate by multiplying three terms:

$$\begin{array}{c} \text{Mass flow} \\ \text{rate} \end{array} = \begin{array}{c} \text{fluid} \\ \text{density} \end{array} \times \begin{array}{c} \text{cross-sectional} \\ \text{area} \end{array} \times \begin{array}{c} \text{fluid} \\ \text{speed} \end{array}$$

$$\dot{m} = \rho Av$$

Example 3.9 Speed of Liquid Oxygen

During liftoff, the space shuttle's liquid oxygen flows from the storage tank to the main engine. If it flows through a discharge pipe of diameter 17 inches, what is the speed of the liquid oxygen in the pipe in feet per second?

Solution: From Example 3.7, the volume flow rate is 16,800 gallons per minute. There are 231 in³ per gallon, so

$$\dot{V} = 16{,}800 \; \frac{\text{gal}}{\text{min}} \cdot 231 \frac{\text{in}^3}{\text{gal}} \cdot \frac{1 \text{ min}}{60 \text{ s}} = 64{,}680 \text{ in}^3/\text{s}$$

The radius of the pipe is 8.5 inches. The cross-sectional area is

$$A = \pi r^2 = \pi (8.5 \text{ in})^2 = 227 \text{ in}^2$$

Solve the volume flow rate equation for v.

$$\dot{V} = Av$$

$$v = \frac{\dot{V}}{A}$$

$$= \frac{64{,}680 \; \frac{\text{in}^3}{\text{s}}}{227 \text{ in}^2} = 285 \text{ in/s}$$

Convert to feet per second.

$$v = 285 \frac{\text{in}}{\text{s}} \cdot \frac{1 \text{ ft}}{12 \text{ in}} = 23.75 \text{ ft/s}$$

The speed of the liquid oxygen in the discharge pipe is 23.75 feet per second.

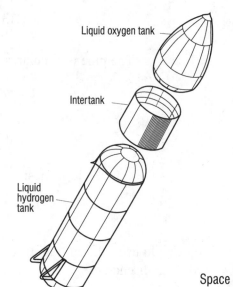

Liquid oxygen tank

Intertank

Liquid hydrogen tank

Figure 3.12
Space shuttle external tank components

Example 3.10 Pipe Diameter for Liquid Hydrogen Flow

You are designing a discharge pipe for the space shuttle's liquid hydrogen tank. The design engineer wants the hydrogen fluid speed to be eight times the oxygen speed. What diameter pipe should you use in the design? The weight density of liquid hydrogen is 4.42 lb/ft³.

Solution: Convert weight density to mass density:

$$\rho = 4.42 \ \frac{\text{lb}}{\text{ft}^3} \cdot \frac{1 \ \text{slug}}{32.2 \ \text{lb}} = 0.137 \ \frac{\text{slug}}{\text{ft}^3}$$

The liquid hydrogen speed is eight times the liquid oxygen speed, found in Example 3.9.

$$v = 8 \times 23.75 \ \text{ft/s} = 190 \ \text{ft/s}$$

From Example 3.8, the mass flow rate of liquid hydrogen is 13.8 slugs/s. Use the mass flow rate equation, and solve for the cross-sectional area.

$$\dot{m} = \rho A v$$

$$A = \frac{\dot{m}}{\rho v}$$

$$= \frac{13.8 \ \dfrac{\text{slugs}}{\text{s}}}{0.137 \ \dfrac{\text{slug}}{\text{ft}^3} \cdot 190 \ \dfrac{\text{ft}}{\text{s}}} = 0.530 \ \text{ft}^2$$

The pipe is circular, so its cross-sectional area is

$$A = \pi r^2$$

$$r = \sqrt{\frac{A}{\pi}} = \sqrt{\frac{0.530 \ \text{ft}^2}{\pi}} = 0.41 \ \text{ft}$$

Convert to inches:

$$r = 0.41 \ \text{ft} \cdot \frac{12 \ \text{in}}{\text{ft}} = 4.9 \ \text{in}$$

You should use a 4.9-in.-radius, or 9.8-in.-diameter pipe for the liquid hydrogen discharge.

Fluid systems that measure and control flow rates include bottling plants for products such as soft drinks, dishwashing liquid, lubricating oil, and bottled water. In these uses, a pump moves the fluid from a mixing tank to a bottling machine. The rate of fluid flow is set so that the bottles are filled quickly.

Figure 3.13
Bottling machine

City water supply systems generally use large-diameter pipes to carry water to homes and business places. In fluid systems that use large-diameter pipes, the speed of the fluid is slow. But the volume flow rate is high. Using smaller pipes and higher flow speeds might also meet the demand. But the work required to move the same amount of water through smaller pipes would be higher and, thus, less efficient.

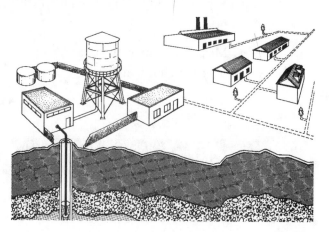

Figure 3.14
A city water supply system

In the case of gases (especially air, which is in common use), it's necessary to put the storage tank as close to the point of use as possible. The flow rate of compressed air through a hose or pipe is reduced when the air has to travel a long distance rather than a short distance. This reduced flow rate is caused by frictional losses between the moving air and the inside surface of the hose or pipe. (You'll learn more about friction in Chapter 4.) Locating the compressor and storage tank close to the point of use makes it easier to maintain the required volume flow rate of a system.

Figure 3.15
Control of flow rate from air compressor to jackhammer is important.

Summary

- Volume flow rate is the volume of fluid moved divided by the time interval over which it is moved.

- Typical volume flow rates are measured in gal/min, ft³/s, liters/s, or m³/s.

- Mass flow rate is the mass of fluid moved divided by the time interval over which it is moved.

- Typical mass flow rates are slugs/s and kg/s.

Exercises

The following relations will be useful when you need to make unit conversions.

$$1 \text{ gal} = 231 \text{ in}^3 = 0.1337 \text{ ft}^3 = 3.785 \times 10^{-3} \text{ m}^3$$

1. Label the following quantities as volume flow rate, mass flow rate, or neither.

   (a) 12 slugs/min   (b) 0.4 cm³/min   (c) 50 g/s   (d) 7.8 L/h

   (e) 6.9 kg/h   (f) 4.2 m²/s   (g) 0.8 gal/s   (h) 2.5 gal/min

2. Some people develop partial blockages of blood flow due to deposits of plaque on the inside walls of their arteries. Suppose a blockage reduces the diameter of an artery by one-half but the speed of blood flow does not change. Does the blood volume flow rate decrease by one-half? Explain your answer.

3. The compressor of a car's air-conditioning system pumps 5 kg of refrigerant in 3 minutes. What is the mass flow rate through the system in kg/min?

4. The pump on a truck used to fight brush fires empties the 1200-gallon tank on the truck in 4.8 minutes. What is the flow rate through the pump in gpm (gallons/minute)?

5. A large diesel truck has a speed of 60 mph. The fuel consumption of the truck at this speed is 7 miles/gallon.

   (a) What is the flow rate, in gpm, through the fuel injection pump on the engine?

   (b) What is the flow rate expressed as in^3/s?

6. The pump for a water-cooling system delivers 18 gpm of water through a pipe with an inside diameter of 1.00 inch.

   (a) What is the speed of water through the pipe in ft/min?

   (b) If the pressure change in the pipe is –23 psi, how much work, in ft·lb, is done in one second to move the water through the pipe?

7. The thrust of a rocket engine, F_{thrust}, can be calculated with mass flow rate. Let v represent the speed of the exhaust gas in m/s, and let $\dot{m}$ represent the "burn rate" or the rate at which fuel is used. $\dot{m}$ is the mass flow rate in kg/s. $\dot{m}$ will always be a negative number since the rocket is using fuel, not making fuel.

$$F_{thrust} = -v\dot{m}$$

   (a) What are the units for thrust using this equation?

   (b) A rocket engine has an exhaust velocity of 12,000 m/s and burns 580 kg of fuel in 2 minutes. Find the thrust of the rocket engine.

8. Mass flow is the critical factor in many industrial chemical reactions. Hydrogen gas feeding a hydrogenation reaction has a density of 1.24×10^{-3} g/cm^3 and a speed of 75.3 cm/s through a pipe with a diameter of 1.27 cm. What is the mass flow rate $\dot{m}$ of hydrogen to the reaction?

9. When a boat's propeller rotates, it moves forward in the water in the same way (but less efficiently) that a screw moves forward when it rotates in a block of wood. The propeller's *pitch* is the horizontal distance the propeller moves forward in one complete revolution, without the influence of drag. For example, a propeller with a 6-in. pitch moves forward 6 inches per revolution.

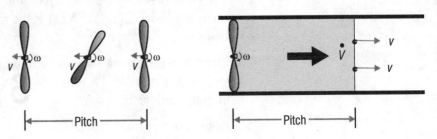

A propeller can also be used in a flowmeter. Water moving past the propeller forces it to rotate. A propeller with a 6-in. pitch will rotate one complete revolution when a column of water 6 inches long flows past the propeller.

(a) Water flows through a pipe containing a flowmeter with a 6-in.-pitch propeller. The propeller turns at 90 rpm. What is the speed, in inches per second, of the water?

(b) The diameter of the pipe is 4.5 inches. What is the pipe's cross-sectional area?

(c) Calculate the volume flow rate of the water, in cubic inches per second.

(d) Calculate the volume flow rate in gallons per minute.

3.3 RATE IN ELECTRICAL SYSTEMS

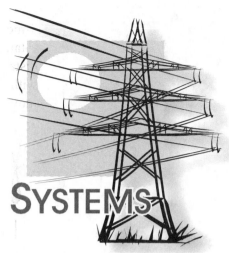

Objectives

- Define electrical current as a rate.

- Describe what is measured by ammeters and voltmeters. Explain how to connect an ammeter and a voltmeter in an electrical circuit.

- Explain why electrons travel at speeds much lower than the speed of light in a conductor.

- Define frequency and period. Explain the relationship between frequency and period.

In mechanical systems, the important rates are speed (rate of change of position) and acceleration (rate of change of velocity). In fluid systems, the important rates are volume flow rate (rate of change of volume) and mass flow rate (rate of change of mass). In electrical systems, or circuits, the most important rate is current. In Section 2.3 you learned that current is rate of electrical charge flow.

INTERNET *connection*

To find out more about rate in electrical systems, follow the links at **www.learningincontext.com**.

Electric Current

When a conductor joins two objects of different electric potential, charge flows from the higher potential to the lower potential. The potential difference, or voltage difference, is the prime mover that causes charge to move. In a solid conductor, such as a copper wire, it is the electrons that move in the circuit.

Current is a measure of the net charge Δq that passes through a cross-sectional area in a time interval Δt. The electric current I is defined by the following ratio:

$$\text{Electric current} = \frac{\text{charge moved}}{\text{time interval}}$$

$$I = \frac{\Delta q}{\Delta t}$$

Charge is measured in coulombs (C). Current is measured in *amperes* (A). If one coulomb of charge flows through a conductor in a time interval of one second, the electric current is one **ampere**. $1 \text{ A} = 1 \text{ C/s}$.

Example 3.11 Charge Flow in a Motor Circuit

A DC electric motor operates an airplane's landing gear. The current in the motor circuit during operation is 6.8 amperes. It takes 10 seconds to raise the landing gear. How much charge flows through any cross section of the circuit while the landing gear is being raised? How many electrons flow through a cross section of the circuit?

Solution: A current of 6.8 amperes is equal to a flow rate of 6.8 coulombs per second.

$$I = 6.8 \text{ A} = 6.8 \text{ C/s}$$

Use the equation for electric current and solve for the charge moved:

$$I = \frac{\Delta q}{\Delta t}$$

$$\Delta q = I\Delta t$$

$$= \left(6.8 \, \frac{\text{C}}{\text{s}}\right)(10 \text{ s})$$

$$= 68 \text{ C}$$

The charge on one electron is 1.602×10^{-19} C:

$$\text{Number of electrons} = \frac{68 \text{ C}}{1.602 \times 10^{-19} \, \dfrac{\text{C}}{\text{electron}}} = 4.24 \times 10^{20} \text{ electrons}$$

In 10 seconds of operation, 68 coulombs of charge or 4.24×10^{20} electrons flow through a cross section of the motor circuit.

Measuring Current and Voltage

You can measure current in electrical circuits with an **ammeter** and potential difference with a **voltmeter**. Each instrument has two terminals, one labeled positive (+) and one labeled negative (−). But the instruments are not connected in the same way.

An ammeter measures *current through* a circuit element. The ammeter is placed in the conducting path, so the current through the circuit element is the same as the current through the ammeter. This type of connection is called a **series connection**. Figure 3.16 shows a simple DC circuit, where a battery provides a potential difference to a light bulb (the load) and an ammeter is connected in series. A schematic diagram of the circuit is shown in Figure 3.17. Notice that the ammeter is in line with, or in series with the load.

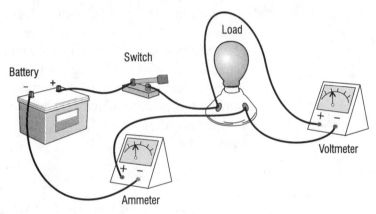

Figure 3.16
A simple DC circuit

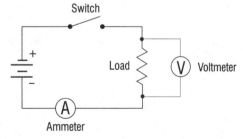

Figure 3.17
A schematic circuit diagram of the DC circuit

A voltmeter measures the potential difference, or *voltage across* a circuit element. The type of connection for measuring voltage, as shown in Figures 3.16 and 3.17, is called a **parallel connection**. The load and the voltmeter appear to be parallel to each other in the circuit diagram. The voltage across the voltmeter is the same as that across the load.

The Speed of Charge Flow

When you close the switch in an electric circuit that contains a battery, a current is generated throughout the circuit almost instantaneously. For example, the light bulb in the circuit in Figure 3.16 appears to glow at the same instant the switch is closed. But in fact there is a slight time delay. The "signal" or electric field from the battery that applies a force on the electrons in the light bulb travels at almost the speed of light through the conductor. But it is *not* the electrons in the conductor that travel at almost the speed of light. It is the electric field. The average speed of the electrons is much less than the speed of light.

A metal conductor has a large number of electrons that move freely about the conductor. These electrons have gained enough energy at room temperature to break their bonds with the metal atoms in the conductor. Since the conductor has a neutral charge, every free electron leaves behind a positive ion. As the free electrons move through the conductor, their paths are constantly being changed by the coulomb forces resulting from interactions between the free electrons and interactions between free electrons and positive ions. A possible random path of a free electron moving through a conductor is shown in Figure 3.18. Between collisions, the average speed of the electron is about 10^6 m/s, or less than one-hundredth the speed of light.

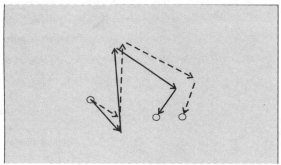

Figure 3.18
A possible path of a free electron in a conductor.
The solid lines show a random path. The dashed lines show
how the random path could be altered by an electric field.

When an electric field, or voltage, is applied to the conductor, a force is exerted on the free electrons (in Figure 3.18, the force is to the right). The force accelerates the electrons between collisions, resulting in a net movement or *drift* in the direction of the force. This drift is the net displacement of the electron along the conductor. Because collisions interrupt the paths of free electrons, the actual **drift velocity** in the conductor is very slow—less than one centimeter per second.

AC Circuits, Frequency, and Period

In AC circuits, current and voltage vary continuously in a certain pattern. Commercial power companies in the United States and Canada generate *60-cycle* alternating current. This means the pattern of variation of current and voltage repeats itself 60 times each second. **Frequency** is a measure of how often a pattern repeats itself. If there are n repetitions, or cycles, of the pattern in a time interval Δt, the frequency f of the pattern is the following ratio:

$$\text{Frequency} = \frac{\text{number of cycles}}{\text{time interval}}$$

$$f = \frac{n}{\Delta t}$$

If f is measured in Hz, then the units of frequency are cycles/second, or **hertz** (Hz).

$$1 \text{ Hz} = 1 \text{ cycle/s.}$$

In calculations, the unit "cycle" is dropped, so you will also use

$$1 \text{ Hz} = 1 \text{ s}^{-1}.$$

The exponent "–1" is shorthand for "reciprocal." You can also write the equation above as

$$1 \text{ Hz} = \frac{1}{1 \text{ s}}.$$

The **period** of a repeating pattern is the time it takes for one complete cycle. The period and frequency are reciprocals. We use T to represent period.

$$T = \frac{1}{f} \quad \text{and} \quad f = \frac{1}{T}$$

If f is measured in Hz, the units of period are seconds.

Figure 3.19 shows current as a function of time for a typical AC circuit. You can measure period from this graph by measuring the time for a complete cycle. Notice that it doesn't matter where in the pattern you start the measurement. You can start where the graph crosses the time axis, at a crest, or at a trough. But you must measure the time interval for a *complete* cycle. For this graph, $T = 4$ ms. The reciprocal is the frequency:

$$f = \frac{1}{T} = \frac{1}{4 \times 10^{-3} \text{ s}} = 250 \text{ s}^{-1} \text{ or } 250 \text{ Hz}$$

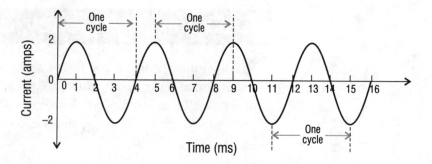

Figure 3.19
Current versus time for a typical AC circuit.
The period is 4 ms and the frequency is 250 Hz.

Voltage and current can also change with a regular pattern that is not smooth like Figure 3.19. In these circuits, voltage is either "on" or "off" and changes abruptly between the two. These patterns are used in microprocessors.

Example 3.12 Period and Frequency in a Microprocessor Circuit

A microprocessor uses a circuit with voltage and current cycles. The current flows in only one direction but alternates in magnitude. The pattern is called a **square wave**. The voltage in the circuit alternates from zero to +3 V, as shown here. The frequency of the square wave is 500 MHz. What is the period?

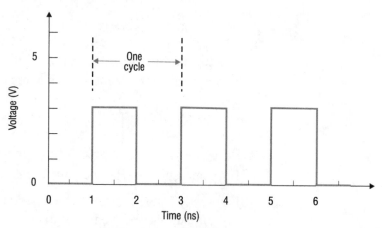

Voltage pattern in a microprocessor circuit

Solution: The period is the reciprocal of the frequency f, where $f = 500$ MHz or 500×10^6 s^{-1}:

$$T = \frac{1}{f} = \frac{1}{500 \times 10^6 \text{ s}^{-1}} = 2 \times 10^{-9}\text{s or 2 ns}$$

The period of the square wave is 2 nanoseconds.

Summary

- Electrical current is a measure of the amount of charge that flows through a cross section of a conductor per unit time. Current is measured in amperes.

- Ammeters measure current. Voltmeters measure voltage. Ammeters are connected in circuits in series. Voltmeters are connected in parallel.

- An electric field applies forces to electrons in a circuit. A change in the electric field travels at nearly the speed of light along a conductor. Electrons travel at speeds much lower than the speed of light.

- Frequency is the rate at which a pattern repeats. Frequency is measured in hertz.

- Period is the time it takes for a pattern to repeat. The period is the reciprocal of the frequency.

Exercises

1. Rate in DC electrical circuits is associated with how fast _____ moves in the circuit.

2. Rate in AC electrical circuits can be associated with both how fast _____ moves in the circuit, and how fast the _____ of charge flow changes.

3. The rate of charge flow in both DC and AC circuits is expressed in units of _____ .

4. To measure the current through a load in a circuit, you connect an ammeter in _____ (series or parallel). To measure the voltage across the load, you connect a voltmeter in _____ (series or parallel).

5. The rate at which the direction of current flow changes in an AC circuit is expressed in units of _____ and is called the _____ of the AC current.

6. A charge of 0.020 coulomb flows from a battery in 0.001 second. What is the current flow during this time period?

7. The gate of a transistor acts like a capacitor and collects charge. If an electron current of 2.6 nanoamperes flows into the gate for 12 microseconds, how much does the charge on the gate change?

8. A transistor gate is positively charged with 45 picocoulombs. The gate is discharged in 3.7 nanoseconds. What is the average current during the time the gate is discharged?

9. An ammeter measures a steady current of 2.5 A flowing through a DC circuit. How long will it take for 2 C of charge to flow past a point in the circuit?

10. Suppose an electric field is applied from the top to the bottom of a conductor.

   (a) What is the direction of the drift velocity of the free electrons in the conductor?

   (b) Explain why the magnitude of the drift velocity is much lower than the actual speed of the free electrons.

11. An ammeter and a voltmeter are used to measure the current through a load and the voltage across the load in a circuit. One of the schematic circuit diagrams below shows the correct way to connect the instruments. Copy the correct diagram and label the ammeter A and the voltmeter V.

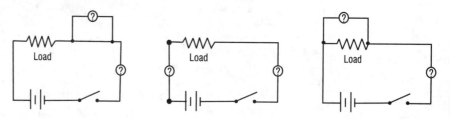

12. The graph of voltage vs time for an AC circuit is shown at the right. The scale for the horizontal axis is 5 microseconds per major division.

   (a) What is the period of the voltage?

   (b) What is the frequency of the voltage?

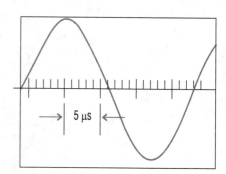

3.4 RATE IN THERMAL SYSTEMS

Objectives

- Define heat flow rate and its SI and English units of measure.
- Describe the heat transfer processes of conduction, convection, and radiation.
- Solve heat transfer rate problems using the heat conduction equation.

Heat Flow Rate

Rate in mechanical, fluid, and electrical systems is the movement of some substance—something that has mass and volume, like automobiles, water, and electrons. Rate in thermal systems is the movement of heat. Heat is not a substance. You learned in Section 1.4 that heat is thermal energy transferred from one body to another because of a temperature difference. The amount of heat that is transferred per unit time is the **heat flow rate**.

If an amount of heat Q is transferred from one body to another in a time interval Δt, the heat flow rate is given by the following ratio

$$\text{Heat flow rate} = \frac{\text{heat transferred}}{\text{time interval}}$$

$$\dot{Q} = \frac{Q}{\Delta t}$$

INTERNET *connection*

To find out more about rate in thermal systems, follow the links at **www.learningincontext.com**.

There are several possible combinations for the units of heat flow rate. Heat transferred can be measured in any energy unit: calories (cal), joules (J), British thermal units (Btu), or foot pounds (ft·lb). The units for time interval can be seconds (s), minutes (min), or hours (h). Therefore, in SI, heat flow rate can be measured in cal/s, cal/min, cal/h, J/s, J/min, or J/h. In the English system, heat flow rate can be measured in Btu/s, Btu/min, Btu/h, ft·lb/s, ft·lb/min, or ft·lb/h.

Table 3.2 gives some useful conversion factors for converting between energy units.

Table 3.2 Energy Conversion Factors

1 cal	=	4.185 J
1 cal	=	3.077 ft·lb
1 Btu	=	1054 J
1 Btu	=	252 cal
1 Btu	=	778 ft·lb
1 ft·lb	=	1.356 J

Example 3.13 Heat Flow Rate in Air Conditioning

Devices are classified by their heat flow rate capacities using the English units "Btu" for "Btu per hour." For example, an air-conditioning unit classified as 15,000 Btu is capable of removing heat from a building at a rate of 15,000 Btu/hr. If this unit runs continuously for 3.5 hours, what amount of heat is transferred? Write the answer in Btu and J.

Solution: $\dot{Q} = \dfrac{Q}{\Delta t}$

$$Q = \dot{Q}\Delta t$$

$$= \left(15{,}000\ \frac{\text{Btu}}{\text{h}}\right)(3.5\ \text{h})$$

$$= 52{,}500\ \text{Btu or } (52{,}500\ \text{Btu})\left(\frac{1054\ \text{J}}{1\ \text{Btu}}\right) = 5.53 \times 10^7\ \text{J}$$

The air-conditioning unit transfers 52,500 Btu or 5.53×10^7 J of heat in 3.5 hours.

Heat Conduction

When you place a pot on a hot stove, heat is transferred from the stove's heating element to the bottom of the pot. The atoms and molecules in the bottom of the pot vibrate faster and faster as the temperature increases. When these energetic particles collide with particles in the side of the pot, they transfer some of their energy. As the atoms and molecules in the side of the pot gain thermal energy, the temperature in the side increases. These particles, in succession, collide with other particles and transfer energy farther up the side of the pot. This process continues until there is no temperature difference on the pot. The transfer of thermal energy arising from a temperature difference between adjacent parts of a body is called **heat conduction**.

Will heat be conducted in an object if the entire object is at the same temperature? In this case, all the molecules in the object have the same average kinetic energy. Half the molecules have energy greater than the average, and half have energy less than the average. A molecule has the same chance of gaining energy in a collision as it does of losing energy. Therefore, there is no net flow of thermal energy in the object. For heat conduction to take place, there must be a temperature difference within an object.

Cool

Hot

Figure 3.20
Heat conduction is the transfer of thermal energy within the same body caused by a temperature difference.

Not all substances have the same ability to conduct heat. For example, the molecules of air and other gases are so far apart that their collision rates are low. Therefore, gases are poor conductors of heat. Molecules of liquids and some nonmetallic solids are closer together, and these materials are better conductors of heat than gases. Metals have the greatest ability to conduct heat. In a metal, many electrons are not tightly bound to atoms and are free to move about the metal. These free electrons are responsible for a metal's ability to conduct heat as well as electrical current. After a collision, a free electron can move past many atoms before colliding and giving up energy. This increase in distance of travel of energetic particles speeds the transfer of energy from high-temperature regions to low-temperature regions.

The **thermal conductivity** k of a material is a measure of its ability to conduct heat. Metals have a large value of k because they are good heat conductors. Wood has a small value of k because it is a poor heat conductor. Wood is a good thermal insulator. This is why wood makes a good handle for a pot.

The rate at which heat is conducted through a slab of material (see Figure 3.21) depends on the thermal conductivity k of the material, the temperature difference ΔT across the slab, the cross-sectional area A through which heat flows, and the thickness Δx of the slab.

$$\text{Heat conduction rate} = -\frac{\text{thermal conductivity} \times \text{cross-sectional area} \times \text{temperature difference}}{\text{thickness}}$$

$$\dot{Q} = -\frac{kA\Delta T}{\Delta x}$$

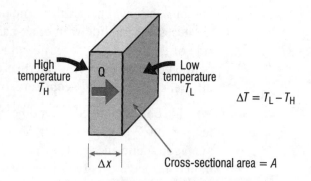

$\Delta T = T_L - T_H$

Cross-sectional area = A

Figure 3.21

The rate of heat conduction $\dot{Q}$ through a slab is equal to $-kA\Delta T/\Delta x$. A "slab" of material has a small thickness Δx compared to the height and width.

We use the same variable name $\dot{Q}$ for heat transfer rate and heat conduction rate. This is because heat conduction is a special case of heat transfer—a case where heat is transferred within the same body. Therefore, the units of heat conduction rate are the same as those for heat transfer rate.

Notice the minus sign in the equation for heat conduction rate. By convention, ΔT means "final temperature minus initial temperature." In the direction of heat conduction the final temperature is T_L and the initial temperature is T_H. The temperature difference $\Delta T = T_L - T_H$ is negative since $T_H > T_L$. Therefore, the heat conduction rate $\dot{Q}$ is positive. Heat flows from a region of high temperature to a region of low temperature.

Table 3.3 gives the thermal conductivity (k) for several substances. Note that metals have higher thermal conductivities than insulating materials such as air or cork board.

Table 3.3 Some Thermal Conductivities

Material	$\left(\dfrac{Btu \cdot in}{h \cdot ft^2 \cdot °F}\right)$	$\left(\dfrac{cal \cdot cm}{s \cdot cm^3 \cdot °C}\right)$
Polyurethane Foam	0.17	5.7×10^{-5}
Air	0.18	6.3×10^{-5}
Fiberglass	0.32	1.1×10^{-4}
White Pine	0.78	2.69×10^{-4}
Water	4.25	1.46×10^{-3}
Glass	5.8	1.99×10^{-3}
Concrete	6.0	2.07×10^{-3}
Steel	350	0.12
Aluminum	1400	0.48
Copper	2700	0.93

Example 3.14 Heat Flow Through Fiberglass

A wall of a house is designed to contain a 3-in. thickness of fiberglass insulation. The wall measures 15 ft by 12 ft. What is the heat flow rate through the insulation if the inside temperature is 68°F and the outside temperature is 32°F?

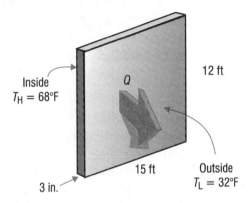

Solution: The cross-sectional area of the wall is

$$A = (15 \text{ ft}) (12 \text{ ft}) = 180 \text{ ft}^2$$

The temperature difference is

$$\Delta T = T_L - T_H = 32°F - 68°F = -36°F$$

The heat transfer rate is

$$\dot{Q} = -kA \frac{\Delta T}{\Delta x}$$

$$= -\left(0.32 \ \frac{\text{Btu} \cdot \text{in}}{\text{h} \cdot \text{ft}^2 \cdot °F} \right) (180 \text{ ft}^2) \left(\frac{-36°F}{3 \text{ in}} \right)$$

$$= 691 \ \frac{\text{Btu}}{\text{h}}$$

Heat flows from the inside of the insulation (high temperature) to the outside (low temperature) at a rate of 691 Btu/h.

If the wall in Example 3.14 is insulated with polyurethane foam instead of fiberglass, will the heat transfer rate increase, decrease, or stay the same?

In addition to conduction, there are two other methods of transferring heat from regions of higher temperature to regions of lower temperature: convection and radiation.

Convection

Refer to Appendix F for a career link to this concept.

Convection is a transfer of heat by movement of fluid. The process is complex and cannot be described by one simple equation. Figure 3.22 shows two bodies with different temperatures, not in contact with each other, but both in contact with a fluid. At the surface of the high-temperature body, fluid gains energy by conduction. This causes the fluid near the surface to expand (the distance between molecules increases when they gain energy). When the fluid expands, it becomes less dense than the surrounding cooler fluid and rises because of the buoyant forces acting on it. When the warm fluid rises, it is replaced by cool fluid. This fluid will, in turn, gain energy from the high-temperature body and rise.

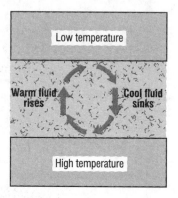

Figure 3.22
Natural convection

The result is a circulation of fluid and transfer of energy due to a temperature difference. Energy is transferred from a high-temperature body to the fluid; the warmed fluid rises and transfers energy to the cooler fluid and low-temperature body. This kind of heat transfer is called *natural convection*. Natural convection takes place in the Earth's atmosphere. The sun heats the surface of the Earth, energy is transferred from the surface to the air, and the air rises and cools at higher altitudes. Since different parts of the Earth's surface absorb heat from the sun more rapidly than others, the air near the surface is heated unevenly. This is what produces convection currents, or winds, in the atmosphere.

Convection can also be forced. In *forced convection*, a fan or pump creates a pressure difference in a heated or cooled fluid, which forces the fluid to circulate. This is how heating and cooling systems work. For example, the human body uses blood as the working fluid in a complex forced convection system for cooling. Thermal energy is released by metabolism inside the body (for example, in muscles) and is transferred to blood. Blood is forced to circulate by the heart (a pump). The warmed blood is pumped to the skin, where thermal energy passes from the blood to the skin. The energy is removed from the skin by convection, by a change of phase (evaporation of moisture from the skin), and by another method called **radiation**.

Radiation

All objects radiate energy in the form of *electromagnetic radiation*. This is the same type of radiation as that emitted by a light bulb, but most electromagnetic radiation is not visible—it has a wavelength shorter or longer than visible light. (You will learn about the characteristics of electromagnetic radiation in Chapter 9.) The rate of energy radiated by an object depends on the object's temperature, surface area, and material composition of the surface. The rate of energy emission increases with the fourth power of the temperature. Radiation transfers energy from one body to another through empty space—it does not use a medium.

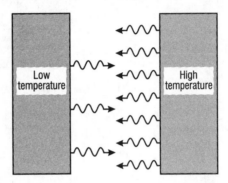

Figure 3.23
A hot object radiates more energy per unit time than an identical cooler object.

In Figure 3.23, a hot object radiates energy, some of which is absorbed by a cooler object. The cooler object also radiates energy, but, because it has a lower temperature, it radiates less than it absorbs. The net transfer of energy is from the hot object to the cooler object. Radiation is the most common means of energy transfer in the universe. Energy is transferred from the sun to all the planets in the solar system by radiation.

Summary

- Heat flow rate is the amount of thermal energy transferred per unit time.

- Heat is transferred from a high-temperature object or region to a low-temperature object or region.

- Heat conduction is the transfer of thermal energy within an object due to a temperature difference between adjacent regions of the object.

- The thermal conductivity of a material is a measure of its ability to conduct heat.

- Convection is a transfer of heat by movement of fluid. Convection can be natural or forced.

- Radiation is a transfer of energy by electromagnetic waves.

Exercises

1. What condition is necessary for heat to flow from one region to another region of the same object?

2. Suppose you leave a metal spoon and a wooden spoon in a refrigerator overnight. The next day you remove the spoons and hold one in each hand. The metal spoon feels colder than the wooden spoon, even though they are the same temperature.

   (a) Referring to Table 3.4, which spoon is a better conductor?

   (b) Explain why the metal spoon feels colder.

3. In choosing a material for a cooking utensil, would you want the material to have a high or low thermal conductivity? Explain your answer.

4. A pine wood door 1.75 in. thick will be removed and replaced by glass. How thick should the glass be if the heat flow rate through the wall is to be unchanged?

5. In an electric water heater, the heating element is located at the bottom of the tank. Why is this advantageous?

6. Why does warm fluid rise in natural convection?

7. The Earth continuously absorbs radiation from the sun. Why doesn't the temperature of the Earth continuously increase?

8. When a lake begins to freeze, ice forms first at the surface. Is conduction, convection, or radiation involved in this process? Explain your answer.

9. A solid copper rod is used as a "heat pipe" to conduct heat from a hot solar panel to a cooling liquid. The cross-sectional area of the rod is 1.2 cm² and the length is 15 cm. The rod is insulated around the side, so the only heat conduction is through the ends of the rod. The solar panel temperature is 115°C and the cooling liquid temperature is 10°C. What is the heat flow rate through the rod?

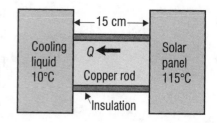

10. The heat flow rate from the solar panel in Exercise 9 must be increased to 10.0 cal/s. If you can change only the temperature of the cooling liquid, what new temperature should you use?

11. A silicon control rectifier (SCR) is a semiconductor device used to control large AC power devices. During operation, current flows through the SCR and heats it. The added thermal energy must be removed or it will destroy the SCR.

    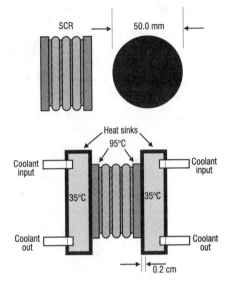

    As shown at the right, an SCR is clamped between two "heat sinks" that contain a low-temperature coolant. The ends of the SCR are separated from the coolant by 0.20 cm of steel. The temperature of the SCR is 95°C, and the temperature of the coolant is 35°C. What is the heat flow rate, in J/s, from each end of the SCR? You can ignore heat flow from the sides of the SCR.

12. A 50-gram sample of water is initially at a temperature of 22°C. The sample is heated until the temperature is 32°C. The specific heat of water is $1.00 \; \dfrac{cal}{g \cdot °C}$.

    (a) How much heat is absorbed by the water, in calories?

    (b) in Btu?

    (c) in joules?

    (d) in ft·lb?

13. Three liters of water evaporate from cooking pots in a commercial kitchen. The water vapor mixes with air in the kitchen, and the mixture passes through the kitchen's air conditioner. In the air conditioner, the mixture is cooled and water vapor condenses back into liquid water. *When water vapor condenses, it releases heat. The amount of heat released is equal to the amount of heat absorbed when the water was evaporated.* The heat released in condensation must be removed by the air conditioner. The air conditioner is rated at 12,000 Btu per hour.

    (a) The heat of vaporization of water is 540 cal/g. How much heat is absorbed by the water when 3 L are evaporated? (The density of water is 1 g/cm³, and there are 1000 cm³ in 1 L.)

    (b) How long will it take for the air conditioner to remove the heat released by the condensing water?

CHAPTER THREE SUMMARY

Rate is an important concept in mechanical, fluid, electrical, and thermal systems. In each system, rate is defined as a measured quantity divided by a time interval.

In mechanical systems, the measured quantity is the distance traveled by an object, or the object's change in position. The distance traveled, or change in position, per unit time is speed. An object's speed can also change. The change in speed divided by the time interval is acceleration. Acceleration is sometimes described as a "rate of a rate." (Can you explain why?)

There are two measured quantities in fluid systems—mass and volume. Rate of change of mass is called mass flow rate, and rate of change of volume is called volume flow rate. When fluid flows through a pipe, mass (or volume) flow rate is the mass (or volume) of fluid that flows past a point on the pipe per unit time.

In electrical systems, the measured quantity is charge. When charge flows through a wire, current is the amount of charge that flows past a point on the wire per unit time. Current is measured in units of coulombs per second, or amperes.

The measured quantity in thermal systems is thermal energy. Heat is thermal energy that flows from a region of lower temperature to a region of higher temperature. Heat transferred per unit time is heat flow rate.

The rates in mechanical, fluid, electrical, and thermal systems can be expressed as a single general ratio:

$$\text{Rate} = \frac{\text{measured quantity}}{\text{time interval}}$$

The measured quantities and rates are summarized in the table below.

System	Measured Quantity	Rate	Equation
Mechanical (Translation)	Position	Speed	$v = \dfrac{\Delta d}{\Delta t}$
	Speed	Acceleration	$a = \dfrac{\Delta v}{\Delta t}$
(Rotation)	Angular position	Angular speed	$\omega = \dfrac{\Delta \theta}{\Delta t}$
	Angular speed	Angular acceleration	$\alpha = \dfrac{\Delta \omega}{\Delta t}$
Fluid	Volume	Volume flow rate	$\dot{V} = \dfrac{\Delta V}{\Delta t}$
	Mass	Mass flow rate	$\dot{m} = \dfrac{\Delta m}{\Delta t}$
Electrical	Charge	Electric current	$I = \dfrac{\Delta q}{\Delta t}$
Thermal	Thermal energy	Heat flow rate	$\dot{Q} = \dfrac{\Delta Q}{\Delta t}$

CHAPTER 4

RESISTANCE

Resistance is the opposition to motion or flow. In some situations, resistance must be overcome—for example to create or maintain motion of objects, or flow of fluids, charge, or heat. In other situations, resistance is useful—for example, to slow or stop motion of objects and to control flow of fluids, charge, and heat.

Mechanical resistance opposes motion between solid surfaces. This opposition is called friction. A force of friction exists whenever one solid object slides against another solid object. The direction of the force is opposite the direction of the object's velocity. For example, when you move a chair by sliding it across the floor, you must exert a force greater than the opposing force of friction. When you apply the brakes on a car, friction between the brake pad and a rotating wheel opposes the wheel's motion and slows its rate of rotation.

$F_{friction}$ F

Fluid resistance opposes the flow of fluids. The resistance is caused by friction between molecules in the fluid. This opposition is called drag when a solid object moves through a fluid (or when a fluid flows past a solid object). To paddle a kayak through water, you must exert a force greater than the opposing force of drag. A sky diver has a terminal speed because the drag force balances the gravitational force. A fluid flowing through a pipe has a pressure drop along the pipe because of drag.

Electrical resistance opposes the flow of electric charge, or current. This resistance is caused by electrons colliding with atoms in the conducting path. Some materials have low resistance, and some have high resistance. For example, a toaster has two wires—a power cord and a heating element. The power cord is made of copper. Copper has a low resistance—it is a good conductor of electricity because it has many electrons that can easily move

in the wire. But the toaster's heating element has a high resistance. In this material, electrons are more tightly bound to the atoms and do not move as easily from place to place. When electrons collide with atoms in the heating element, they transfer energy to the atoms. This is the source of heat.

Thermal resistance opposes the flow of heat. Some materials have low thermal resistance and some have high resistance. Metals have low thermal resistance—they are good conductors of heat. The metal handle on a pot of boiling water is hot because the pot conducts heat to the handle. You can safely handle the pot if you use a potholder between your hand and the metal. A potholder has a high thermal resistance—it is not a good conductor of heat.

4.1 RESISTANCE IN MECHANICAL SYSTEMS

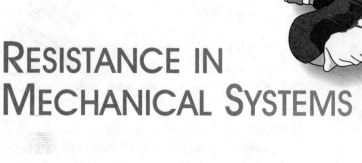

Objectives

- State Newton's second law of motion and use it to solve problems involving force, mass, and acceleration.

- Calculate an object's weight, given its mass.

- Explain the difference between static and kinetic friction.

- Use the linear model to calculate the force of friction between two surfaces.

- Explain how lubrication and rolling reduce friction.

**INTERNET** *connection*

To find out more about resistance in mechanical systems, follow the links at **www.learningincontext.com**.

In Section 1.1 you learned that the motion of a body in equilibrium is described by Newton's first law of motion:

Every object will remain at rest, or will continue to move in a straight line with constant speed unless the object is acted on by a net force.

A book sitting on a table is in equilibrium. The weight of the book is the force of gravity acting downward. The table pushes upward on the book with an equal and opposite force. Since the vector sum of these two forces is zero, no net force is acting on the book and it remains at rest.

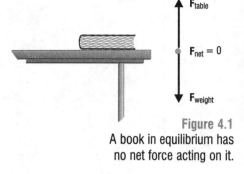

Figure 4.1
A book in equilibrium has no net force acting on it.

Suppose you push the book and exert a net force in a horizontal direction from left to right. The book will begin to move, or be *accelerated*, in the direction of the net force. If you push with twice the force, the acceleration will double. If you push with three times the force, the acceleration will triple. In other words, the acceleration of the book is directly proportional to the force acting on the book.

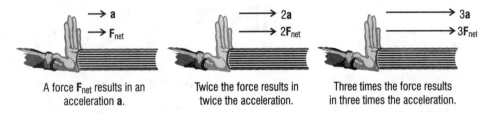

A force F_{net} results in an acceleration **a**.

Twice the force results in twice the acceleration.

Three times the force results in three times the acceleration.

Figure 4.2
Acceleration of an object is directly proportional to the force acting on the object.

Now suppose you use the same net force to accelerate more than one book. For an equal force, two books are accelerated at one-half the rate of one book. Three books are accelerated at one-third the rate, and so on. The acceleration of the books is inversely proportional to the mass.

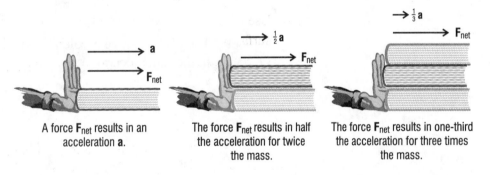

A force F_{net} results in an acceleration **a**.

The force F_{net} results in half the acceleration for twice the mass.

The force F_{net} results in one-third the acceleration for three times the mass.

Figure 4.3
The acceleration of an object is indirectly proportional to the mass of the object.

The relationship between acceleration, net force, and mass is **Newton's second law of motion**:

The acceleration of an object is directly proportional to the net force acting on the object and inversely proportional to the mass of the object.

Mathematically, Newton's second law is:

$$\text{Acceleration} = \frac{\text{net force}}{\text{mass}}$$

$$a = \frac{\mathbf{F}_{net}}{m} \quad \text{or} \quad \mathbf{F}_{net} = m\mathbf{a}$$

In the SI system, force is measured in newtons (N). One newton is the force required to accelerate a 1-kg mass 1 m/s².

$$1 \text{ N} = (1 \text{ kg}) (1 \text{ m/s}^2) = 1 \text{ kg} \cdot \text{m/s}^2$$

In the English system, force is measured in pounds (lb). One pound is the force required to accelerate a 1-slug mass 1 ft/s².

$$1 \text{ lb} = (1 \text{ slug}) (1 \text{ ft/s}^2) = 1 \text{ slug} \cdot \text{ft/s}^2$$

Example 4.1 Newton's Second Law and a Car's Motion

In performance testing, a 1250-kg car accelerates from 0 to 100 km/h in 8.2 seconds. What is the average net force pushing the car during the test?

Solution: First convert the final speed to m/s:

$$v_f = \left(100 \ \frac{\text{km}}{\text{h}}\right) \left(1000 \ \frac{\text{m}}{\text{km}}\right) \left(\frac{1 \text{ h}}{3600 \text{ s}}\right) = 27.8 \ \frac{\text{m}}{\text{s}}$$

The car's average acceleration is the ratio of change in speed to the time interval:

$$a_{ave} = \frac{\Delta v}{\Delta t} = \frac{v_f - v_i}{\Delta t}$$

$$= \frac{27.8 \frac{\text{m}}{\text{s}} - 0 \frac{\text{m}}{\text{s}}}{8.2 \text{ s}}$$

$$= 3.39 \text{ m/s}^2$$

Use Newton's second law to calculate the force.

$$F_{ave} = m a_{ave}$$

$$= (1250 \text{ kg}) (3.39 \text{ m/s}^2)$$

$$= 4238 \text{ N} \qquad \left[N = \text{kg} \cdot \text{m/s}^2\right]$$

The average net force pushing the car is 4240 N.

Calculating Weight and Mass

You can use Newton's second law to relate an object's weight to its mass. In this case, the acceleration is that experienced by the object in the Earth's gravitational field. We use the symbol $\mathbf{F}_g$ to represent gravitational force, or weight.

You have experienced gravitational acceleration if you have ever stepped off a diving board. While standing on the board, your weight $\mathbf{F}_g$ acting downward is balanced by an upward force exerted on you by the board. When you step off, the upward force is removed and a net force $\mathbf{F}_g$ is acting downward. You accelerate in the direction of this force, toward the surface of the pool.

When an object is in a gravitational field and gravity is the only force acting on the object, it accelerates in the direction of the force. This acceleration is called **gravitational acceleration**. We use the symbol $\mathbf{g}$ to represent gravitational acceleration. On the surface of the Earth, the direction of $\mathbf{g}$ is the same as $\mathbf{F}_g$, toward the center of the Earth and the magnitude is 9.80 m/s² or 32.2 ft/s².

If an object's mass is m, you can use Newton's second law to calculate its weight:

$$\mathbf{F} = m\mathbf{a} \;\rightarrow\; \mathbf{F}_g = m\mathbf{g}$$

Example 4.2 Weight Measured by a Scale

A 65-kg person stands on a bathroom scale. What force does the scale exert on the person?

Solution: Two forces are acting on the person—the force of gravity, or the person's weight, F_g and the force of the scale F_{scale}. These two forces must be in equilibrium, since the person is standing still and is not being accelerated.

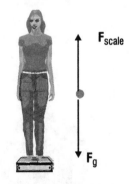

$$F_{scale} = F_g = mg$$

$$= (65 \text{ kg}) (9.80 \text{ m/s}^2)$$

$$= 637 \text{ N} \qquad \left[N = kg \cdot m/s^2 \right]$$

The scale exerts a force of 637 N upward on the person.

Notice in Example 4.2 that g is used to calculate force, even though nothing is being accelerated. If the force F_g is balanced by another force, there is no acceleration. But Newton's second law still holds, and you can calculate F_g using its equivalent, mg.

What does it feel like to be in an elevator when the elevator accelerates upward? You feel heavier, because the floor of the elevator is pushing upward with greater force than when you are standing still or moving at constant speed.

Example 4.3 Weight Measured During Acceleration

The person from Example 4.2 is placed on a scale in an elevator. The elevator accelerates upward at a rate of 2.5 m/s². What weight does the scale read during the acceleration?

Solution: Since the person is being accelerated upward, a net force $\mathbf{F}_{net}$ is acting upward. This force is the vector sum of the force of the scale (upward) and the force of gravity (downward). Let upward be the positive direction:

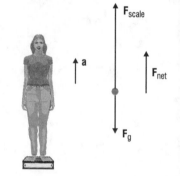

$$F_{net} = F_{scale} - F_g$$
$$F_{scale} = F_{net} + F_g$$
$$= ma + mg$$
$$= m(a + g)$$
$$= (65 \text{ kg}) (2.5 \text{ m/s}^2 + 9.80 \text{ m/s}^2)$$
$$= 800 \text{ N}$$

The scale reads 800 N during the acceleration.

Refer to Appendix F for a career link to this concept.

Friction Forces

When you push an object across a surface, such as the books in Figures 4.2 and 4.3 or the crate in Figure 4.4, across a surface, the force you apply to the object must be *greater than* the opposing force of **friction**. To accelerate an object that is standing still, you must overcome friction. To keep an object moving at constant speed, you also must apply a force to overcome friction. In either case, the force of friction resists motion.

Friction is a result of irregularities in the surfaces of objects.

Figure 4.4
Magnified view of two surfaces in contact

At a microscopic level, all surfaces have irregular "hills and valleys." The "hills" are the points of contact between surfaces. At these points, an electrical force of attraction, or bonding, occurs between atoms in the two surfaces. To begin sliding one surface over the other, you must break the bonds. The force required to overcome this initial attraction is called the **static friction** force. When the surfaces are moving, a weaker force of attraction still exists between atoms in the surfaces. You also must exert a force to overcome this attraction to maintain a constant speed. This force is called the **kinetic friction** force. Static friction is usually greater than kinetic friction.

A Linear Model for Friction Forces

Friction forces are very complicated, and no model can predict the forces accurately and reliably for all situations. However, a simplified linear model can be used to calculate the forces, which agree reasonably well with measured data.

The model is based on three observations about friction:

- The friction force depends on whether or not the surfaces are sliding (static or kinetic friction).

- The friction force depends on the materials of which the surfaces are made.

- The friction force depends on how hard the surfaces are pressed together. This is called the **normal force** between the surfaces. The direction of the normal force is perpendicular to the surfaces that are in contact.

Friction opposes motion. In other words, the direction of the friction force is opposite the direction of the applied force. According to the linear model, the magnitude of the friction force is proportional to the normal force N. The constant of proportionality is called the **coefficient of friction** μ (the Greek letter *mu*). The coefficient of static friction is μ_s and the coefficient of kinetic friction is μ_k.

$$\begin{array}{ccc}
\text{Maximum friction} & = & \text{coefficient of} \\
\text{force} & & \text{friction}
\end{array} \times \begin{array}{c} \text{normal} \\ \text{force} \end{array}$$

$$F_{\text{static}} \leq \mu_s N$$

$$F_{\text{kinetic}} \leq \mu_k N$$

Some typical values for μ_s and μ_k for various surface materials are shown in Table 4.1.

Table 4.1 Coefficients of Friction (Approximate Values)

Surface	μ_s	μ_k
Wood on wood	0.5	0.2
Wood on concrete	0.6	0.4
Rubber on dry concrete	0.8	0.7
Rubber on wet concrete	0.65	0.57
Steel on steel (dry)	0.78	0.58
Steel on steel (oiled)	0.11	0.05
Steel on Teflon	0.04	0.04

To illustrate the forces in these equations, suppose you are pushing a crate with a force **F** directed to the right. You increase the magnitude of **F** until you get the crate moving (see Figure 4.5 on the next page):

(a) At first, $F < F_{\text{static,max}}$ and the crate does not move. Notice that $F_{\text{static,max}} = \mu_s N$. As you increase F, the force of friction F_{static} increases to exactly match F so that $F_{\text{static}} = F$.

(b) At the instant F becomes greater than $F_{\text{static,max}}$, a net force exists on the crate and it accelerates to the right. According to Newton's second law, the acceleration is proportional to the net force.

(c) With the crate moving, you must apply a force $F = F_{\text{kinetic}}$ to keep it moving at constant speed.

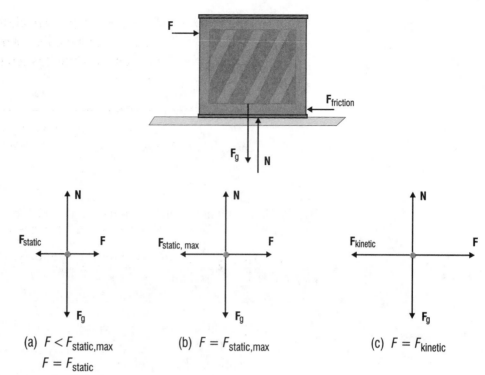

(a) $F < F_{static,max}$
$F = F_{static}$

(b) $F = F_{static,max}$

(c) $F = F_{kinetic}$

Figure 4.5
Forces acting on a crate

Example 4.4 Forces on a Crate

The crate in Figure 4.5 is made of wood and weighs 85 pounds. To slide the crate across a concrete floor:

(a) What force is required to get the crate moving?

(b) What force is required to keep the crate moving at constant speed?

Solution: (a) To get the crate moving, you apply a force **F** and gradually increase the magnitude of **F** until it just exceeds the opposing force $\mathbf{F}_{static,max}$. At the instant before it moves, the crate is in equilibrium (see Figure 4.5b). The vertical forces are balanced:

$$N = F_g = 85 \text{ lb}$$

The horizontal forces are also balanced. From Table 4.1, $\mu_s \approx 0.6$.

$$F = F_{static,max} = \mu_s N$$
$$= (0.6)(85 \text{ lb})$$
$$= 51 \text{ lb}$$

To get the crate moving, the applied force must exceed 51 lb.

(b) When the crate moves at constant speed, there is no acceleration, and therefore no net force acting on the crate. In the vertical direction, the normal force still equals the weight of the crate. In the horizontal direction, the applied force now equals the force of kinetic friction (see Figure 4.5c). From Table 4.1, $\mu_k \approx 0.4$.

$$F = F_{\text{kinetic}} = \mu_s N$$
$$= (0.4)\,(85\ \text{lb})$$
$$= 34\ \text{lb}$$

To keep the crate moving at constant speed, the applied force must equal 34 lb.

Lubricants

Lubricants reduce friction by keeping the two sliding surfaces apart with a thin layer of fluid. Figure 4.6 shows what happens when two surfaces slide with lubrication. The two objects—piston ring and cylinder wall—no longer touch each other.

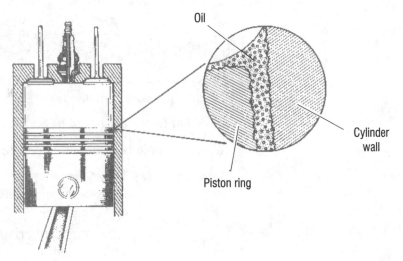

Oil
Cylinder wall

Piston ring

Figure 4.6
Effects of lubricants on friction

The lubricant between the surfaces moves in layers. The layer nearest the cylinder wall is stationary. Each layer farther away moves a little faster. The layer nearest the piston ring is moving as fast as the moving surface. Friction is no longer the result of tiny hills and valleys sliding past one another. Now friction is the result of fluid layers sliding past one another. This internal friction in the fluid is called *viscosity*. You will learn more about viscosity in the next section.

Proper lubrication reduces frictional forces between surfaces. This reduces the wear on the surfaces and the heat generated at the surfaces.

Rolling Friction

Another way to reduce friction is to roll an object over a surface, rather than slide it. Figure 4.7 shows a circular surface rolling on a flat surface. The surfaces don't scrape past one another as they do in sliding friction. This is why the force of rolling friction is always much less than that of sliding friction. An object fitted with wheels or other rolling surfaces moves with much less force than a similar object fitted with skids.

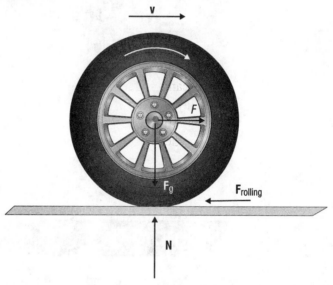

Figure 4.7
The force of rolling friction is much less than the force of sliding friction because there is less movement between surfaces.

Bearings are mechanical devices used to reduce friction in rotating systems. Sometimes bearings are lubricated to reduce friction even more.

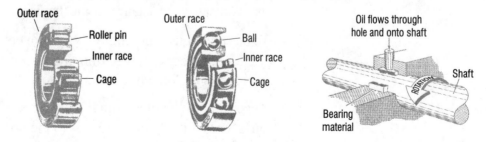

Figure 4.8
Bearings and lubrication reduce friction.

In some mechanical systems, friction is needed. For example, the brakes in your car use friction to slow the angular speed of the wheels and, in turn, the forward motion of the car. A friction clutch is used in some automobiles with manual-shift transmissions to transfer torque from the engine to the wheels. Friction is used in conveyer belt systems to move objects (see Figure 4.9). These systems work only if friction is present between the surfaces.

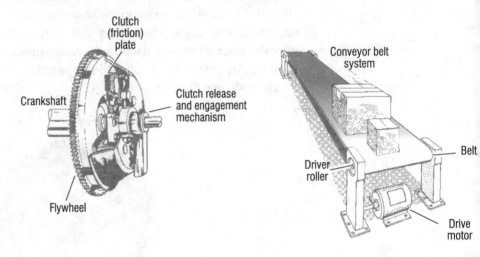

Figure 4.9
Mechanical systems that use friction

Summary

- Newton's second law of motion states the relationship among the net force acting on an object, the mass of the object, and its acceleration: $F = ma$.

- An object's weight is the force exerted on the object by gravity. $F_g = mg$. Near the surface of the Earth, the gravitational acceleration is $g = 9.80$ m/s² or 32.2 ft/s².

- Friction causes resistance in mechanical systems.

- To start an object moving, you must overcome the force of static friction. To keep an object moving at constant speed, you must overcome the force of kinetic friction.

- According to the linear model, the force of friction between two surfaces is directly proportional to the normal force pushing the surfaces together.

- Lubrication and rollers reduce friction. Lubricants separate the two sliding surfaces with a layer of fluid.

1. In Section 3.1 you learned that acceleration is the rate of change of velocity, $\frac{\Delta v}{\Delta t}$. In this section, you learned that acceleration is the ratio of force to mass, $\frac{F}{m}$. Are both these equalities true? Explain.

2. A small basket contains 1 kg of strawberries, and a large basket contains 2 kg. Does the large basket also contain twice the weight of the small basket? Explain.

3. Push a book slowly across a tabletop with your hand. Why is it harder to start the book sliding from a position of rest than it is to keep the book sliding when it is moving?

4. Suppose you drop an empty water bottle and an identical full water bottle from the same height. Which bottle will hit the ground first? Explain your answer.

5. Show that the units of g in the equation $g = F/m$ are m/s^2.

6. At liftoff, a 232,000-kg Delta II space launch vehicle is accelerated upward with a force exerted by its rocket engines. This force is called thrust. The Delta II rocket engines produce a thrust of 3.11 million newtons.

   (a) What is the net force acting on the Delta II at liftoff?

   (b) What is the acceleration of the Delta II at liftoff?

   (c) Following liftoff, the acceleration of the Delta II is not constant; it increases. Explain why this happens. (At liftoff, approximately 90% of the weight of the Delta II is rocket fuel.)

7. In hockey, a player takes a slap shot by striking the puck with a stick in an attempt to propel the puck into the opponent's goal. Suppose that, in a slap shot, a force of 39 N causes a puck to accelerate at 230 m/s^2.

   (a) What is the mass of the hockey puck?

   (b) What acceleration would a 20-N force produce?

8. A 21-kg shipping box is at rest on a wooden floor. The coefficient of static friction between the box and the floor is 0.35, and the coefficient of kinetic friction is 0.28.

   (a) Find the magnitude of the horizontal force required to make the box start to slide.

   (b) Find the magnitude of the horizontal force required to keep the box sliding at a constant velocity.

9. An apple drops from a tree and falls straight down.

   (a) What is the acceleration at the instant the apple drops?

   (b) What is the velocity at the instant the apple drops?

   (c) What is the acceleration after 1 second of free fall?

   (d) What is the velocity after 1 second of free fall?

10. The illustration at the right shows a tire and a wheel on a car that is traveling to the left. When the driver applies the brakes, a force is exerted on the wheel at a distance from its axis of rotation. This force creates a torque that reduces the angular speed of the wheel. The reduction in angular speed slows the car—the car decelerates (or accelerates to the right). Thus, a braking force is applied to the car in the direction opposite its velocity This braking force is exerted between tire and the road surface.

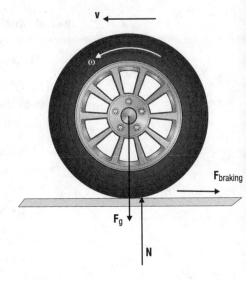

The braking force is the force of friction between the tire and the road. Suppose that, for a tire and a dry asphalt road, $\mu_s = 0.75$ and $\mu_k = 0.60$. The mass of the car and driver is 1460 kg.

   (a) Calculate the normal force the road exerts on the tire. (Remember, th car has four tires.)

   (b) What is the maximum braking force that can be exerted on one tire before the brakes "lock" and the tire starts to skid?

   (c) What is the maximum braking force exerted on the tire if the brakes lock and the tire skids?

11. Would the maximum braking force from Exercise 10 increase or decrease under the following conditions? Explain your answers.

   (a) More people get into the car.

   (b) It starts raining.

12. A figure skater has a mass of 53 kg. The coefficient of kinetic friction between the ice and her skate is 0.15.

   (a) If the skater has only one skate touching the ice, what are the magnitude and direction of the normal force between the skate and ice?

   (b) What are the magnitude and direction of the kinetic friction force when the skater glides on one skate?

   (c) How much work must be done to move the skater 35 meters across the ice?

13. Your weight is the force exerted on you by gravity. In Newton's universal law of gravitation, this is the mutual force of attraction between you and the Earth. It is caused by your mass and the mass of the Earth. The force is given by the equation

$$F_g = G\frac{m_1 m_2}{d^2}$$

where $G = 6.67 \times 10^{-11} \frac{\text{N}\cdot\text{m}^2}{\text{kg}^2}$. Let $m_1 = m_{\text{Earth}} = 5.97 \times 10^{24}$ kg and $m_2 = m$ (your mass). Since you are on the surface of the Earth (or very near it), d is the distance from the center to the surface, or the radius of the Earth:

$$d = r_{\text{Earth}} = 6.37 \times 10^6 \text{ m.}$$

In Newton's second law, your weight is the force of gravity that causes you to accelerate (in the absence of a balancing force) toward the center of the Earth. This force is the product of your mass and the acceleration of gravity.

$$F_g = mg$$

Your weight is the same for both interpretations of force:

$$mg = \frac{G\frac{m_{\text{Earth}}\, m}{F_{\text{Earth}}^2}}{}$$

Solve this equation for g, and compare your numerical result to the standard value. Does g depend on your mass?

4.2 RESISTANCE IN FLUID SYSTEMS

Objectives

- Define drag.

- Explain the difference between laminar and turbulent flow.

- Explain the difference between frictional drag and pressure drag.

- Define viscosity and explain how it can be measured.

- Explain why a freely falling object has a terminal speed.

- Use Stokes' law and Poiseuille's law to solve problems involving fluid resistance.

INTERNET connection

To find out more about resistance in fluid systems, follow the links at **www.learningincontext.com.**

When one solid object slides against another, a force of friction opposes the motion. The direction of the force is opposite the direction of the object's velocity. When a solid object moves through a fluid, there is also a force that opposes the motion. This force is called **drag**. When a boat moves through water or when an airplane moves through air, a drag force is exerted in the direction opposite the velocity of the boat or airplane.

You can feel a drag force when you stand in a high wind or when you put your hand out the window of a moving car. In the first case, you are stationary and the fluid is moving past you; in the second case you are moving past the fluid. Drag occurs only when there is *relative movement* between an object and a fluid.

Laminar (Streamlined) and Turbulent Flow

The drag exerted on an object by a fluid depends on many factors. The most important are the speed of the object (or fluid), the size and shape of the object, and the physical properties of the fluid. These factors make it difficult to calculate drag exactly, but you can make approximations.

The simplest approximation is to ignore drag forces when they are small. For example, you can usually ignore drag for an object moving slowly in fluids such as air or water. But even very slow speeds produce significant drag in fluids such as molasses and motor oil.

When drag forces cannot be ignored, you can make two approximations about the fluid flow—the flow can be *laminar* or *turbulent*. **Laminar**, or **streamlined flow** is a slow, smooth flow over a surface, in which the paths of individual particles do not cross. Each path is called a *streamline*, as illustrated in Figure 4.10. The fluid speed at the surface is zero, and fluid moves in theoretical layers, or *laminates*, with increasing speed away from the surface. Drag is produced by the friction between successive layers of fluid. This is called **frictional drag**.

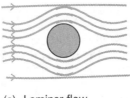
(a) Laminar flow

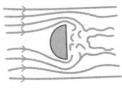
(b) Turbulent flow

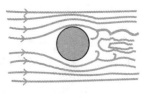
(c) Turbulent flow

Figure 4.10
Laminar and turbulent flows around obstacles.
A turbulent wake can be created by a different shape or a higher fluid speed.

Turbulent flow is irregular flow with eddies and whorls causing fluid to move in different directions. Turbulence is produced by high speeds, by shapes that are not streamlined, and by sharp bends in the path of a fluid. Turbulence produces the visible wake behind a moving boat and an invisible wake behind a moving airplane or car.

Changing the direction of the fluid into eddies and whorls requires work. When the fluid does work, the pressure drops. (Remember, $W = -V\Delta P$.) Thus, the fluid pressure in the wake is less than the fluid pressure in the streamlined flow. This pressure difference causes a force to act on the object in the direction opposite its relative velocity. This force is called **pressure drag**.

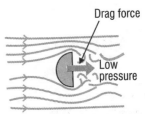

Figure 4.11
Turbulence creates a region of low pressure in the fluid. The higher pressure over the front surface area of the object causes a drag force.

Frictional drag and pressure drag both increase as speed increases.
Figure 4.12 shows how the total drag force on an automobile increases as its speed increases. (The axes do not have a scale because numerical values of drag depend on the aerodynamic design of the automobile. But the linear and nonlinear shape of the graph is similar for all designs.)

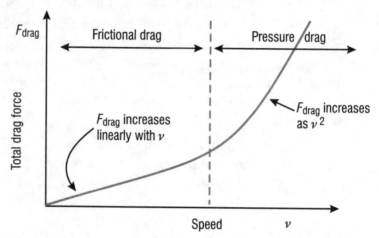

Figure 4.12
The drag force on a car increases as the car's speed increases.

At low speeds, the drag force on the car is frictional drag. The force increases linearly with speed. This means that doubling the speed doubles the frictional drag force.

At higher speeds, turbulence and pressure drag are more and more important. This force increases as the square of the speed. Doubling the speed increases the pressure drag by a factor of four.

Viscosity

Friction between two solid surfaces causes a resistance to movement between the surfaces. On a microscopic level, the resistance is due to electrical forces between atoms and molecules in the surfaces of the solids. Electrical forces also exist between atoms and molecules of a fluid. These forces create internal friction in the fluid, which causes a resistance to movement. **Viscosity** is the property of a fluid that describes this internal friction. We use the Greek letter η (eta) to represent viscosity. Molasses and bubble gum have high resistance to internal movement, and high viscosities. Air and water have much lower viscosities.

Viscosity for fluid resistance is similar to the coefficients of friction for mechanical resistance, but viscosity is not a simple coefficient. For example, Figure 4.13 shows a layer of fluid of thickness Δy between two plates. The bottom plate is held in place, and the top plate (of area A) is pulled to the right at a constant speed v. The fluid in contact with the top plate moves with the plate at speed v, and the fluid in contact with the bottom plate remains motionless. The speed of the fluid between the top and bottom varies linearly. Electrical forces between layers of fluid resist this variation in motion between layers. (The top plate "drags" layers of fluid with it. This is the source of the word that describes the resistance.) The force F is required to overcome the resistance and keep the plate moving at constant speed.

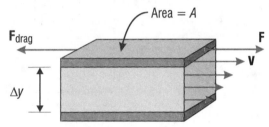

Figure 4.13
The viscosity η of a fluid can be measured by pulling a plate at constant speed across a layer of the fluid.

$$\eta = \frac{F\Delta y}{Av}$$

When the plate moves to the right at constant speed, no *net* force is acting on the plate. Therefore, the fluid exerts a force of friction, or drag force F_{drag} on the plate to the left, opposing motion. The magnitude of the drag force equals F.

As long as the plate speed v is not so large that turbulence occurs, the fluid flow between the plates is laminar. The force F required to maintain a constant speed for most fluids in laminar flow is found to be:

- proportional to A and v, and

- inversely proportional to the thickness of the fluid layer, Δy.

The proportionality constant is the viscosity of the fluid.

$$F_{drag} = F = \eta\frac{Av}{\Delta y}$$

Viscosity has units of (pressure) (time). The SI units for viscosity are $\frac{N}{m^2}\cdot s$ or Pa·s. The English units are $\frac{lb}{ft^2}\cdot s$ or psi·s.

Different fluids resist motion differently, and therefore have different viscosities. Table 4.2 lists values of viscosity for several fluids.

Table 4.2 Viscosities of Common Fluids

Fluid	Temperature °C	Viscosity Pa · s
Gases		
Air	0	1.7×10^{-5}
	20	1.9×10^{-5}
	100	2.2×10^{-5}
Water Vapor	100	1.3×10^{-5}
Liquids		
Water	0	0.0018
	20	0.0010
	100	0.00028
Blood	37	~0.005
Cooking Oil	20	~0.01
Motor Oil	20	1
Corn Syrup	20	8
Molten Lava	950	1000

The viscosity of most liquids decreases as the temperature increases. For example, cold honey is very "thick" and difficult to pour (high viscosity). But if you heat honey in a microwave oven it becomes "watery" (lower viscosity). As the temperature increases, the molecules in the honey become less and less tightly bound to each other. Thus, the force required to separate the molecules also becomes less.

On the other hand, the viscosity of most gases increases with temperature. Forces between gas molecules are exerted only during collisions, and there are more collisions per second with higher temperature.

Motor oil is rated by viscosity by the Society of Automotive Engineers (SAE). Oil with an SAE10 rating has lower viscosity than SAE40 oil (at the same temperature). Oil rated as 10W40 has a viscosity at low engine temperatures equivalent to SAE10 (at low temperatures) and a viscosity at higher engine temperatures equivalent to SAE40 (at higher temperatures).

Stokes' Law

In 1845, the Irish mathematician and physicist George Stokes used viscosity and the equations of fluid flow to predict the drag force on a sphere moving through a fluid. The result is called **Stokes' law**. It applies to objects moving at low enough speeds that the flow of fluid around the objects is streamlined, or laminar. In these cases, there is no turbulence and the only drag force on the objects is due to frictional drag.

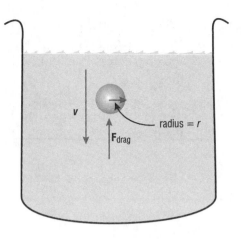

Figure 4.14
The drag force on a sphere
moving through a fluid
opposes the sphere's velocity.

The drag force acts in the direction opposite the object's velocity (it opposes motion). According to Stokes' law, the drag force equals the product of a constant (6π for a sphere), the radius r of the object, the speed v of the object (or the relative speed between the object and fluid), and the fluid's viscosity η:

$$F_{drag} = 6\pi r v \eta$$

Terminal Speed

When an object moves through a fluid, the drag force on the object increases as the speed increases. If you drop a baseball from a high tower, it has a very low speed and very small drag at first. The force of gravity (weight) acting downward is greater than the drag force acting upward. Therefore, a net force acts downward on the baseball and it accelerates downward. As the speed increases the drag increases, until at some point the upward drag equals the weight. At this point the forces acting on the baseball are balanced and it no longer accelerates. The speed becomes constant. The **terminal speed** of a falling object is the constant speed that occurs when the drag force equals the gravitational force.

The terminal speed of a baseball is about 40 m/s, but the terminal speed of a basketball is only about 20 m/s. Which ball has a greater drag force at any given speed?

Example 4.5 Terminal Speed of a Dust Particle

When volcanoes erupt, rocks, dust, and ash are thrown into the atmosphere. These particles fall back to Earth at terminal speeds that depend on their size. The terminal speed of a particle in a volcanic dust cloud can be estimated using a sphere to model the particle.

Estimate the terminal speed of a 50-μm-diameter particle if the density of the volcanic material is 2500 kg/m³.

Solution: When the particle moves at terminal speed, no net force is acting on it. The force of gravity equals the drag force. Use Stokes' law to calculate the drag force.

The radius r of the particle is one-half the diameter:

$$r = \frac{50 \ \mu m}{2} = 25 \ \mu m \text{ or } 2.5 \times 10^{-5} \text{ m}$$

The mass m of the particle is the product of the density ρ and volume V. The volume of a spherical particle is $\frac{4}{3} \pi r^3$:

$$m = \rho V$$

$$= \left(2500 \ \frac{kg}{m^3}\right)\left[\frac{4}{3}\pi\left(2.5 \times 10^{-5} m\right)^3\right]$$

$$= 1.64 \times 10^{-10} \text{ kg}$$

The weight of the particle is F_g:

$$F_g = mg = (1.64 \times 10^{-10} \text{ kg})(9.80 \text{ m/s}^2)$$

$$= 1.61 \times 10^{-9} \text{ kg·m/s}^2 \text{ or } 1.61 \times 10^{-9} \text{ N}$$

Use Stokes' law, and equate the drag to the weight. Solve for the speed v. Use the value of viscosity from Table 4.2 for air at 20°C:

$$F_{drag} = F_g$$

$$6\pi r v \eta = 1.61 \times 10^{-9} \text{ N}$$

$$v = \frac{1.61 \times 10^{-9} \text{ N}}{6\pi r \eta}$$

$$= \frac{1.61 \times 10^{-9} \text{ N}}{6\pi\left(2.5 \times 10^{-5} m\right)\left(1.9 \times 10^{-5} \ \frac{N}{m^2}\cdot s\right)}$$

$$= 0.18 \text{ m/s or 18 cm/s}$$

The terminal speed of a 50-μm particle of volcanic dust is about 18 centimeters per second.

Refer to Appendix F
for a career link
to this concept.

Poiseuille's Law

Poiseuille's law gives the volume flow rate of a fluid flowing through a tube or pipe. Like Stokes' law, Poiseuille's law applies to laminar flow. Figure 4.15 illustrates laminar flow in a pipe. The fluid layer at the center moves the fastest, and layers nearer the wall move more slowly. (Fluid in contact with the wall does not move.)

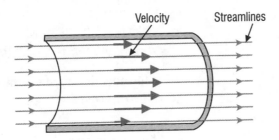

Velocity   Streamlines

Figure 4.15
Cross section through the center of a pipe, showing laminar flow. The fluid at the center of the pipe has the highest speed. The speed decreases closer to the wall of the pipe.

Jean Louis Poiseuille was a physician who was also trained as a physicist and mathematician. In the mid-1840s, he experimented with water flowing through glass capillary tubes as a simulation of blood flowing through small blood vessels. Poiseuille learned that the rate at which fluid flows through a tube increases proportionately to the pressure applied and to the fourth power of the radius of the tube.

According to Poiseuille's law, the volume flow rate $\dot{V}$ (m³/s) of a fluid of viscosity η through a tube or pipe of radius r and length L is:

$$\dot{V} = -\frac{\pi}{8}\frac{r^4 \Delta P}{\eta L}$$

In this equation, ΔP is the change in pressure of the fluid as it flows the length L. The internal friction of the fluid causes the pressure to *decrease* as the fluid flows. Therefore, $\Delta P = P_2 - P_1$ is *negative* because $P_2 < P_1$. With a negative ΔP, $\dot{V}$ is positive.

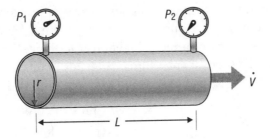

P_1 P_2

$\dot{v}$

r

L

Figure 4.16
A fluid's viscosity, or internal friction, causes the pressure to drop along the direction of flow.

Example 4.6 Blood Flow Rate

The flow rate of blood through a vein is 3.2 cm³/s. The diameter of the vein is 3.6 mm. If the pressure drops by 1100 Pa between two points in the vein, estimate the length of the vein between the points.

Solution: Convert units of $\dot{V}$ and r to SI:

$$\dot{V} = 3.2 \frac{cm^3}{s} \cdot \frac{1 \ m^3}{10^6 \ cm^3} = 3.2 \times 10^{-6} \ m^3/s$$

$$r = d/2 = (3.6 \ mm)/2 = 1.8 \ mm = 1.8 \times 10^{-3} \ m$$

Solve the equation for Poiseuille's law for the length L. Use the value of viscosity from Table 4.2:

$$\dot{V} = -\frac{\pi}{8} \frac{r^4 \Delta P}{\eta L}$$

$$L = -\frac{\pi}{8} \frac{r^4 \Delta P}{\eta \dot{V}}$$

$$= -\frac{\pi}{8} \frac{(1.8 \times 10^{-3} \ m)^4 (-1100 \ Pa)}{(0.005 \ Pa \cdot s)\left(3.2 \times 10^{-6} \ \dfrac{m^3}{s}\right)}$$

$$= 0.28 \ m \quad \text{or} \quad 28 \ cm$$

The vein is about 28 cm long.

Factors Affecting Flow Through a Pipe

Resistance decreases the flow rate $\dot{V}$ of fluid through a pipe. Poiseuille's law shows how this resistance depends on three factors: (1) the radius (or cross-sectional area) of the pipe, (2) the length of the pipe, and (3) the viscosity of the fluid. These dependencies can be illustrated using graphs of volume flow rate versus pressure drop. For each graph, you can define a "fluid resistance" R as the ratio of the prime mover to the volume flow rate. The prime mover in fluid systems is pressure change, or in this case pressure drop. Pressure drop is $-\Delta P$. (ΔP is negative, so pressure drop and fluid resistance are positive.)

$$R = \frac{\text{pressure drop}}{\text{volume flow rate}} = \frac{-\Delta P}{\dot{V}}$$

Therefore, R is the slope of each line graphed on the following pages. A high-resistance pipe has a large slope, and a low-resistance pipe has a small slope.

(1) Dependence on Radius

Compare the flow of a fluid through two pipes of the same length, but one with a small radius and the other with a large radius. The larger pipe has a greater cross-sectional area and can move a greater volume of fluid per second. This pipe also has a lower resistance to flow than the smaller pipe. According to Poiseuille's law, the volume flow rate increases as the fourth power of the radius. If the radius of the large pipe is twice the radius of the small pipe, the volume flow rate is sixteen times higher (if $r \rightarrow 2r$, then $r^4 \rightarrow 16r^4$).

Figure 4.17 shows graphically the effect of increasing the pipe radius. The volume flow rates and pressure drops are shown for water flowing through a 1-m length of pipe for three pipe radii. Which graph has the highest slope? The highest resistance? For a pressure drop of 25 Pa, if you increase the radius of the pipe from 1.0 cm to 1.5 cm, you increase the cross-sectional area, decrease the flow resistance, and increase the volume flow rate from 98.2 cm³/s to 497 cm³/s.

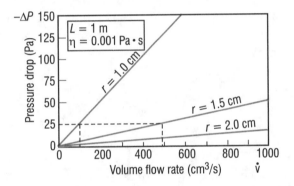

Figure 4.17
Fluid resistance decreases as pipe radius and cross-sectional area increase.

(2) Dependence on Length

Figure 4.18 shows how fluid resistance changes when the pipe length changes. Longer pipes have higher fluid resistance. If you double the length of a pipe, you double the resistance and the volume flow rate is halved. Volume flow rate is inversely proportional to length.

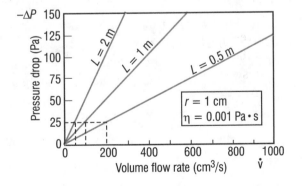

Figure 4.18
Fluid resistance increases as pipe length increases.

(3) Dependence on Viscosity

Figure 4.19 shows how resistance varies with the viscosity of the fluid. Which graph has the highest slope? The highest resistance? Volume flow rate is inversely proportional to viscosity. If you use a fluid with half the viscosity, you double the volume flow rate.

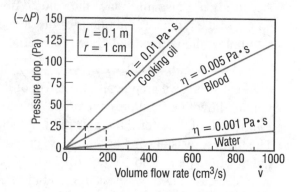

Figure 4.19
Fluid resistance increases as viscosity increases.

If the flow becomes turbulent, resistance increases rapidly. As illustrated in Figure 4.20, bends and Ts in a pipe or air duct cause turbulence. When it is important to maintain laminar flow and reduce resistance, designers use curves with radii as large as possible rather than abrupt changes in the path of a fluid.

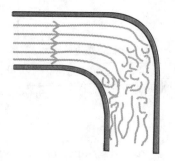
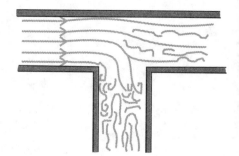

Figure 4.20
Abrupt changes in the direction of fluid flow can cause turbulence and increase resistance.

Obstructions or restrictions also cause turbulence. For example, the grill of a car is an obstruction that causes turbulence, affecting the aerodynamic drag of an automobile. Filters in air ducts are restrictions. Figure 4.21 shows the pressure drops along an air duct containing a filter. There is a small pressure drop from P_1 to P_2 (exaggerated in the graph) along the length of the duct, and there is a much larger drop from P_2 to P_3 because of the filter. If the filter is dirty, the pressure drop is even larger. In fact, a clogged filter can almost stop airflow.

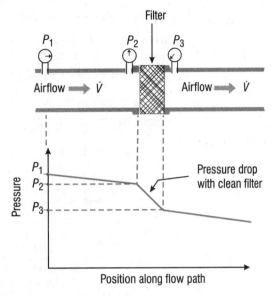

(a) Pressure vs position for a clean filter

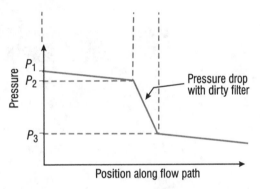

(b) Pressure vs position for a dirty filter. The volume flow rate for this situation is lower than that for (a).

Figure 4.21
Pressure drop along the flow path for an air duct and filter. Note the pressure drop from P_1 to P_2 is exaggerated, as is the drop from P_3 to the right.

Summary

- Drag is the force that opposes the motion of an object moving through a fluid or the force a moving fluid exerts on a stationary object.

- Laminar flow is slow, smooth flow over a surface, where particles follow streamlines. The streamlines define theoretical layers of fluid that do not mix. The friction between successive layers of fluid is called frictional drag.

- Turbulent flow is irregular flow with eddies and whorls that mix the fluid. Turbulence causes a wake behind a moving object. The pressure difference between the fluid outside the wake and the fluid inside the wake causes pressure drag.

- Drag increases with speed. When turbulence is created, pressure drag increases more rapidly than friction drag.

- Viscosity is the property of a fluid that describes its internal friction. The SI units of viscosity are Pa·s.

- Stokes' law can be used to calculate the drag force on a sphere moving at constant speed in a viscous fluid.

- When the drag equals the gravitational force acting on a falling body, the body falls at a constant speed, called the terminal speed of the body.

- Poiseuille's law can be used to calculate the volume flow rate or pressure drop of a viscous fluid flowing through a tube or pipe.

Exercises

1. Drag on an object moving through a stationary fluid _____ (increases or decreases) as the object's speed increases.

2. If a fluid flows past a stationary object, the drag on the object _____ (increases or decreases) as the fluid speed increases.

3. Fluid resistance increases as flow becomes _____ (laminar or turbulent).

4. Why do downhill ski racers and bicycle racers wear specially formed clothing and helmets, and form their bodies in the shape of an egg?

5. The forces acting on four objects moving through a fluid are shown below. The force vectors are drawn to scale. Which object(s) moves at constant velocity?

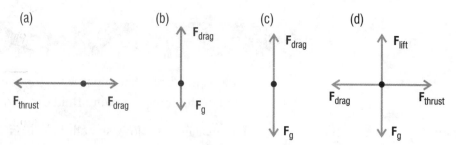

6. Two metal plates are separated by a 1.5-mm thickness of motor oil, as shown in Figure 4.13. The top plate measures 12 cm by 15 cm.

   (a) What force is required to move the top plate at a constant speed of 0.4 cm/s? Use the value of viscosity in Table 4.2.

   (b) If the force on the top plate is halved, what is the plate's speed?

7. (a) The plate in Exercise 6 moves to the right at a constant speed of 0.4 cm/s. What are the magnitude and direction of the drag force on the plate?

   (b) The oil between the plates is replaced with water at 20°C. What is the drag force on the top plate when it moves to the right at a constant 0.4 cm/s?

   (c) The water is replaced with air at 20°C. What is the drag force for the same motion of the top plate?

   (d) Suppose you are approximating the drag force on a plate moving through a fluid at 0.4 cm/s. For which fluid—oil, water, or air—are you most accurate when you say the drag force is approximately zero?

8. A sky diver falls at a terminal speed of 14 ft/s with her parachute open. Her weight plus the weight of her clothing and gear is 168 lb. What are the magnitude and direction of the drag force on the sky diver?

9. Metal particles produced in a milling machine are collected in an oil tank. The particles can be modeled as spheres. One particle is 1.5 mm in diameter and weighs 7.4×10^{-5} N. What is the terminal speed of the particle in the oil if the oil's viscosity is 2.8 Pa·s?

10. The volume flow rates and pressure drops for two pipes are graphed below.

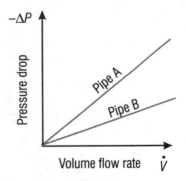

   (a) Which pipe has the higher resistance?

   (b) If the pipes are the same length, which one has the larger diameter?

   (c) If the pipes have the same diameter, which one is longer?

11. (a) Solve the Poiseuille's law equation for fluid resistance.

$$R = \frac{-\Delta P}{\dot{V}} = ?$$

What are the SI units of this quantity?

(b) A 40-cm length of copper tubing has an internal diameter of 0.32 cm. Calculate the resistance of the tubing when water at 20°C flows through it.

(c) What is the water flow rate through the tubing when there is a pressure drop of 1.5 kPa between the tubing inlet and its outlet?

(d) A second, identical 40-cm length of tubing is connected to the outlet of the first length. What is the water flow rate through the combined length if the pressure drop is 1.5 kPa?

12. A 12-inch-diameter pipeline transports crude oil 54.4 miles. The maximum pressure in the pipeline is 950 psi. The pressure drop is 850 psi. The viscosity of the oil is 1.9×10^{-4} psi·s.

(a) Find the volume flow rate (in in³/s) of crude oil through the pipeline.

(b) Calculate the amount of work (in ft·lb) that must be done by pumps to operate the pipeline for one second.

(c) Suppose the pipeline is replaced with one whose diameter is 14 inches. What is the pressure drop required to produce the same flow rate as in (a)?

13. The two water pipes shown below have the same diameter and length. The water flow rate through the pipes is the same, but the pressure drop is not the same. What could cause the difference in pressure drop? Explain.

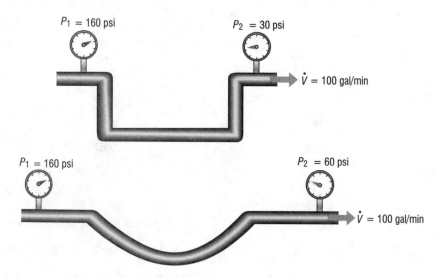

$P_1 = 160$ psi $P_2 = 30$ psi $\dot{V} = 100$ gal/min

$P_1 = 160$ psi $P_2 = 60$ psi $\dot{V} = 100$ gal/min

14. The piston in an air compressor has a diameter of 12.5 cm and a height of 15.0 cm. There is a 0.0127-cm space between the piston and cylinder wall filled with lubricating oil. The oil has a viscosity of 0.35 Pa·s. If the average speed of the piston is 43.0 m/s, what is the average drag on the piston caused by the lubricating oil?

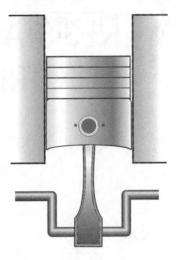

15. The speed of a sailboat is limited by the drag of water on the hull. At low speeds, you can use a laminar flow model to estimate drag. The water touching, or *wetting* the hull moves with the boat. Successive layers of water slide against each other, with each layer moving at a lower speed than previous layers. At a distance of approximately 0.3 mm, water does not slide in layers. You can use this distance as the thickness of the fluid layer in the viscosity equation.

   (a) When moving at constant velocity, a sailboat has a wetted hull surface area of 21.5 m². The sails apply a force of 223 N in the direction the boat is moving. What is the speed of the boat? (Assume the water's temperature is 20°C.)

   (b) If the sailboat has a winged keel that reduces the wetted surface by 15%, what is the speed of the boat?

4.3 RESISTANCE IN ELECTRICAL SYSTEMS

Objectives

- Explain the differences among conductors, insulators, and semiconductors.

- Define electrical resistance.

- Solve problems using resistance, voltage, and current.

- Describe a material that obeys Ohm's law.

- Calculate the resistance of a wire, given the resistivity of the material and the size of the wire.

- For circuits with resistors in series and in parallel, calculate total resistance, current through each resistor, and voltage drop across each resistor.

INTERNET connection

To find out more about resistance in electrical systems, follow the links at **www.learningincontext.com**.

In the last lesson you learned that, when fluid flows through a pipe, there is resistance to the flow. The amount of fluid resistance depends on the size of the pipe and the material composition of the fluid. Similarly, when charge flows through a wire, there is resistance to the flow. The amount of resistance depends on the size of the wire and its material composition. Electrical resistance of materials and devices varies over a wide range of values—more than any other physical property.

Conductors, Insulators, and Semiconductors

All substances can be ranked by their ability to conduct electric current. For example, charge can flow readily through conductors. Metals, some liquids, and plasmas are good **conductors** because they contain many free electrons. These electrons move easily through the material if an electric field (or potential difference) is applied. In a conductor, electrons flow easily, but there is always some electrical resistance that inhibits flow. However, in some materials resistance disappears at very low temperatures. These materials are called *superconductors*.

Most nonmetallic solids (such as wood, plastic, glass, rubber, and minerals) are **insulators**. In these materials, electrons are tightly bound to atoms or molecules and cannot move easily from place to place. Insulators conduct very small currents even when large potential differences are applied.

Some substances (such as silicon, germanium, gallium, and arsenic) are intermediate in their ability to conduct charge. These are called **semiconductors**. In pure form, semiconductors are better insulators than conductors. But if small amounts of impurities are added (about one atom in ten million) semiconductors become good conductors. Microprocessors and computer chips for data storage are made with semiconductor materials.

Electrical Resistance

A copper wire is a conductor. Free electrons move throughout the wire, but not in straight lines. The electrons continuously bump into copper atoms and other electrons. Each collision causes the electrons to change direction. If a potential difference is applied between the ends of the wire, the electrons are accelerated between collisions away from the negative end of the wire toward the positive end.

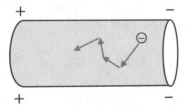

Figure 4.22
Electrical resistance to charge flow
is caused by collisions in the wire.

When faster-moving electrons collide with metal atoms, they transfer energy to the atoms and slow down. Energy transferred from the free electrons to the metal atoms increases the wire's internal energy, and its temperature. These collisions between electrons and atoms inhibit the free flow of electrons. This is the source of electrical resistance to current.

Figure 4.23 shows the similarities between an electric circuit and a closed fluid system. In the fluid system, a pump is the source of pressure difference (the prime mover in a fluid system). If you increase the pressure difference produced by the pump, you will increase the fluid flow rate in the system. In the electric circuit, a power supply is the source of potential difference (the prime mover in an electrical system). If you increase the potential difference, you will increase the charge flow rate, or current.

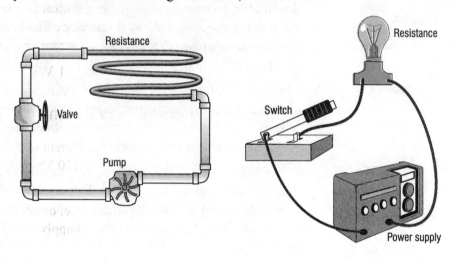

Figure 4.23
Similarities between a closed fluid system and an electric circuit

In the fluid system above, the fluid flows through a long, thin tube. This tube creates drag, or resistance to the flow. The pressure drops as the fluid flows through the resistance. (What makes up for the pressure drop?) In the electrical system, a lamp creates resistance to the current. The voltage drops as charge flows through the resistance. (What makes up for this voltage drop?)

All pipes and tubes resist fluid flow, and all electrical devices resist charge flow. In the last section, we defined a fluid resistance with a ratio involving the prime mover and a flow rate:

$$\text{Fluid resistance} = \frac{\text{pressure drop}}{\text{volume flow rate}}$$

Electrical resistance is defined with a similar ratio:

$$\text{Electrical resistance} = \frac{\text{voltage drop}}{\text{charge flow rate}}$$

Charge flow rate is current. Therefore, **electrical resistance** R is defined as the ratio of the potential difference or voltage drop ΔV across a device and the resulting current I that flows through the device.

$$\text{Resistance} = \frac{\text{potential difference}}{\text{current}}$$

$$R = \frac{\Delta V}{I}$$

The unit of electrical resistance is the **ohm** Ω (the Greek letter *omega*). From the definition, a device has a resistance of 1 ohm when a potential difference of 1 volt across the device causes a current of 1 ampere to flow through it.

$$1\ \Omega = 1\ \text{V/A}$$

Example 4.7 Resistance of a Lamp

The lamp in Figure 4.23 draws a current of 0.91 A when the power supply produces a potential difference of 110 V. What is the resistance of the lamp?

Solution: The potential difference, or voltage drop, across the lamp is the voltage of the power supply.

$$R = \frac{\Delta V}{I} = \frac{110\ \text{V}}{0.91\ \text{A}} = 121\ \text{V/A} \quad \text{or} \quad 121\ \Omega$$

The lamp's resistance is 121 ohms.

Ohm's Law

In 1826, the German physicist Georg Simon Ohm discovered that the ratio of potential difference to current is constant for most conductors. Thus, the resistance of most conductors does not vary as the magnitude or direction of the applied potential difference changes. Today we say that a device obeys **Ohm's law** if its resistance is constant, independent of potential difference and current.

$$\Delta V = IR$$

Although most conductors obey Ohm's law (at least for a limited range of voltage), many important devices do not. For example, Figure 4.24a on the next page shows the relationship between ΔV and I for a metallic conductor, where ΔV is directly proportional to I. What is the slope of the line in this graph? Is it constant? Figure 4.24b shows a similar graph for a semiconductor device where R is not constant—it decreases when V increases.

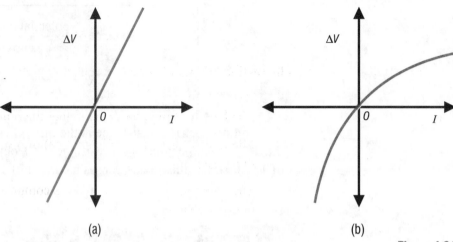

(a)

(b)

Figure 4.24
Graphs of the relationship between I and ΔV for
(a) a conductor that obeys Ohm's law, and
(b) a semiconductor device that does not obey Ohm's law.

Thus, Ohm's law is not a fundamental principle obeyed by all materials and devices. But the definition of resistance always applies to all devices. The resistance of a device is given by $R = \Delta V/I$ whether or not R is constant as the voltage changes.

Example 4.8 Ohm's Law in a Flashlight Bulb

New cells in a flashlight produce a total potential difference of 3.0 V. The flashlight bulb draws a current of 1.7 A with the new cells. As they are used, the cells degrade and their voltage output declines. If the bulb obeys Ohm's law, what current flows through the bulb when the cells produce a total potential difference of 2.5 V?

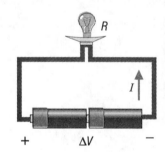

Solution: Use Ohm's law for the flashlight bulb. The resistance is the same for both potential differences. Let I represent the unknown current.

$$R = \frac{\Delta V}{I} = \frac{3.0 \text{ V}}{1.7 \text{ A}} = \frac{2.5 \text{ V}}{I}$$

$$I = \frac{(2.5 \text{ V})(1.7 \text{ A})}{3.0 \text{ V}} = 1.4 \text{ A}$$

When the potential difference is 2.5 V, the current flowing through the bulb is 1.4 A.

Resistivity

In Section 4.2, you learned that the amount of resistance to fluid flow through a pipe depends on three things:

- The length of the pipe—the longer the pipe, the greater the resistance.
- The radius (or cross-sectional area) of the pipe—the smaller the pipe, the greater the resistance.
- The material of which the fluid is composed—the higher the viscosity, the greater the resistance.

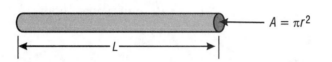

Figure 4.25
A longer, thinner pipe has a greater resistance to fluid flow. A longer, thinner wire has a greater resistance to charge flow.

Similarly, a wire has a resistance to charge flow that depends on:

- The length of the wire—the longer the wire, the greater the resistance.
- The radius (or cross-sectional area) of the wire—the smaller the wire, the greater the resistance.
- The material of which the wire is composed—the higher the *resistivity*, the greater the resistance.

Resistivity is a measure of the capacity of a material to resist electric charge flow. If a wire of unit cross-sectional area is made of the material, its resistivity is the resistance per unit length of the wire. In SI, the units of resistivity are $\Omega \cdot m$. The Greek letter ρ (rho) is used to represent resistivity. If the length L and cross-sectional area A of a wire are known, the wire's resistance R can be calculated:

$$R = \rho \frac{L}{A}$$

The resistivities of various materials are listed in Table 4.3.

Table 4.3 Approximate Resistivities (at 20°C)

Material	ρ ($\Omega \cdot m$)	Material	ρ ($\Omega \cdot m$)
Conductors		Semiconductors	
Copper	1.7×10^{-8}	Silicon	3.5×10^{-8}
Gold	2.4×10^{-8}	Carbon	1.4×10^{-5}
Aluminum	2.6×10^{-8}	Germanium	0.5
Iron	12×10^{-8}		
Mercury	98×10^{-8}	Insulators	
Nichrome Wire	112×10^{-8}	Glass	10^{12}
		Quartz	10^{17}

Example 4.9 Resistance of a Copper Wire

In the United States, wire is manufactured in standard sizes set by the American wire gage system. For example, No. 14 wire has a diameter of 1.63 mm. What is the resistance of a 100-m length of No.14 copper wire?

Solution: The radius of the wire is one-half the diameter. The cross-sectional area of the wire is

$$A = \pi r^2 = \pi \left(\frac{1.63 \text{ mm}}{2} \right)^2 = 2.09 \text{ mm}^2$$

Convert A to square meters. Use the conversion factor 1 m = 10^3 mm. Square both sides: $(1 \text{ m})^2 = (10^3 \text{ mm})^2 = 10^6 \text{ mm}^2$.

$$A = 2.09 \text{ mm}^2 \cdot \frac{1 \text{ m}^2}{10^6 \text{ mm}^2}$$

$$= 2.09 \times 10^{-6} \text{ m}^2$$

From Table 4.3, for copper at room temperature, $\rho = 1.7 \times 10^{-8}$ $\Omega \cdot$m.

$$R = \rho \frac{L}{A} = (1.7 \times 10^{-8} \text{ } \Omega \cdot \text{m}) \left(\frac{100 \text{ m}}{2.09 \times 10^{-6} \text{ m}^2} \right)$$

$$= 0.81 \text{ } \Omega$$

The resistance of 100 m of No. 14 copper wire is 0.81 Ω.

Example 4.10 Voltage Drop Across a Copper Wire

A 5.6-A current flows in the copper wire of Example 4.9. What is the potential difference between the ends of the wire?

Solution: Solve $R = \dfrac{\Delta V}{I}$ for ΔV:

$$\Delta V = RI$$

$$= (0.81 \text{ } \Omega)(5.6 \text{ A})$$

$$= 4.5 \text{ V}$$

The potential difference between the ends of the wire is 4.5 volts.

Figure 4.26 shows a simple **series** circuit. Two lamps are connected in series with a power supply. When the switch is closed, there is only one path for current. Charge flows from the negative terminal of the power supply, through each lamp in turn, and into the positive terminal of the power supply.

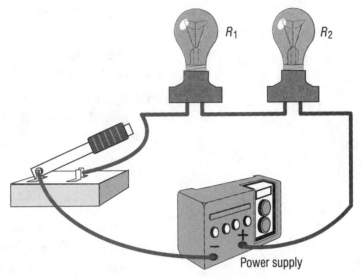

Figure 4.26
Two lamps connected in series with a power supply

This simple circuit illustrates four important rules for series circuits:

1. Since the current has only one path, the current through each lamp, and everywhere in the series circuit, is the same.

2. The current is resisted by the first lamp, and then by the second lamp, in turn. The total resistance in a series circuit is the sum of the individual resistances along the path of the current.

3. From $\Delta V = RI$, the voltage drop across each lamp is the product of the lamp's resistance and the current.

4. The sum of the voltage drops across the lamps equals the total potential difference of the power supply. The total potential difference also equals the product of the total circuit resistance and the current.

Notice what happens when there is a break, or an *open circuit*, anywhere in the path of the current of a series circuit. For example, opening the switch or burning out one of the lamp filaments creates an open circuit in Figure 4.26. When this happens, charge flow stops at the break. As a result of rule 1, charge flow stops everywhere in the circuit. Thus, when electrical elements are connected in series, an open circuit stops the current everywhere.

Example 4.11 Resistance in Series

The lamps in Figure 4.26 have resistances of 90 Ω and 70 Ω. The power supply produces 120 V.

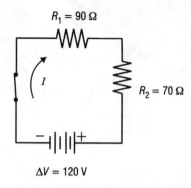

a. What is the current I through the circuit?

b. What is the voltage drop across each lamp?

Solution: First find the total resistance R_{total} of the circuit. Since the lamps are connected in series, R_{total} is the sum of the individual resistances (rule 2):

$$R_{total} = R_1 + R_2$$
$$= 90 \text{ Ω} + 70 \text{ Ω} = 160 \text{ Ω}$$

a. To calculate the current, replace R_1 and R_2 by the single, equivalent resistance R_{total}. Use the definition of resistance.

$$R_{total} = \frac{\Delta V_{total}}{I_{total}}$$

$$I_{total} = \frac{\Delta V_{total}}{R_{total}} = \frac{120 \text{ V}}{160 \text{ Ω}} = 0.75 \text{ A}$$

b. Let ΔV_1 be the voltage drop across R_1, and ΔV_2 be the voltage drop across R_2. Each voltage drop is the product of resistance and current (rule 3). The current through each resistance is the same (rule 1): $I_1 = I_2 = I_{total}$.

$$\Delta V_1 = R_1 I_1 \qquad\qquad \Delta V_2 = R_2 I_2$$
$$= (90 \text{ Ω}) (0.75 \text{ A}) \qquad\qquad = (70 \text{ Ω}) (0.75 \text{ A})$$
$$= 67.5 \text{ V} \qquad\qquad = 52.5 \text{ V}$$

Check: The sum of the voltage drops should equal ΔV_{total}.

$$\Delta V_{total} \overset{?}{=} \Delta V_1 + \Delta V_2$$
$$120 \text{ V} \overset{?}{=} 67.5 \text{ V} + 52.5 \text{ V}$$
$$120 \text{ V} \overset{?}{=} 120 \text{ V} \checkmark$$

Figure 4.27 shows the two lamps connected in **parallel** with the power supply. When the switch is closed, part of the current from the power supply flows through one lamp and part flows through the other lamp.

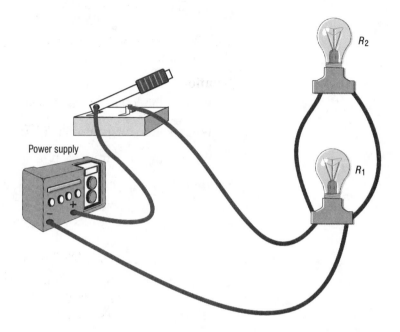

Figure 4.27
Two lamps connected in parallel with a power supply

This example illustrates four important rules for parallel circuits:

1. The total current through the circuit equals the sum of the currents through all the lamps.

2. Because there are multiple paths for current, the overall resistance of the circuit is decreased. The total resistance for the lamps connected in parallel is less than the resistance of either lamp. You can calculate the total resistance R_{total} using reciprocals: The reciprocal of R_{total} equals the sum of the reciprocals of the individual resistances.

$$\frac{1}{R_{total}} = \frac{1}{R_1} + \frac{1}{R_2}$$

3. From $I = \dfrac{\Delta V}{R}$, the current through each lamp is the ratio of the voltage drop across the lamp to the resistance of the lamp.

4. The voltage drop across the lamps is the same, and equals the potential difference of the power supply.

Example 4.12 Resistance in Parallel

The lamps in Figure 4.27 have resistances of 90 Ω and 70 Ω. The power supply produces 120 V.

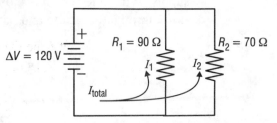

a. What is the total current I_{total} in the circuit?

b. What is the voltage drop across each lamp?

c. What is the current in each lamp?

Solution: First find the total resistance R_{total} of the circuit. Since the lamps are connected in parallel, use reciprocals (rule 2):

$$\frac{1}{R_{total}} = \frac{1}{R_1} + \frac{1}{R_2}$$

$$\frac{1}{R_{total}} = \frac{1}{90 \ \Omega} + \frac{1}{70 \ \Omega}$$

$$\frac{1}{R_{total}} = \frac{70 \ \Omega + 90 \ \Omega}{(90 \ \Omega)(70 \ \Omega)} = \frac{160 \ \Omega}{6300 \ \Omega^2}$$

To find R_{total}, find the reciprocal of $\frac{1}{R_{total}}$:

$$R_{total} = \frac{6300 \ \Omega^2}{160 \ \Omega}$$

$$= 39.4 \ \Omega$$

a. To calculate the current, replace R_1 and R_2 by the single, equivalent resistance R_{total}.

$$R_{total} = \frac{\Delta V_{total}}{I_{total}}$$

$$I_{total} = \frac{\Delta V_{total}}{R_{total}} = \frac{120 \ V}{39.4 \ \Omega} = 3.05 \ A$$

b. Let ΔV_1 be the voltage drop across R_1 and ΔV_2 be the voltage drop across R_2. The voltage drop across all lamps is the same, and equals the potential difference of the power supply (rule 4). Therefore,

$$\Delta V_1 = \Delta V_2 = \Delta V_{\text{total}} = 120 \text{ V}$$

c. Let I_1 be the current through R_1 and I_2 be the current through R_2.

$$I_1 = \frac{\Delta V_1}{R_1} \qquad\qquad I_2 = \frac{\Delta V_2}{R_2}$$

$$= \frac{120 \text{ V}}{90 \text{ }\Omega} \qquad\qquad = \frac{120 \text{ V}}{70 \text{ }\Omega}$$

$$= 1.33 \text{ A} \qquad\qquad = 1.71 \text{ A}$$

Check: The sum of the currents should equal I_{total}.

$$I_{\text{total}} \overset{?}{=} I_1 + I_2$$

$$3.05 \text{ A} \overset{?}{=} 1.33 \text{ A} + 1.71 \text{ A}$$

$$3.05 \text{ A} \overset{?}{=} 3.04 \text{ A} \quad \checkmark \quad (\text{within rounding error})$$

Resistors

In the examples above, the lamps provide resistance in the circuits. The connecting wires also have resistance, but it is so small that we usually ignore it. Sometimes, additional resistance is needed in a circuit to reduce current. A **resistor** is an electrical device that has a specific resistance. Resistors are made of long wires, carbon, or semiconductors. The value of resistance is labeled on the outside of a resistor.

Suppose you needed to reduce the total current in the circuit of Example 4.12 to less than 2.0 A. The total resistance should be greater than 120 V/2.0 A or 60 Ω. The circuit already has a resistance of 39.4 Ω, so you need to add at least (60 Ω – 39.4 Ω) or 20.6 Ω. Therefore, you can reduce the current to less than 2.0 A if you add a 21-Ω resistor in series.

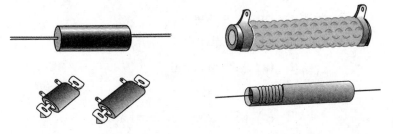

Figure 4.28
Resistor types

Summary

- Electrical resistance is the opposition to charge flow in electric circuits. The mathematical value of resistance is the ratio of potential difference across a device to current through the device. $R = \Delta V/I$. ($\Omega = V/A$)

- If a material obeys Ohm's law, its resistance is constant, and $\Delta V = IR$.

- The resistance of a wire depends on the length and cross-sectional area of the wire and the resistivity of the material composition of the wire. $R = \rho L/A$.

- For resistors connected in series in a circuit, the total resistance is the sum of the individual resistances. The current is the same everywhere in the circuit. The sum of the voltage drops across the resistors equals the total voltage produced by the source.

- For resistors connected in parallel in a circuit, the reciprocal of the total resistance is the sum of the reciprocals of the individual resistances. The voltage drop is the same across each resistor. The total current in the circuit equals the sum of the currents through all resistors.

Exercises

1. Electrical resistance in a wire is a measure of the opposition to the flow of _____.

2. Copper wire and metallic solder are
   (a) conductors
   (b) semiconductors
   (c) insulators

3. The resistance of a wire *does not* depend on which of the following?
   (a) wire material
   (b) wire mass
   (c) wire cross-sectional area
   (d) wire length

4. The resistivity of a wire depends on
   (a) wire material
   (b) wire mass
   (c) wire cross-sectional area
   (d) wire length

5. The graph at the right shows the relationship between current and voltage for two resistors. Does resistor A or resistor B have the greater resistance?

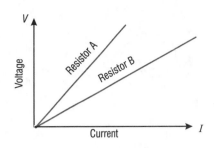

6. (a) What is the current through each resistor in the series circuit shown at the right?

   (b) What is the voltage drop across each resistor?

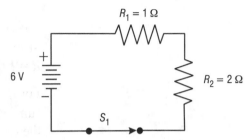

7. (a) What is the total current through the parallel circuit shown at the right?

   (b) What is the voltage drop across each resistor?

   (c) What is the current through each resistor?

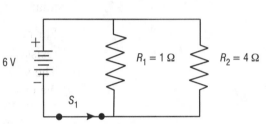

8. (a) Sketch a circuit diagram showing three lamps connected in series with a power supply.

   (b) If one lamp burns out, what happens to the other two? Explain.

   (c) The intensity of light from a lamp depends on the current in the lamp filament. A high current causes a lamp to burn brightly, while a lower current causes dimming. If more lamps are connected in series to the circuit, what happens to the light intensity of each lamp?

9. In the electrical circuit in your home, why are appliances, lighting, and outlets connected in parallel and not in series? Give two reasons.

10. Copper wires are available in a range of diameters. Number 12 wire is 2.05 mm in diameter, and number 00 wire is 9.27 mm in diameter. To carry a large current with a small drop in voltage, would you expect number 12 or number 00 wire to be used? Explain your answer.

11. The *mean free path* of electrons in a metal is the average distance traveled between collisions with atoms. The mean free path of electrons in metal A is greater than the mean free path in metal B. How would you expect the resistivity of metal A to compare to the resistivity of metal B?

12. Tell whether each of the following describes an open circuit or a closed circuit.

   (a) There is a break in the path of the current.

   (b) There is no charge flow in the circuit.

   (c) Current is measured in the circuit with an ammeter.

13. A circuit consists of a power supply and a single resistor.

   (a) What happens to the current through the resistor if the potential difference of the power supply doubles?

   (b) If the potential difference of the power supply does not change but a second identical resistor is connected in series, what happens to the current through the circuit?

14. What is the resistance of a car's headlamp if it draws a current of 2.5 amperes when connected to the car's 12-volt circuit?

15. An electric car has a 120-V power supply (ten 12-V batteries). The resistance of the motor is 0.21 Ω. What is the current through the motor?

16. (a) Draw a circuit diagram to show a 24-V battery and two resistors and an ammeter in series. The resistors have resistances of 12 Ω and 20 Ω.

   (b) What is the reading on the ammeter?

   (c) What is the voltage drop across each resistor?

17. (a) Draw a circuit diagram to show a 24-V battery and two resistors and a voltmeter in parallel. The resistors have resistances of 12 Ω and 20 Ω.

   (b) What is the reading on the voltmeter?

   (c) What is the current through each resistor?

18. Three 25-Ω resistors are connected in parallel and placed across a 60-V power supply.

   (a) What is the equivalent resistance of the parallel circuit?

   (b) What is the current through the power supply?

   (c) What is the current through each resistor?

19. As metal pipe is manufactured, it is inspected for flaws using a magnetic imaging process. The pipe is magnetized with current flowing through an aluminum rod inserted through the center of the pipe, as shown at the right. The rod has a diameter of 3.5 cm and is 13.7 m long.

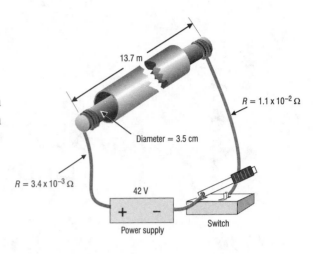

Copper cables connect the rod to the terminals of a power supply. The resistance of each cable is shown above. When the switch is closed, a potential difference of 42 V is applied to the circuit.

(a) What is the resistance of the aluminum rod?

(b) What is the total resistance of the electrical circuit?

(c) Calculate the current in the circuit.

20. A portable electric heater draws a current of 10 amperes when it is connected directly to a household 120-volt outlet. The heater is connected to a 75-foot-long extension cord, which has a resistance of 1.8 ohms. The extension cord is plugged into a 120-volt outlet.

(a) What is the total resistance of the extension cord and heater?

(b) What current will flow through the circuit with the extension cord?

(c) What percentage of the heater's rated current of 10 A flows through the heater when it is connected through the extension cord?

21. Two resistors in series form a *voltage divider*, as shown at the right. Write your answers for (a) and (b) as fractions, not decimals.

(a) Calculate the total resistance R_{total} of the circuit. What is the ratio $\dfrac{R_2}{R_{total}}$?

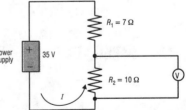

(b) Calculate the voltage measured by the voltmeter across R_2. This is called the *output voltage* of the divider. The power supply voltage is called the *input voltage*. What is the ratio of output to input voltage?

(c) Compare your answers for (a) and (b). Explain how you could use a voltage divider to get an output voltage of $x\%$ of an input voltage.

4.4 RESISTANCE IN THERMAL SYSTEMS

Objectives

- Describe a situation in which you would use a material with a high thermal conductivity and a situation in which you would use a material with a high thermal resistance.

- Explain the analogy among fluid resistance, electrical resistance, and thermal resistance.

- Describe the relationship among temperature drop, thermal resistance, and heat flow rate. Use the relationship to solve problems involving heat conduction.

- Calculate thermal resistance for a single layer or multiple layers of different materials.

INTERNET connection

To find out more about resistance in thermal systems, follow the links at **www.learningincontext.com.**

Resistance in mechanical systems (friction) opposes the motion of solid objects. In fluid systems, resistance opposes the flow of fluids. Resistance in electrical systems opposes the flow of charge, or current. In thermal systems, resistance opposes the flow of heat.

You learned in Section 3.4 that heat flow rate through a material increases with the thermal conductivity of the material. The bottom of a pan is made of a metal with a high thermal conductivity. This means the heat flow rate will be high when a temperature difference exists between a cooking surface and food inside the pan. You can also say the *thermal resistance* of the bottom of the pan is very low. **Thermal resistance** is a measure of an object's ability to oppose heat transfer.

Figure 4.29
A pan has a low thermal resistance or a high thermal conductivity.

Materials with high thermal resistance are used to insulate an object or a region of space. A region is insulated if its surroundings do not affect the region. For example, the walls of a refrigerator have a layer of insulation to increase their thermal resistance. With the insulation, there is a low heat flow rate from the warm air outside to the cold interior of the refrigerator.

Figure 4.30
The walls and door of a refrigerator have a high thermal resistance.

Thermal Resistance

In Section 4.2, we wrote a ratio for fluid resistance in laminar flow through a tube or pipe. In Section 4.3, we wrote a similar ratio for electrical resistance in charge flow through electrical devices. These ratios compared the prime mover in each system to a flow rate.

For the fluid system, we wrote resistance as the ratio of pressure drop to volume flow rate.

$$R_{fluid} = \frac{\text{pressure drop}}{\text{volume flow rate}} = \frac{-\Delta P}{\dot{V}}$$

$$\Delta P = P_f - P_i$$

$$\text{Pressure drop} = -\Delta P = P_i - P_f$$

(The negative sign is used to make pressure drop positive. Remember, in the direction of fluid flow, pressure decreases, so ΔP is negative.)

For electrical systems, resistance is the ratio of voltage drop to charge flow rate.

$$R_{electrical} = \frac{\text{voltage drop}}{\text{charge flow rate}} = \frac{\Delta V}{I}$$

$$\text{Voltage drop} \quad \text{or} \quad \text{Potential difference} = \Delta V$$

(By convention, a negative sign is not used for voltage drop or potential difference. Remember, ΔV does not mean $V_{final} - V_{initial}$.)

In thermal systems, the prime mover is temperature difference and the flow rate is heat flow rate. Therefore, we define thermal resistance as the ratio of temperature drop to heat flow rate.

$$R_{thermal} = \frac{\text{temperature drop}}{\text{heat flow rate}} = \frac{-\Delta T}{\dot{Q}}$$

$$\Delta T = T_2 - T_1$$

$$\text{Temperature drop} = -\Delta T = T_1 - T_2$$

(The negative sign is used to make temperature drop positive. Remember, heat flows from a high-temperature region to a low-temperature region. ΔT will be negative since $\Delta T = T_{low} - T_{high}$.)

Notice the units of thermal resistance

$$R_{thermal} = \frac{\text{temperature drop}}{\text{heat flow rate}} \rightarrow \frac{\text{°C}}{\text{cal/s}} \quad \text{or} \quad \frac{\text{°F}}{\text{Btu/s}}$$

When working problems, you can simplify the units in the denominator.

$$\frac{\text{°C}}{\text{cal/s}} = \frac{\text{s} \cdot \text{°C}}{\text{cal}} \qquad \frac{\text{°F}}{\text{Btu/s}} = \frac{\text{s} \cdot \text{°F}}{\text{Btu}}$$

Figure 4.31 shows a slab, or wall, of thickness Δx and composed of a material whose thermal conductivity is k. The area of the slab is A. The left face of the slab has a temperature T_1 and the right face has a temperature T_2, where $T_1 > T_2$. The temperature decreases linearly from T_1 to T_2 through the thickness of the slab.

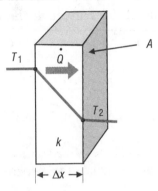

Figure 4.31
Heat flows through a wall from the high-temperature side to the low-temperature side.

You learned in Section 3.4 that heat flows from high temperature to low temperature through the slab, at a rate $\dot{Q}$ given by the heat conduction equation:

$$\dot{Q} = \frac{-kA\Delta T}{\Delta x}$$

Divide both sides of the equation by $-\Delta T$:

$$\frac{\dot{Q}}{-\Delta T} = \frac{kA}{\Delta x}$$

The reciprocal of the left side is R_{thermal}, so find the reciprocal of both sides:

$$R_{\text{thermal}} = \frac{-\Delta T}{\dot{Q}} = \frac{\Delta x}{kA}$$

You can use thermal resistance to solve heat flow problems, just like you use electrical resistance to solve charge flow problems. In electrical circuits, the voltage drop across a resistor is proportional to the current. In heat flow problems, the temperature drop across a slab is proportional to the heat flow rate.

$$-\Delta T = R_{\text{thermal}}\,\dot{Q}$$

Example 4.13 Temperature Inside a Refrigerator

A refrigerator wall measures 92 cm by 168 cm and contains a 5-cm thickness of fiberglass insulation. The heat flow rate through the fiberglass is 4.65 cal/s. If the temperature on the outside of the fiberglass is 21°C, what is the temperature on the inside?

The thermal conductivity of the fiberglass is

$$k = 1.1 \times 10^{-4} \, \frac{\text{cal} \cdot \text{cm}}{\text{s} \cdot \text{cm}^2 \cdot {}^\circ\text{C}}.$$

Solution: The area of the wall is

$$A = 92 \text{ cm} \times 168 \text{ cm} = 1.55 \times 10^4 \text{ cm}^2.$$

Calculate the thermal resistance:

$$R_{\text{thermal}} = \frac{\Delta x}{kA} = \frac{5 \text{ cm}}{\left(1.1 \times 10^{-} \, \dfrac{\text{cal} \cdot \text{cm}}{\text{s} \cdot \text{cm}^2 \cdot {}^\circ\text{C}}\right)\left(1.55 \times 10 \text{ cm}^2\right)}$$

$$R_{\text{thermal}} = 2.93 \, \frac{\text{s} \cdot {}^\circ\text{C}}{\text{cal}} \quad \text{or} \quad 2.93 \, \frac{{}^\circ\text{C}}{\text{cal/s}}$$

The temperature drop is proportional to the heat flow rate:

$$-\Delta T = R_{\text{thermal}} \, \dot{Q}$$

$$-(T_2 - T_1) = \left(2.93 \, \frac{\text{s} \cdot {}^\circ\text{C}}{\text{cal}}\right)\left(4.65 \, \frac{\text{cal}}{\text{s}}\right) = 13.6 {}^\circ\text{C}$$

$$T_1 - T_2 = 13.6 {}^\circ\text{C}$$

$$21 {}^\circ\text{C} - T_2 = 13.6 {}^\circ\text{C}$$

$$T_2 = (21 - 13.6) {}^\circ\text{C} = 7.4 {}^\circ\text{C}$$

The temperature inside the refrigerator is 7.4°C.

The figure shows, to the right of the problem statement, a wall labeled 168 cm, 92 cm, with $T_1 = 21{}^\circ\text{C}$ and $\Delta x = 5$ cm.

Thermal Resistance in Series

Walls are often constructed with layers of materials of different thicknesses and different thermal conductivities. For example, Figure 4.32 shows a wall made with two layers. Thermal energy is not created or lost within the wall. Therefore, the heat flow rate through both layers must be the same, and each must equal the heat flow rate through the entire wall. So you can write a single equation for $\dot{Q}$ using the overall temperature drop $-\Delta T_{\text{overall}}$, from T_1 to T_3, and the total thermal resistance R_{total}.

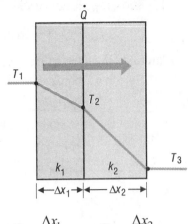

$$\dot{Q} = \frac{-\Delta T_{\text{overall}}}{R_{\text{total}}}$$

Overall
temperature $= -\Delta T_{\text{overall}}$
drop

$$= -(T_3 - T_1)$$

$$= T_1 - T_3$$

$$R_1 = \frac{\Delta x_1}{k_1 A} \qquad R_2 = \frac{\Delta x_2}{k_2 A}$$

Figure 4.32
The thermal resistance of two materials in series
is the sum of the individual resistances.

Heat flows through each resistance, one at a time, just like current flows
through each resistance in a series circuit. You can calculate the total thermal
resistance in the same way that you calculate total electrical resistance for
series circuits—it is the sum of the individual resistances.

$$R_{\text{total}} = R_1 + R_2$$

Example 4.14 Heat Flow Through a Composite Wall

A house wall consists of an inner layer of sheetrock ½ in. thick, a middle
layer of insulation 3 in. thick, and an outer layer of brick 4 in. thick. The
wall measures 25 ft by 12 ft. The thermal conductivity of each
construction material is shown in the table. Calculate the heat flow rate
through the wall if the inside temperature is 68°F and the outside
temperature is 30°F.

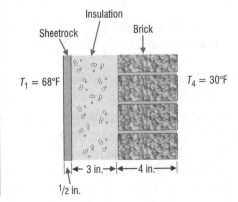

Material	Thermal Conductivity $\frac{\text{Btu} \cdot \text{in}}{\text{h} \cdot \text{ft}^2 \cdot °\text{F}}$
Sheetrock	5.2
Insulation	0.32
Brick	4.8

Solution: The area of the wall is

$$A = 25 \text{ ft} \times 12 \text{ ft} = 300 \text{ ft}^2$$

Calculate the thermal resistance of each layer, where $R_{\text{thermal}} = \dfrac{\Delta x}{kA}$:

$$R_1 = \frac{0.5 \text{ in}}{\left(5.2 \dfrac{\text{Btu} \cdot \text{in}}{\text{h} \cdot \text{ft}^2 \cdot {}^\circ\text{F}}\right)(300 \text{ ft}^2)} = 0.00032 \frac{\text{h} \cdot {}^\circ\text{F}}{\text{Btu}}$$

$$R_2 = \frac{3 \text{ in}}{\left(0.32 \dfrac{\text{Btu} \cdot \text{in}}{\text{h} \cdot \text{ft}^2 \cdot {}^\circ\text{F}}\right)(300 \text{ ft}^2)} = 0.031 \frac{\text{h} \cdot {}^\circ\text{F}}{\text{Btu}}$$

$$R_3 = \frac{4 \text{ in}}{\left(4.8 \dfrac{\text{Btu} \cdot \text{in}}{\text{h} \cdot \text{ft}^2 \cdot {}^\circ\text{F}}\right)(300 \text{ ft}^2)} = 0.0028 \frac{\text{h} \cdot {}^\circ\text{F}}{\text{Btu}}$$

The total resistance is the sum:

$$R_{\text{total}} = R_1 + R_2 + R_3 = (0.00032 + 0.031 + 0.0028) \frac{\text{h} \cdot {}^\circ\text{F}}{\text{Btu}}$$

$$R_{\text{total}} = 0.034 \frac{\text{h} \cdot {}^\circ\text{F}}{\text{Btu}} \quad \text{or} \quad 0.034 \frac{{}^\circ\text{F}}{\text{Btu/h}}$$

The heat flow rate through the wall is the ratio of overall temperature drop to total resistance:

$$\dot{Q} = -\frac{\Delta T_{\text{overall}}}{R_{\text{total}}} = \frac{-(30 - 68){}^\circ\text{F}}{0.034 \dfrac{{}^\circ\text{F}}{\text{Btu/h}}}$$

$$\dot{Q} = 1118 \text{ Btu/h}$$

Round to two significant figures. The rate of heat flow through the wall is 1100 Btu per hour.

Insulation, or high thermal resistance, is important when you want to keep the temperature of something in a container constant, or to minimize the heat flow rate through a container. In addition to insulating refrigerators and homes, high thermal resistance is used to insulate water heaters, water pipes, and thermos bottles. Water supply and sewer pipes are buried, so they are insulated by soil. A *dewar* is an insulated container for holding extremely cold materials such as liquid nitrogen. Insulation in a dewar is provided by a vacuum. Can you explain why a vacuum is a very good insulator?

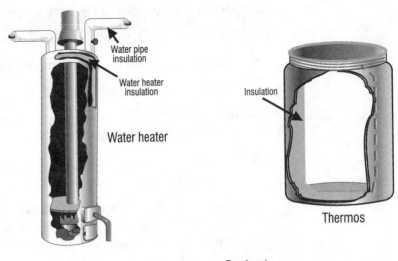

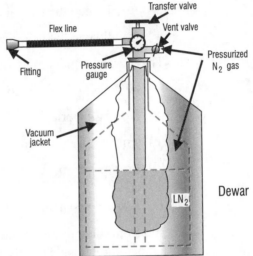

Figure 4.33
A water heater and connecting pipes, thermos, and dewar are insulated to reduce heat flow rates.

Summary

- Materials with high thermal resistance are used for thermal insulation. The heat flow through these materials is low.

- Fluid resistance, electrical resistance, and thermal resistance are defined as the ratio of the prime mover in each system to a flow rate.

- In thermal systems, the temperature drop between two points is proportional to the heat flow rate between the points. The constant of proportionality is the thermal resistance.

- When a wall or slab has multiple layers of different materials, the total thermal resistance for the slab is the sum of the resistances of the layers.

Exercises

1. Thermal resistance is the opposition to the flow of _____.

2. Thermal resistance is the ratio of _____ to _____.

3. In the definition of thermal resistance, explain why the temperature drop $(-\Delta T)$ is a positive quantity.

4. If temperature is measured in °C and heat flow rate is measured in cal/s, what are the units of thermal resistance?

5. A thermos bottle is surrounded by a material with a high thermal resistance. Explain why the following are equivalent reasons for using the thermos bottle to store hot chocolate:

   It will keep the temperature of the hot chocolate high for a long time.

   It will keep the heat flow rate low.

6. The thermal conductivity of a material depends on

   (a) thickness of the material

   (b) type of material

   (c) temperature difference across the material

   (d) surface area of the material

7. The thermal resistance of a building is $0.05 \dfrac{\text{h} \cdot {}^\circ\text{C}}{\text{kcal}}$. What is the heat flow rate from the building if the temperature inside is 20°C and the temperature outside is 5°C?

8. An architect designs an office building with large windows. Each window has length L, width W, and thickness Δx. How can the architect reduce the heat flow rate through each window?

   (a) Use a material with a higher thermal conductivity.

   (b) Increase L and/or W.

   (c) Increase Δx.

   (d) All of the above.

9. A window in Exercise 8 measures 10 feet by 12 feet and is 1 inch thick. It is made with a material whose thermal conductivity is $3.2 \dfrac{\text{Btu} \cdot \text{in}}{\text{h} \cdot \text{ft}^2 \cdot {}^\circ\text{F}}$.

   (a) What is the thermal resistance of the window?

   (b) What is the heat flow rate through the window if the inside temperature is 70°F and the outside temperature is 0°F?

10. A house ceiling consists of an inner layer of plaster (1/8 in. thick) over a layer of sheetrock (1/2 in. thick) with an outer layer of insulation (6 in. thick). The total surface area of the ceiling is 2500 ft². Calculate the heat flow rate through the ceiling if the inside temperature is 70°F and the temperature above the insulation is 25°F. The thermal conductivity of each material is shown in the table.

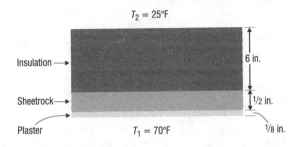

Material	Thermal Conductivity $\dfrac{\text{Btu} \cdot \text{in}}{\text{h} \cdot \text{ft}^2 \cdot °\text{F}}$
Insulation	0.28
Sheetrock	5.2
Plaster	6.0

11. Draw a graph showing the relationship between temperature drop $(-\Delta T)$ and heat flow rate $(\dot{Q})$ for the ceiling in Exercise 10. Use the graph to estimate the temperature drop across the ceiling for a heat flow rate of 3000 Btu/h.

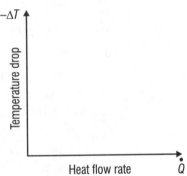

12. A polyurethane foam cooler measures 3 ft × 2 ft × 1.5 ft (inside dimensions). The thermal conductivity of the foam is $0.20 \dfrac{\text{Btu} \cdot \text{in}}{\text{h} \cdot \text{ft}^2 \cdot °\text{F}}$.

The thickness of the sides, bottom, and top of the cooler is 1.5 inches. The cooler is filled with canned drinks, water, and ice. What is the heat flow rate into the cooler when the outside temperature is 95°F? Assume the temperature is 32°F on all inside surfaces, and 95°F on all outside surfaces.

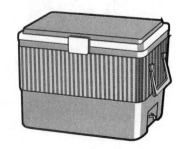

13. An air-conditioning duct has a rectangular cross section measuring 12 inches by 18 inches. It is wrapped with a fiberglass insulation blanket 3 inches thick. The duct is 21 feet long. Refrigerated air flowing through the duct has an average temperature of 42°F. The duct runs through a ceiling space that has a temperature of 110°F. The thermal conductivity of the insulation is $0.32 \dfrac{\text{Btu} \cdot \text{in}}{\text{h} \cdot \text{ft}^2 \cdot {}^\circ \text{F}}$.

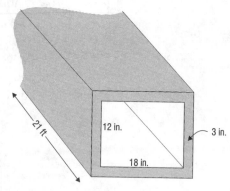

(a) As shown in the cutaway diagram above, the duct consists of four walls, with each wall measuring 21 feet in length. Calculate the total area of the inside surface of the duct.

(b) Heat flows through each wall of the duct from the high-temperature region outside to the low-temperature region inside. What is the total heat flow rate from the ceiling space into the duct?

(c) What thickness of insulation would be required to reduce the heat flow rate to 1/3 the value found in (b)?

14. The living quarters for a research group near the Arctic Ocean are elevated, so they are not in contact with the permafrost. This allows cold air to circulate under the buildings to remove heat, which would otherwise melt and damage the permafrost. Each building is in the shape of a box (or rectangular prism), with dimensions 20 ft by 40 ft by 8 ft. The walls, floor, and ceiling of the building are insulated with 12 inches of a material whose thermal conductivity is $0.32 \dfrac{\text{Btu} \cdot \text{in}}{\text{h} \cdot \text{ft}^2 \cdot {}^\circ \text{F}}$. You can neglect the insulation value of the other construction materials.

(a) Calculate the total surface area of the walls, the floor, and the ceiling of a building.

(b) The heater in a building maintains a constant indoor temperature of 50°F, while the outside temperature is −40°F (no wind chill). How many Btu per hour must the heater produce?

(c) One of the buildings has a heater with an output of 10,000 Btu/h. How cold can it get outside the building and maintain 50°F inside the building?

CHAPTER FOUR SUMMARY

When a net force acts on a body, the body accelerates. Newton's second law of motion describes the relationship between the net force, the body's mass, and the body's acceleration ($F = ma$).

Whenever there is motion, there is opposition or resistance to the motion.

Mechanical resistance is opposition to motion of a solid object when it is in contact with another solid object. This opposition is called friction. A linear model of friction describes the forces adequately in many situations. According to this model, the force of friction is proportional to the normal force between the objects ($F_{static} \leq \mu_s N$, and $F_{kinetic} = \mu_k N$).

Fluid resistance is opposition to fluid flow. Drag is the force that resists motion of an object moving through a fluid (or a fluid moving past a stationary object). Drag increases as speed increases. Resistance causes fluid pressure to drop as fluid flows through a pipe, tube, or duct ($R_{fluid} = -\Delta P / \dot{V}$). The resistance depends on the radius of the pipe, the length of the pipe, and the viscosity of the fluid.

Electrical resistance is opposition to charge flow. Resistance causes a potential difference, or voltage drop, as current flows through a conductor ($R = \Delta V / I$). The resistance of a wire depends on the length of the wire, its cross-sectional area, and the resistivity of its material composition.

Thermal resistance is opposition to heat flow. Heat flows through a wall from a region of high temperature to a region of low temperature. The thermal resistance of the wall is the ratio of the temperature drop to the heat flow rate ($R_{thermal} = -\Delta T / \dot{Q}$). Thermal resistance depends on the thickness of the wall, its cross-sectional area, and the thermal conductivity of its material composition.

CHAPTER 5

ENERGY

A **property** of an object or a system is a quality or trait belonging to the system. A volleyball's mass, volume, weight, diameter, color, speed, and height above the floor are all properties of the volleyball. *Energy* is also a property. **Energy** is the property that enables something to do work.

For example, a moving volleyball has energy. Energy of motion is called **kinetic energy**. A volleyball's kinetic energy enables the ball to do work when it strikes a net and forces the net to deform.

Objects can also have energy because of their position. This type of energy is called **potential energy**. When a volleyball is tossed up prior to a serve, its higher position in the Earth's gravitational field gives the ball the ability to do work when it falls to a lower position. This property is gravitational potential energy. When a volleyball flies into the net, the deformed, stretched net gains elastic potential energy. This gives the net the ability to do work on the ball, stopping its motion and forcing it to move in the opposite direction.

Work, kinetic energy, and potential energy are closely related. When the volleyball flies into the net, some of its kinetic energy is converted into potential energy. The amount of energy converted equals the work done on the ball by the force of the net. When the net forces the ball to move in the opposite direction, some of the stored potential energy is converted into work. If there were no friction, the amount of potential energy lost by the net would equal the amount of work done on the ball.

Potential energy can also be stored in electrical devices called capacitors and inductors. In a capacitor, energy is stored in an electric field. In an inductor, energy is stored in a magnetic field. In both devices, the amount of energy stored equals the work done in creating the fields.

The **internal energy** of a system is the sum of the microscopic kinetic and potential energies of all the atoms and molecules that make up the system. Internal energy is useful in solving problems in thermal systems, such as refrigerators and engines. We will be concerned mostly with *changes* in internal energy. For example, the internal energy of the working fluid of a refrigerator changes when work is done on the fluid (as in the refrigerator's compressor) and when heat is transferred to the fluid (as in the refrigerator's evaporator).

A system's **total energy** is the sum of its kinetic, potential, and internal energies. *The total energy of an isolated system never changes.* (An isolated system is one in which no mass, work, or energy is allowed to enter or leave.) This is called the **law of conservation of energy**, and it is one of the most important and useful concepts in physics.

5.1
ENERGY IN MECHANICAL AND FLUID SYSTEMS I

Objectives

- Explain the relationship between kinetic energy and motion.

- Calculate the kinetic energy of an object when it is in translational motion and when it is in rotational motion.

- Explain the similarities between the equations for translational and rotational kinetic energies.

- Explain the relationship between the work done on an object or fluid and the change in kinetic energy.

- Use the work-energy theorem to solve problems in mechanical and fluid systems.

INTERNET *connection*

To find out more about energy in mechanical and fluid systems, follow the links at **www.learningincontext.com.**

Refer to Appendix F for a career link to this concept.

Kinetic Energy

An object or a fluid in motion can do work. A moving hammer can do work on a nail. Hot exhaust gas leaving a jet engine can do work on an airplane. Therefore, the moving hammer and exhaust gas have energy. Energy that is due to mass in motion is called **kinetic energy**. Mathematically, kinetic energy KE is the product of one-half the mass m of the object and the square of its speed v.

$$\text{Kinetic energy} = \tfrac{1}{2}\,(\text{mass})(\text{speed})^2$$

$$\text{KE} = \tfrac{1}{2}\,mv^2$$

The unit for kinetic energy is the same as the unit for work. In SI, kinetic energy is measured in joules. For example, a 2-kg object moving at 1 m/s has a kinetic energy of $\tfrac{1}{2}$ (2 kg)(1 m/s)^2 = 1 kg·m²/s² or 1 N·m or 1 J. In English units, energy is measured in foot-pounds.

Kinetic energy increases linearly with mass. Suppose a 1-kg hammer and a 2-kg hammer are moving at the same speed. The 2-kg hammer has twice the kinetic energy of the 1-kg hammer, and can do twice the work.

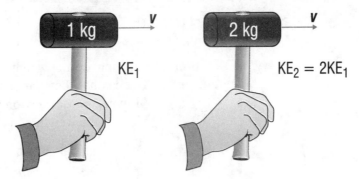

Figure 5.1
A 2-kg hammer has twice the kinetic energy of a 1-kg hammer moving at the same speed.

Kinetic energy increases with the square of the speed. Suppose a 1-kg hammer is moving twice as fast as another 1-kg hammer. The faster hammer has four times the kinetic energy of the slower hammer, and can do four times the work.

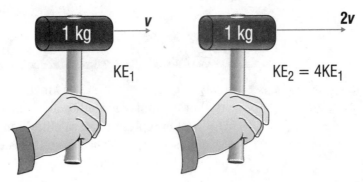

Figure 5.2
A hammer moving twice as fast as an identical hammer has four times the kinetic energy.

Example 5.1 Kinetic Energy of a Volleyball

After a serve, a 0.27-kg volleyball is moving at 22 m/s. What is the kinetic energy of the volleyball?

Solution: $KE = \frac{1}{2}mv^2$

$$= \frac{1}{2}(0.27 \text{ kg})(22 \text{ m/s})^2$$

$$= 65.3 \text{ kg·m}^2/\text{s}^2 \quad \text{or} \quad 65.3 \text{ J}$$

The kinetic energy of the volleyball is 65.3 joules.

Example 5.2 Kinetic Energy in a Shot

Just before it strikes the ground, an 8.8-lb shot in a shot-put competition is moving at 38 ft/s. What is the kinetic energy of the shot?

Solution: First convert the weight of the shot (pounds) to mass (slugs). You can use the relationship that one slug weighs 32.2 pounds. Or, you can use Newton's second law, with the force of gravity equal to the weight and $a = g$:

$$m = \frac{F}{a} = \frac{8.8 \text{ lb}}{32.2 \text{ ft/s}^2} = 0.273 \text{ lb·s}^2/\text{ft} \quad \text{or} \quad 0.273 \text{ slug}$$

$$KE = \frac{1}{2}mv^2$$

$$= \frac{1}{2}\left(0.273\frac{\text{lb·s}^2}{\text{ft}}\right)\left(38\frac{\text{ft}}{\text{s}}\right)^2$$

$$= 197 \text{ ft·lb}$$

The kinetic energy of the shot is 197 foot-pounds.

Kinetic Energy in Rotational Systems

A body in circular motion has kinetic energy since it is moving and can do work. For example, a satellite in circular orbit around the Earth has kinetic energy. Let ω represent the satellite's angular speed (in radians per second). Let r represent the distance from the satellite to the center of rotation, which is the center of the Earth.

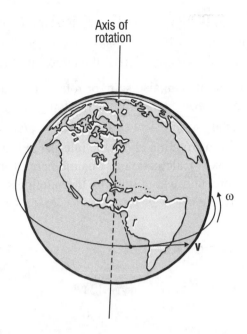

Axis of
rotation

ω

v

r

Figure 5.3
A satellite in circular orbit
is a rotational system.

The linear speed v of the satellite is the product of r and ω. If r is measured in meters and ω is measured in rad/s, what are the units of v?

$$v = r\omega$$

The satellite's kinetic energy can be written as follows:

$$\text{KE} = \tfrac{1}{2}mv^2 = \tfrac{1}{2}mr^2\omega^2$$

The product mr^2 is called the **moment of inertia** of the satellite. We use the symbol I to represent moment of inertia. The kinetic energy equation for a body in rotation can be written as follows.

$$\frac{\text{Kinetic}}{\text{energy}} = \tfrac{1}{2}\left(\frac{\text{moment}}{\text{of inertia}}\right)(\text{angular speed})^2$$

$$\text{KE} = \tfrac{1}{2}I\omega^2$$

This is the same equation as that for the kinetic energy of a body in translation, but moment of inertia replaces mass and angular speed replaces linear speed.

The moment of inertia of a body in rotational motion is usually not easy to calculate. For the satellite, the equation $I = mr^2$ was based on an important assumption about the mass and its location relative to the axis of rotation. When we said, "let r represent the distance from the satellite to the center of rotation," we did not say what part of the satellite we would measure r from. Instead, we assumed that all the satellite mass was concentrated at a single point, and we measured from that point. This point is called the satellite's *center of mass*. Using the center of mass, you can treat the satellite as a particle—as if it has mass but no size. The motion of the center of mass represents the motion of the entire satellite for rotation around the Earth.

A satellite can also spin, or rotate about an axis through its center of mass. The kinetic energy of this motion is not the same as the kinetic energy of the orbital motion. The equation $KE = \frac{1}{2}I\omega^2$ still holds, but ω is now the angular speed of rotation about the internal axis and I is the moment of inertia about this axis. Calculation of this moment of inertia is more complicated than before, because of the way the satellite's mass is distributed around the axis of rotation.

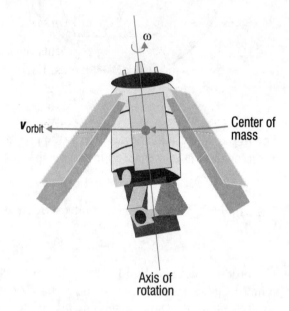

Figure 5.4
A spinning satellite has rotational kinetic energy, not the same as its orbital kinetic energy.

To see how to calculate the moment of inertia of this type of object, look at the compact disc shown in Figure 5.5. Think of all the particles that make up the CD. They have different distances from the axis of rotation, and they may have different masses. Two of these particles are shown in the figure— one on the outside rim of the CD and one on the inside rim. The particles have masses m_1 and m_2, and they are located distances r_1 and r_2 from the axis of rotation.

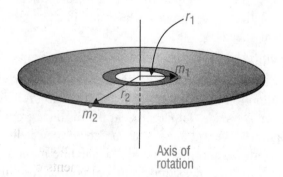

Figure 5.5
The moment of inertia of a CD is the sum of the moments of all the particles that make up the CD.

The moment of inertia of the two particles is the sum $m_1r_1^2 + m_2r_2^2$. But the CD contains many more than two particles, and the moment of inertia of the entire CD is the sum of all the particles' moments:

$$I = m_1r_1^2 + m_2r_2^2 + m_3r_3^2 + \ldots$$

The symbol "$+ \ldots$" means to continue the sum for all particles. It is possible to find this sum using the tools from a branch of mathematics called *calculus*. For an object in the shape of the CD (an annular cylinder), the result is

$$I = \tfrac{1}{2}m(r_1^2 + r_2^2)$$

where m is the total mass of the CD ($m = m_1 + m_2 + m_3 + \ldots$).

Figure 5.6 lists the formulas for moments of inertia for the point particle, annular cylinder, and five other shapes. Each formula contains the mass of the object and a distance (radius or length), but the formulas are different. For each shape, the axis of rotation also is specified. Notice that (d) and (h) are the same shape but the axes are different. The moment of inertia changes when the axis changes.

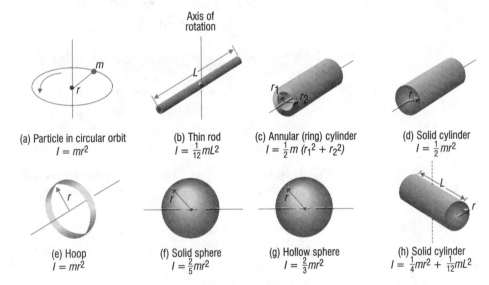

Axis of rotation

(a) Particle in circular orbit
$I = mr^2$

(b) Thin rod
$I = \tfrac{1}{12}mL^2$

(c) Annular (ring) cylinder
$I = \tfrac{1}{2}m\,(r_1^2 + r_2^2)$

(d) Solid cylinder
$I = \tfrac{1}{2}mr^2$

(e) Hoop
$I = mr^2$

(f) Solid sphere
$I = \tfrac{2}{5}mr^2$

(g) Hollow sphere
$I = \tfrac{2}{3}mr^2$

(h) Solid cylinder
$I = \tfrac{1}{4}mr^2 + \tfrac{1}{12}mL^2$

Figure 5.6
Moment of inertia formulas for different-shaped objects.
In each case, m is the mass of the object.

Moment of inertia in rotational kinetic energy is analogous to mass in translational kinetic energy, but they are not the same. You can demonstrate the difference with a simple activity. You will need two metersticks, four 100-gram weights, and some masking tape. Tape two weights to one meterstick, at the 40- and 60-cm marks. Tape the other two weights to the other meterstick, at the 10- and 90-cm marks. The total masses of the metersticks are the same, but the moments of inertia are different.

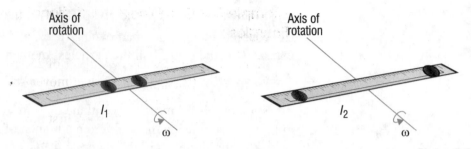

Figure 5.7
The masses are the same, but $I_2 > I_1$. You can tell the difference by rotating each meterstick about an axis through the center of mass.

Hold each meterstick at the 50-cm mark. The center of mass is also at the 50-cm mark. Mass is a property that describes an object's resistance to change in translational motion. Hold each meterstick horizontally, and move it up and down. Do they have the same mass?

Moment of inertia is a property that describes an object's resistance to change in rotational motion. Rotate each meterstick about an axis through the center of mass and perpendicular to the length, as shown in Figure 5.7. Which one is harder to rotate? This one has a greater moment of inertia.

Example 5.3 Rotational and Kinetic Energy of a Flywheel

A flywheel is being tested as a possible energy-storage device for automobiles. The flywheel is in the shape of a solid cylinder with a radius of 0.25 m. The mass of the flywheel is 68 kg, and it spins at an angular speed of 6200 rpm. What is the kinetic energy of the flywheel?

Solution: First find the moment of inertia. The formula for a solid cylinder is given in Figure 5.6(d):

$$I = \tfrac{1}{2}mr^2$$

$$= \tfrac{1}{2}(68 \text{ kg})(0.25 \text{ m})^2$$

$$= 2.125 \text{ kg·m}^2$$

Use this value in the equation for rotational kinetic energy. Convert angular speed to radians per second:

$$\text{KE} = \tfrac{1}{2}I\omega^2$$

$$= \tfrac{1}{2}(2.125 \text{ kg·m}^2)\left(6200\frac{\text{rev}}{\text{min}} \cdot \frac{1 \text{ min}}{60 \text{ s}} \cdot \frac{2\pi \text{ rad}}{\text{rev}}\right)^2$$

$$= 4.5 \times 10^5 \text{ kg·m}^2/\text{s}^2 \quad \text{or} \quad 4.5 \times 10^5 \text{ J}$$

The kinetic energy of the flywheel is 4.5×10^5 joules.

Example 5.4 Combined Translational and Rotational Kinetic Energies

A 7.2-kg bowling ball has a diameter of 25 cm. When the ball is rolled down an alley, the center of the ball moves at a horizontal speed of 4.2 m/s. The ball rotates at a rate of 34 rad/s. What is the kinetic energy of the bowling ball when it strikes the first pin?

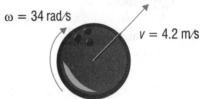

Solution: The bowling ball has translational and rotational motion. The total kinetic energy is the sum of the two kinetic energies:

$$KE = KE_{translational} + KE_{rotational} = \tfrac{1}{2}mv^2 + \tfrac{1}{2}I\omega^2$$

First calculate $KE_{translational}$:

$$\tfrac{1}{2}mv^2 = \tfrac{1}{2}(7.2 \text{ kg})(4.2 \text{ m/s})^2 = 64 \text{ kg·m}^2/\text{s}^2 \quad \text{or} \quad 64 \text{ J}$$

Now find the moment of inertia of the bowling ball. The ball is a solid sphere. The formula is given in Figure 5.6(f):

$$I = \tfrac{2}{5}mr^2 = \tfrac{2}{5}(7.2 \text{ kg})(\tfrac{0.25}{2}\text{ m})^2 = 0.045 \text{ kg·m}^2$$

Calculate $KE_{rotational}$:

$$\tfrac{1}{2}I\omega^2 = \tfrac{1}{2}(0.045 \text{ kg·m}^2)(34 \text{ rad/s})^2 = 26 \text{ kg·m}^2/\text{s}^2 \text{ or } 26 \text{ J}$$

Find the sum:

$$KE = \tfrac{1}{2}mv^2 + \tfrac{1}{2}I\omega^2 = 64 \text{ J} + 26 \text{ J} = 90 \text{ J}$$

The kinetic energy of the bowling ball is 90 joules.

The Work-Energy Theorem

A hockey puck slides across the ice at an initial speed v_i and with an initial kinetic energy KE_i. A skater strikes the puck and exerts a force in the direction of motion. This force accelerates the puck. The puck's speed increases to a value v_f. Since $v_f > v_i$, the final kinetic energy KE_f is greater than KE_i. Where did the extra kinetic energy come from?

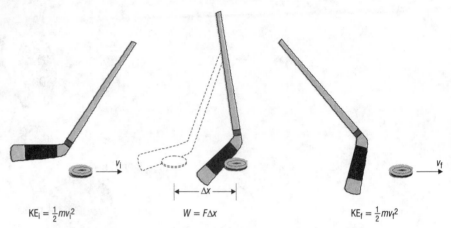

$$KE_i = \tfrac{1}{2}mv_i^2 \qquad W = F\Delta x \qquad KE_f = \tfrac{1}{2}mv_f^2$$

Figure 5.8
Work done on a hockey puck increases its kinetic energy.

The skater applies a force to the puck to accelerate it down the ice. This force is applied over a distance Δx. Therefore, the skater does work on the puck. This work is responsible for the puck's increase in kinetic energy. In general, when work is done on an object, its kinetic energy changes, and the work done equals the change in kinetic energy.

$$W = KE_f - KE_i$$

Or, using the delta symbol:

$$W = \Delta KE$$

This relationship is called the **work-energy theorem**. The theorem was established in the nineteenth century by the English physicist James Prescott Joule. The SI unit of energy and work is named in his honor.

The work-energy theorem establishes an alternative definition of work: a measure of the energy that is transmitted by a force, such as a contact, gravitational, electrical, or magnetic force. In the example above, the work done by the hockey player can be measured by the energy transmitted to the puck (ΔKE).

The work-energy theorem also applies to fluids. Remember, a pressure (or force per unit area) can do work on a fluid ($W = P\Delta V$ or $-V\Delta P$). Work done on a fluid changes the fluid's kinetic energy. You will use the relationship between work and energy for fluids in the next section.

Example 5.5 Work Done on a Pickup

A 2150-kg truck accelerates from 25 km/h to 40 km/h. What work is done by the engine? Neglect friction and drag.

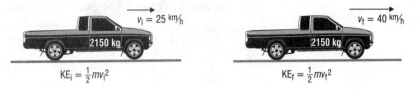

$KE_i = \frac{1}{2}mv_i^2$ $KE_f = \frac{1}{2}mv_f^2$

Solution: Convert the initial and final speeds to meters per second:

$$v_i = 25\frac{km}{h} \cdot \frac{1000 \text{ m}}{km} \cdot \frac{1 \text{ h}}{3600 \text{ s}} \qquad v_f = 40\frac{km}{h} \cdot \frac{1000 \text{ m}}{km} \cdot \frac{1 \text{ h}}{3600 \text{ s}}$$

$$v_i = 6.94 \text{ m/s} \qquad\qquad v_f = 11.1 \text{ m/s}$$

Calculate the truck's initial and final kinetic energies:

$$KE_i = \frac{1}{2}mv_i^2 \qquad\qquad\qquad KE_f = \frac{1}{2}mv_f^2$$

$$= \frac{1}{2}(2150 \text{ kg})(6.94 \text{ m/s})^2 \qquad = \frac{1}{2}(2150 \text{ kg})(11.1 \text{ m/s})^2$$

$$= 5.18 \times 10^4 \text{ J} \qquad\qquad = 1.32 \times 10^5 \text{ J}$$

Now use the work-energy theorem:

$$W = \Delta KE = KE_f - KE_i$$

$$W = 1.32 \times 10^5 \text{ J} - 5.18 \times 10^4 \text{ J}$$

$$= 8.02 \times 10^4 \text{ J}$$

The engines does 8.02×10^4 joules of work.

Summary

- Energy is a property that enables something to do work.

- Kinetic energy is energy that an object has due to its motion.

- An object has kinetic energy if it is in translational motion ($KE = \frac{1}{2}mv^2$) or if it is in rotational motion ($KE = \frac{1}{2}I\omega^2$).

- The moment of inertia I is a property that describes an object's resistance to change in rotational motion.

- When work is done on an object, its kinetic energy changes by an amount equal to the work done.

1. Is kinetic energy a scalar or a vector quantity? Can the kinetic energy of an object ever be negative? Explain your answers.

2. A bicycle racer and her bike have a combined weight of 128 lb. She pedals the bike 0.35 mile in 1.0 minute at a constant speed. What is her kinetic energy?

3. If you double the speed of an object, by how much do you increase its kinetic energy?

4. Car A is accelerated from 0 to 50 km/h. Car B, which has half the mass of car A, is accelerated from 0 to 100 km/h. Which car's engine does more work?

5. A 2500-kg truck slows from 100 km/h to 72 km/h when the driver applies the brakes. What are the initial and final kinetic energies? How much work is done by the truck's brakes?

6. If the brakes of the truck in Exercise 5 did half as much work, what would be the truck's final speed?

7. If the brakes of the truck in Exercise 5 did twice as much work, what would be the truck's final speed?

8. What quantity in a rotational system is analogous to mass in a translational system? What are the SI units of this quantity?

9. When calculating rotational kinetic energy, what units for angular speed must be used?

10. A 75-gram hailstone has a terminal speed of 180 m/s. How much work can the hailstone do when it hits a shingle on the roof of a house?

11. If a large airplane has to make an emergency landing, it may have to "dump" (or drain) fuel in the air to reduce its weight. An airliner dumps 20,000 pounds of fuel before landing at a speed of 120 mph. By how much does the airliner reduce its kinetic energy for touchdown by dumping the fuel?

12. A flywheel between an air compressor and its drive motor dampens torque variations. The moment of inertia of the flywheel is 8640 kg·m². What is the kinetic energy of the flywheel when it rotates at 441 rpm?

13. The flywheel in Exercise 12 slows from 441 rpm to 440 rpm in ¼ revolution. Calculate the work done on the flywheel during the ¼ revolution.

14. An underground water pipeline has a diameter of 0.92 m. The pipeline is 85 km long. If the pipe is completely full of water and the water flows at a speed of 3.1 m/s, what is the kinetic energy of the water? The density of water is 1000 kg/m³.

15. You are designing the wheels for a solar-powered-car competition. You can use a solid, annular, or hoop design, approximated by the illustrations below. The mass of each wheel is 0.75 kg.

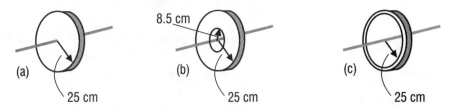

(a) 25 cm   8.5 cm (b) 25 cm   (c) 25 cm

Suppose the car starts from rest and 1 joule of work is transmitted to each wheel, resulting in rotational motion of the wheel. Calculate the angular speed, in revolutions per minute, for each wheel. Which design would you use? Explain your choice.

16. A wind-powered electrical generator has a propeller diameter of 8.5 m. In a 24-hour period, the average speed of air flowing through the generator is 6.7 m/s. You can model this air as that contained in a tube of length l.

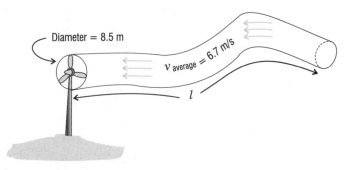

Diameter = 8.5 m $v_{average}$ = 6.7 m/s l

(a) Calculate the length of the tube and the volume of air that flows through the generator in the 24-hour period.

(b) The air has an average density of 1.15 kg/m³. How much kinetic energy is contained in the wind?

(c) How much energy does the generator extract from the wind during this 24-hour period if it is 30% efficient?

17. A 1000-kg telecommunication satellite is placed in a *geostationary* orbit. In this orbit, the satellite completes exactly one revolution of the Earth in 24 hours. The radius of a geostationary orbit is 42,160 km.

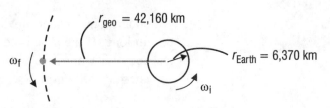

r_{geo} = 42,160 km

r_{Earth} = 6,370 km

(a) Calculate the moment of inertia of the satellite in the geostationary orbit. Calculate the angular speed of the satellite, in radians per second. What is the satellite's kinetic energy in geostationary orbit?

(b) The satellite is launched from the Guiana Space Center, near the Earth's equator. Before launch, the satellite's angular speed is approximately the same as that calculated in (a). Explain why this is true.

(c) The radius of the Earth is 6370 km. What is the satellite's moment of inertia just before it is launched into space? What is the satellite's kinetic energy just before it is launched into space?

(d) The launch vehicle does work to change the satellite's kinetic energy and to lift the satellite (and its own mass) in the Earth's gravitational field. How much work is done to change the satellite's kinetic energy?

5.2 ENERGY IN MECHANICAL AND FLUID SYSTEMS II

Objectives

- Explain the relationship between gravitational potential energy and an object's position in a gravitational field.

- Explain the relationship between elastic potential energy and an object's position.

- Describe the relationship between work done on a system and its potential energy.

- Explain the law of conservation of energy.

- Solve problems using the law of conservation of energy.

- Explain Bernoulli's principle.

- Use Bernoulli's equation to solve problems in fluid flow.

INTERNET *connection*

To find out more about energy in mechanical and fluid systems, follow the links at **www.learningincontext.com**.

In the last section, you learned that objects and fluids in motion have energy because they have the ability to do work. Energy of motion is called kinetic energy and is calculated by $KE = \frac{1}{2}mv^2$ for translational motion and $KE = \frac{1}{2}I\omega^2$ for rotational motion. You also learned that, when work is done on an object, the object's kinetic energy changes by an amount equal to the work done. This is the work-energy theorem.

Gravitational Potential Energy

What happens when you toss a ball straight up into the air (with no rotation)? You give the ball an initial speed and kinetic energy. But the Earth's gravity exerts a force on the ball, which slows it down. (Drag also slows the ball, but we will neglect this force for now.) At some height h above the point at which you released the ball, it stops moving upward and begins moving downward. At this height the speed of the ball, and therefore its kinetic energy, is zero.

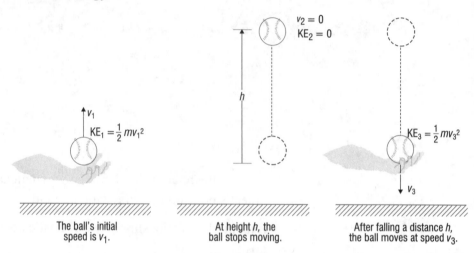

The ball's initial speed is v_1.

At height h, the ball stops moving.

After falling a distance h, the ball moves at speed v_3.

Figure 5.9
The round trip of a tossed ball

You can write a relationship between h and the ball's initial speed v_1 using the work-energy theorem:

$$W = \Delta KE$$

For the upward motion, work is done in slowing the ball by the force of gravity (or weight) mg, where m is the mass of the ball and g is the acceleration of gravity. This force is directed downward, while the ball's displacement is upward. Since force and displacement are in opposite directions, work is negative.

$$-mgh = KE_2 - KE_1$$

When the ball reaches height h, it stops moving, so $KE_2 = 0$.

$$-mgh = 0 - KE_1$$

$$mgh = KE_1$$

Since $KE_1 = \frac{1}{2}mv_1^2$, we can write the following equality: (What property of mathematics do we use?)

$$mgh = \frac{1}{2}mv_1^2$$

From height h, the ball accelerates downward under the force of gravity. This time gravity acts in the same direction as displacement, and work is positive. Let v_3 represent the speed of the ball when it returns to your hand. You can write the following equation from the work-energy theorem:

$$mgh = KE_3 - KE_2$$

$$mgh = KE_3 - 0$$

$$mgh = KE_3 = \tfrac{1}{2}mv_3{}^2$$

Notice that $mgh = KE_1$ and $mgh = KE_3$. Therefore, $KE_1 = KE_3$. (What property of mathematics allows you to make this conclusion?) In other words, by the time the ball returns to your hand, it has recovered all its original kinetic energy. The ball loses kinetic energy on the way up, until it is zero, and then gains kinetic energy on the way down, until all the original kinetic energy is back. What happens to the kinetic energy during this process—where does it go?

As the ball rises, it gains the *potential* for doing work. This potential is realized when the ball drops from height h and does work on your hand as you catch the ball. The amount of work the ball can do because of its height above your hand is called its **gravitational potential energy**. As the ball rises, it loses kinetic energy and gains potential energy.

We use the symbol PE to represent potential energy. We have shown that an object of mass m raised to a height h near the surface of the Earth can do an amount of work mgh, where g is the acceleration of gravity. Therefore, gravitational potential energy PE_g is defined as follows:

$$\begin{array}{c} \text{Gravitational} \\ \text{potential energy} \end{array} = (\text{mass})\left(\begin{array}{c}\text{gravitational} \\ \text{acceleration}\end{array}\right)(\text{height})$$

$$PE_g = mgh$$

The units of potential energy are the same as kinetic energy and work—joules (J) in the SI system and ft-lb in the English system.

In calculation of gravitational potential energy, the height h is measured from a reference level that you select. The reference level is where you decide $h = 0$ and $PE_g = 0$. Example 5.6 demonstrates the importance of the reference level.

Example 5.6 More Than One Potential Energy

(a) A 1-kg picture hangs one meter above a floor. What is the gravitational potential energy of the picture with respect to the floor?

(b) The floor is nine meters above the ground. What is the gravitational potential energy of the picture with respect to the ground?

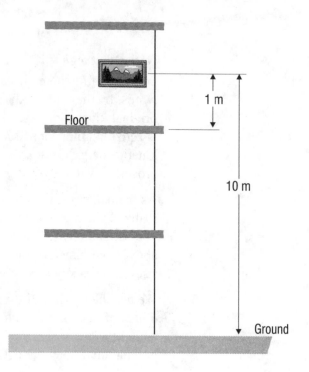

Solution:

(a) Measured "with respect to the floor" means the floor is the reference level. Therefore, h is 1 m:

$$PE_g = mgh = (1 \text{ kg})(9.80 \text{ m/s}^2)(1 \text{ m}) = 9.8 \text{ kg} \cdot \text{m}^2/\text{s}^2 \text{ or } 9.8 \text{ J}$$

(b) Measured with respect to the ground, h is 10 m:

$$PE_g = mgh = (1 \text{ kg})(9.80 \text{ m/s}^2)(10 \text{ m}) = 98 \text{ kg} \cdot \text{m}^2/\text{s}^2 \text{ or } 98 \text{ J}$$

Notice that, when you specify a reference level, you are defining the potential energy to be zero at that level. In Example 5.6(a), the height is measured above the floor. The floor is the reference level, and if the picture is moved to the floor $PE_g = mg(0) = 0$. In Example 5.6(b), where does $PE_g = 0$?

Example 5.7 Potential Energy and Work of a Pump

A submersible pump is in a 185-ft-deep well. It pumps water at a rate of 1 ft³ per second from the well into a tank's inlet 15 ft above the ground. What is the potential energy of 1 ft³ of water at the tank's inlet, using the pump's location as the reference level? How much work is done by the pump each second? The weight density of water is 62.4 lb/ft³.

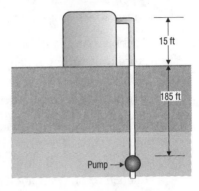

Solution: Each second, the pump moves 1 ft³ of water. Calculate the weight of this water:

$$\text{Weight} = \rho_w V = (62.4 \text{ lb/ft}^3)(1 \text{ ft}^3) = 62.4 \text{ lb}$$

For calculation of the water's potential energy using the pump's location as the reference level, the height h is 185 ft + 15 ft = 200 ft. The weight of the water is mg.

$$PE_g = mgh = \text{weight} \cdot h = 62.4 \text{ lb} \cdot 200 \text{ ft}$$

$$PE_g = 12,480 \text{ ft} \cdot \text{lb}$$

The potential energy of the water at height h is the same as the work done by the pump in lifting the water a height h.

Each second the pump does the following amount of work:

$$W_{\text{pump}} = PE_g = 12,480 \text{ ft} \cdot \text{lb}$$

So far, you have seen how an object or fluid has potential energy because of its position in the Earth's gravitational field. Actually, it is more accurate to say the *system* has potential energy. In these cases the system consists of the object (or fluid) and the Earth. The object has potential energy because it is in the gravitational field of the Earth. The Earth also has potential energy, since it is in the gravitational field of the object. The Earth exerts a force on the object, and the object exerts an equal but opposite force on the Earth. The forces can do work on the system, accelerating the object toward the Earth and the Earth toward the object. But we can usually ignore the acceleration of the Earth since it is usually so small that it cannot be measured. (Can you describe a situation where a force does have a noticeable effect on the Earth?)

Elastic Potential Energy

A system can also have potential energy because of an object's position when other types of forces act on it. As with gravity, these forces have magnitudes that depend on the object's position. For example, when you stretch a rubber band it exerts a *restoring force* that increases in magnitude as you increase the distance stretched. When you release the rubber band, it returns to its original shape (assuming you did not stretch it too far).

A rubber band is *elastic*. Elasticity is an object's or material's tendency to return to its original shape after being stretched. On the other hand, a piece of chewing gum is *inelastic*. If you stretch the gum, it does not exert a restoring force and it does not tend to return to its original shape.

Springs are made of elastic materials, usually metal. Like all elastic materials, the elasticity of a spring is due to electric forces acting between atoms in the metal. Figure 5.10 shows an elastic system composed of a spring with a mass attached to one end and fixed at the other end. On the right end of the spring, the mass and spring can move freely (without friction) left-to-right. The left end of the spring is fixed in place and cannot move.

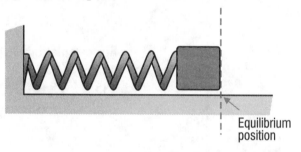

Equilibrium position

Figure 5.10
A spring-mass elastic system. At the equilibrium position, the spring exerts no force on the mass.

The **equilibrium position** of the spring is its unstretched position—where the spring does not exert a restoring force. If you push or pull the mass and displace the mass and spring from the equilibrium position, *the spring exerts a restoring force in the opposite direction*. If you push the mass to the left, the spring pushes to the right, toward the equilibrium position. Most springs exert restoring forces that are directly proportional to the displacement. (This is true as long as the displacement is less than the *elastic limit* of the spring. If you extend or compress a spring farther than the elastic limit, the spring will be permanently deformed, like the chewing gum.) Let F represent the restoring force exerted by the spring, and let x represent the displacement.

$$F = -kx$$

The negative sign in the equation above is very important. It indicates that the restoring force of the spring is in the direction **opposite** the displacement.

The proportionality constant k is called the **spring constant**. It has units of force per unit distance—for example, N/cm or lb/in. A "stiff" spring has a high value of k; a "soft" spring has a low value.

When a spring is compressed (or extended) it exerts a force through a distance, and therefore does work. This work is stored in the spring as **elastic potential energy**. You can calculate the work and energy as follows.

Suppose the spring from Figure 5.10 is compressed, by pushing the mass from the equilibrium position to the left a distance x. Since it starts at equilibrium, the initial force of the spring is $F_i = 0$. The final force is $F_f = -kx$. The average force exerted by the spring during the compression is

$$F_{average} = \frac{F_i + F_f}{2} = \frac{0 + (-kx)}{2} = -\tfrac{1}{2}kx$$

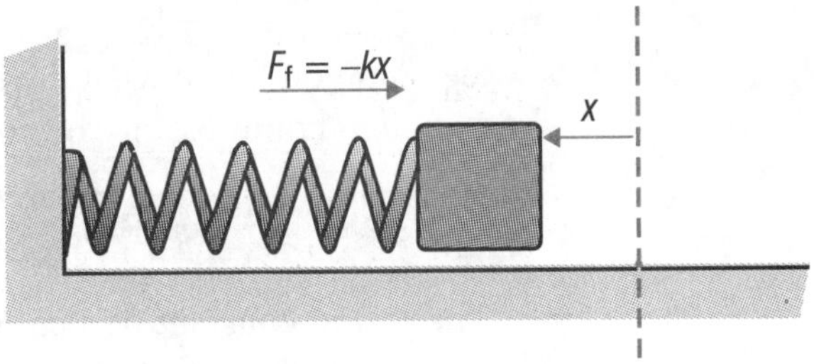

Figure 5.11
A compressed spring exerts a restoring force.
The work done by the spring is stored as elastic potential energy.

The work done by the spring is the product of the average force and the displacement. Since the spring force and displacement are in opposite directions, the work is negative.

$$W_{spring} = F_{average} \bullet x = -\tfrac{1}{2}kx \bullet x = -\tfrac{1}{2}kx^2$$

If there is no friction in the system, the work done *by* the spring is the opposite of the work done *on* the spring (by whoever pushed the mass to the left). This work is stored in the spring as elastic potential energy $PE_{elastic}$. This is the amount of work the spring can do as a result of its change in shape.

$$\begin{array}{c}\text{Elastic}\\\text{potential energy}\end{array} = \tfrac{1}{2}\,(\text{spring constant})\left(\begin{array}{c}\text{spring}\\\text{displacement}\end{array}\right)^2$$

$$PE_{elastic} = \tfrac{1}{2}kx^2$$

Suppose the mass and compressed spring in Figure 5.11 are released. The spring exerts a net force on the mass to the right and accelerates the mass in the direction of the net force. As the mass accelerates, the spring's stored potential energy is converted to kinetic energy. When the mass reaches the equilibrium position (where $x = 0$) PE = 0 but the mass has maximum KE. Its inertia causes it to continue moving to the right, extending the spring. As the spring extends, kinetic energy is converted to potential energy. Now the spring exerts a force to the left, and the mass will slow down, eventually stop, and begin moving to the left. This process continues, with the mass vibrating right to left and back again, alternately converting potential and kinetic energies. This process is called **simple harmonic motion**.

A car's coil spring is an application of elastic potential energy. When you drive over a bump or depression and your car's wheel suddenly moves upward or downward, work is done on the coil spring. The spring stores an amount of potential energy equal to this work. Stored energy is returned to the wheel by lowering or raising it to its original position while keeping the rest of the car nearly level. (Not all the stored energy is returned to the wheel. Do you know what device in the car eliminates the simple harmonic motion that compressing the coil spring would otherwise cause?)

Example 5.8 Elastic Potential Energy in an Auto Spring

The spring constant of a car's front coil spring is 1.8×10^5 N/m. When a front tire of the car rolls over a rock, the spring is compressed 15 cm (or 0.15 m) from its equilibrium position. How much potential energy is stored in the spring at the point of maximum compression?

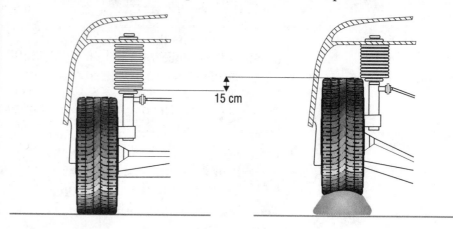

15 cm

Solution: $PE_{elastic} = \frac{1}{2} kx^2$

$\qquad = \frac{1}{2} (1.8 \times 10^5 \text{ N/m})(0.15 \text{ m})^2$

$\qquad = 2025 \text{ N·m, or } 2025 \text{ J}$

The coil spring stores 2025 joules of potential energy.

Several other applications of elastic potential energy are illustrated in Figure 5.12. When a golfer strikes a golf ball, the club compresses one side of the ball. The work done by the club is stored as elastic potential energy in the ball. The elastic potential energy is converted to kinetic energy as the golfer keeps the club in contact with the ball during the follow-through of the swing. The ball accelerates off the club as it returns to its original shape.

(a) Compressed golf ball   (b) Bow and stretched string   (c) Bent pole

Figure 5.12
Applications of elastic potential energy

When an archer pulls the string on a bow, she does work, which is stored in the bow as elastic potential energy. This energy is converted to kinetic energy when the archer releases the string and it accelerates the arrow.

A pole-vaulter begins a vault by sprinting forward to gain kinetic energy. Some of this energy is converted to work when she plants one end of the pole in the box and bends the pole. This work is stored in the pole as elastic potential energy. The potential energy is converted back to work and kinetic energy as the pole straightens and lifts the vaulter upward. The work of the pole and the vaulter's kinetic energy are converted to gravitational potential energy as she clears the crossbar. Her gravitational potential energy is converted back again to kinetic energy as she falls into the pit.

Conservation of Energy

The examples above demonstrate how potential energy can be converted to kinetic energy, and vice versa. There are also other forms of energy that take part in energy conversion. Internal energy, for example, must be included when drag or friction is important. A soccer ball rolling across a grass field eventually stops due to friction. As it slows down, its potential energy is constant but it loses kinetic energy. Total energy is not *lost*, it is transformed from one type to another. The ball's initial kinetic energy is transformed to thermal energy in the grass and the ball. (What happens to the temperature of the grass and ball?)

Scientists have studied various forms of energy, and its transformation from one form to another, for over 150 years. Their conclusion is one of the most important generalizations in science: the law of **conservation of energy**.

In an isolated system, energy is conserved—it cannot be created or destroyed. Energy can change form, but the total amount of energy in the system does not change.

We can demonstrate the law of conservation of energy using the example from the beginning of the section. Suppose the mass of the ball is 1 kg and you toss it straight upward with an initial speed of 10 m/s. We define potential energy to be zero at the point of release of the ball. So the total energy of the ball is the following sum:

$$\text{Total energy} = \text{PE}_g + \text{KE} = 0 + \tfrac{1}{2}mv^2$$

$$= \tfrac{1}{2}(1 \text{ kg})(10 \text{ m/s})^2$$

$$= 50 \text{ J}$$

If we neglect energy transfer to the air through drag forces, the total energy of the ball does not change; it remains 50 J throughout its rise. Just as the ball is released, all its energy is kinetic. Energy is converted from kinetic to potential as the ball rises, but the total energy is constant. Table 5.1 lists the potential, kinetic, and total energies at six heights. Will the ball ever reach a height of 5.2 m? Why?

Table 5.1 Potential, kinetic, and total energies of a 1-kg ball tossed upward at 10 m/s

Height		PE = mgh	KE = $\tfrac{1}{2}mv^2$	PE + KE
5.1 m	$v = 0$ m/s	50 J	0 J	50 J
4.0		39.2	10.8	50
3.0		29.4	20.6	50
2.0		19.6	30.4	50
1.0		9.8	40.2	50
0	$v = 10$ m/s	0	50	50

Example 5.9 Total Energy of a Cliff Diver

A cliff diver dives from a height of 50 feet above the water surface. How far is he from the water when his speed is 40 ft/s? Neglect air drag.

Solution: Let PE_1 and KE_1 represent the diver's potential and kinetic energies before he jumps. Let PE_2 and KE_2 represent the energies at the point at which his speed is 40 ft/s.

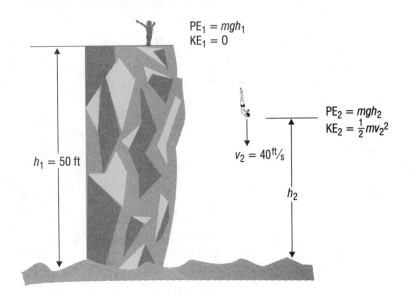

Since total energy is conserved and the only forms of energy are potential and kinetic,

$$\text{Total energy} = PE_1 + KE_1 = PE_2 + KE_2$$

$$mgh_1 + \tfrac{1}{2}mv_1^2 = mgh_2 + \tfrac{1}{2}mv_2^2$$

$$m(32.2 \text{ ft/s}^2)(50 \text{ ft}) + \tfrac{1}{2}m(0)^2 = m(32.2 \text{ ft/s}^2)(h_2) + \tfrac{1}{2}m(40 \text{ ft/s})^2$$

Each term of this equation contains m, so divide both sides by m, and it cancels. The only unknown is h_2. It has units of feet.

$$(32.2)(50) + 0 = 32.2\, h_2 + \tfrac{1}{2}(1600)$$

$$1610 = 32.2\, h_2 + 800$$

$$h_2 = \frac{1610 - 800}{32.2} = 25.2 \quad \text{or} \quad 25.2 \text{ ft}$$

The cliff diver is 25.2 feet above the water when his speed reaches 40 ft/s.

Do you think a fluid will have higher, lower, or the same pressure when it is moving compared to the pressure when the fluid is standing still? Compare your answer to the results of two simple experiments, illustrated in Figure 5.13. First, hold a piece of notebook paper just under your lower lip. Blow hard across the top surface. The paper moves upward. In the second experiment, turn on a water faucet until you establish a slow, steady stream of water. Hold a spoon from the end of the handle, with the back of the spoon just touching the stream. The spoon moves toward the stream.

The paper rises when you
blow across the top surface.

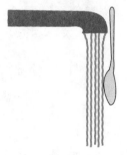

The spoon moves to the left when
water runs across the back surface.

Figure 5.13
Two demonstrations of Bernoulli's principle

The notebook paper and the spoon move because a net force is acting on them. The force is due to atmospheric pressure acting over a surface area. The pressure below the notebook paper is greater than the pressure in the moving air. The pressure to the right of the spoon is greater than the pressure in the moving water. These experiments demonstrate a relationship between the velocity and pressure of a moving fluid. The relationship was first recognized by a Swiss scientist named Daniel Bernoulli in the mid-1700s. **Bernoulli's principle** states:

As the velocity of a fluid increases, the pressure in the fluid decreases.

You may have seen how fluid velocity can increase. For example, water flowing in a stream speeds up when it passes through a narrow part of the stream. You could have predicted this increase in Section 3.2. You learned that the mass flow rate $\dot{m}$ of a fluid is the product of density ρ, cross-sectional area A of the flow, and fluid speed v: $\dot{m} = \rho A v$. If water flows continuously through a stream or pipe, mass flow rate into a narrow section must equal mass flow rate out. (There is no place in a pipe for fluid to be stored, removed, or inserted.) Therefore, $\dot{m}$ must be constant. If the density stays the same but A decreases, v must increase. This is illustrated in Figure 5.14 for a pipe with a gradual reduction in cross section.

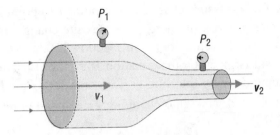

Figure 5.14
The velocity of water increases in the narrower section of a pipe. The pressure decreases.

Since the speed in the narrow section increases, so does kinetic energy. In Figure 5.14, $v_2 > v_1$. This means the fluid mass is accelerated from left to right. A net force is acting from left to right causing the acceleration and doing work on the fluid. In fluid systems, a net force per unit area means there is a pressure difference. Therefore, $P_1 > P_2$. *As the velocity of the fluid increases, the pressure in the fluid decreases.*

Bernoulli also applied energy conservation to fluid flow, as shown in Figure 5.15. Total energy is conserved in a fluid flowing between two points, through a curved pipe of nonuniform cross section. For simplicity, assume there is no viscosity in the fluid, so no energy is "lost" due to internal friction, drag, or turbulence ("lost" means converted to internal energy).

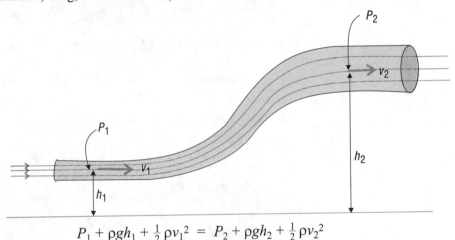

$$P_1 + \rho g h_1 + \tfrac{1}{2}\rho v_1^2 = P_2 + \rho g h_2 + \tfrac{1}{2}\rho v_2^2$$

Figure 5.15
Bernoulli's equation for two points in a fluid

In solving fluid-flow problems, it is usually simpler to use density instead of mass. The density of a fluid is constant in many processes. When we use density instead of mass, energy becomes energy per unit volume. For example, when you divide KE and gravitational PE by volume V, you get:

$$KE = \tfrac{1}{2}mv^2 \qquad\qquad PE_g = mgh$$

$$\frac{KE}{V} = \tfrac{1}{2}\frac{m}{V}v^2 \qquad\qquad \frac{PE_g}{V} = \frac{m}{V}gh \qquad [\rho = \frac{m}{V}]$$

$$\frac{KE \text{ per unit}}{\text{volume}} = \tfrac{1}{2}\rho v^2 \qquad \frac{PE_g \text{ per unit}}{\text{volume}} = \rho g h$$

The fluid pressure changes from point 1 to point 2. Since there are no other sources of work or energy, the pressure change must be caused by work done by the fluid. Remember from Section 2.2 that work done by a given volume of fluid is given by the equation $W = -\Delta P(V)$. Therefore, the work per unit volume done by the fluid is $W/V = -\Delta P$, or $P_1 - P_2$. Energy is conserved, so all this work goes into changing kinetic and potential energies.

$$P_1 - P_2 = (\tfrac{1}{2}\rho v_2{}^2 - \tfrac{1}{2}\rho v_1{}^2) + (\rho g h_2 - \rho g h_1)$$

If you rearrange this equation to get all the same subscripted variables on the same side, the result is **Bernoulli's equation**:

$$P_1 + \rho g h_1 + \tfrac{1}{2}\rho v_1{}^2 = P_2 + \rho g h_2 + \tfrac{1}{2}\rho v_2{}^2$$

The quantity $P + \rho g h + \tfrac{1}{2}\rho v^2$ represents total energy per unit volume. Bernoulli's equation states that this quantity is constant everywhere in the fluid.

Notice that, if fluid viscosity is not negligible, the quantity $P + \rho g h + \tfrac{1}{2}\rho v^2$ is not constant—it decreases in the direction of the flow.

Example 5.10 Flow Through a Constriction

A constriction is built into a 3-cm-radius pipe to measure the flow rate of water. The pipe has a 2-cm radius at the narrow part. When the water pressure in the narrow part of the pipe is 110.6 kPa, the pressure in the wide part is 115.4 kPa. What is the mass flow rate $\dot{m}$ of water through the pipe? The density of water is 1000 kg/m³.

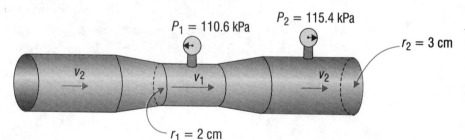

Solution: The mass flow rate is $\dot{m} = \rho A v$ and is constant. Therefore $\rho A_1 v_1 = \rho A_2 v_2$. Solve this equation for v_1. The pipe is circular, so $A = \pi r^2$.

$$v_1 = \frac{\rho A_2 v_2}{\rho A_1} = \frac{A_2}{A_1} v_2 = \frac{\pi (0.03 \text{ m})^2}{\pi (0.02 \text{ m})^2} v_2 = 2.25 v_2$$

Substitute this result into Bernoulli's equation and solve for v_2. The height of the fluid does not change, so $h_1 = h_2$, and the PE$_\text{g}$ terms cancel.

$$P_1 + \rho g h_1 + \tfrac{1}{2}\rho v_1^2 = P_2 + \rho g h_2 + \tfrac{1}{2}\rho v_2^2$$

$$P_1 + 0 + \tfrac{1}{2}\rho(2.25v_2)^2 = P_2 + 0 + \tfrac{1}{2}\rho v_2^2$$

$$\tfrac{1}{2}\rho(2.25^2 v_2^2 - v_2^2) = P_2 - P_1$$

$$4.0625 v_2^2 = \frac{2(P_2 - P_1)}{\rho}$$

$$4.0625 v_2^2 = \frac{2(1.154 \times 10^5 \text{ Pa} - 1.106 \times 10^5 \text{ Pa})}{1000 \text{ kg/m}^3}$$

$$v_2 = \sqrt{\frac{9.6 \text{ m}^2/\text{s}^2}{4.0625}} = 1.54 \text{ m/s}$$

Now calculate the mass flow rate:

$$\dot{m} = \rho A_2 v_2 = (1000 \text{ kg/m}^3)\pi(0.03 \text{ m})^2(1.54 \text{ m/s})$$

$$\dot{m} = 4.35 \text{ kg/s}$$

The mass flow rate of water through the pipe is 4.35 kilograms per second.

The lifting force of a wing on an airplane is another application of Bernoulli's principle. Streamlines in the flow of air past a wing are shown in Figure 5.16. The wing divides air into two parts: One part flows over the top surface of the wing and the other flows along the bottom surface. Air flowing over the top of the wing travels farther than air flowing along the bottom, but in the same amount of time. This means the speed of air above the wing is greater than the speed below the wing. The difference in speed leads to a lower pressure over the top of the wing. The average pressure difference times the area of the wing is the lifting force produced by the wing.

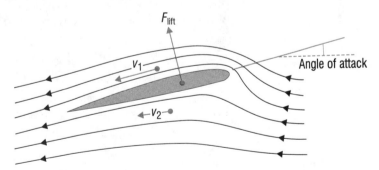

Figure 5.16
Streamlines show air flow around a wing. Air speed is higher where the streamlines are closer together.

At higher speeds, the pressure difference and the lift are higher. But, for any wing design, at some speed and angle of attack the air flow becomes turbulent. The lifting force of a wing is lowered by turbulent air flow.

Summary

- Potential energy is energy that something has because of its position.

- In a gravitational field, $PE_g = mgh$.

- Elastic potential energy is energy stored in a spring or other material that exerts a restoring force when it is stretched or compressed.

$$PE_{elastic} = \frac{1}{2} kx^2$$

- Work done on a system can be stored as potential energy.

- The law of conservation of energy states that in an isolated system energy can change form, but the total energy does not change.

- Bernoulli's principle states that as the velocity of a fluid increases, the pressure in the fluid decreases.

- Bernoulli's equation states that, for a nonviscous, laminar fluid flow where the density does not change, $P + \rho gh + \frac{1}{2} \rho v^2$ is constant. This is a statement of conservation of energy for the fluid.

Exercises

1. Is energy the same as force? How are they related?

2. If you lift a 50-lb barbell 6 ft off the floor, how much work do you do? By how much do you change the barbell's potential energy? If you drop the barbell from 6 ft, what is its kinetic energy just before it hits the floor?

3. A 90-kg box is stored on a warehouse shelf 8.2 meters above the floor.

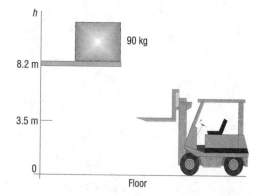

(a) What is the box's gravitational potential energy relative to the floor?

(b) What is the box's gravitational potential energy relative to a forklift 3.5 m above the floor?

4. Shareka weighs 490 N. She rides an escalator in a mall to a level 6.7 m below her starting location. What is Shareka's change in gravitational potential energy?

5. (a) How much potential energy does a 55.2-kg rock-climber gain when she climbs a vertical distance of 35 m?

   (b) Does your answer to (a) change if the climber follows a zig-zag path instead of a straight-line path up the rock? Explain.

6. A 0.60-kg basketball drops from the top of a building, 8 meters above the ground. Marc is located 5 meters above the ground, and Maria is on the ground. They choose their own locations as the reference levels for the ball's gravitational potential energy.

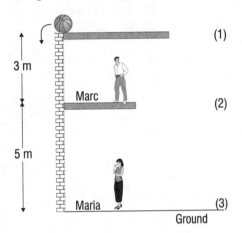

Calculate the potential energy and kinetic energy of the ball, as seen by Marc and Maria at three locations: (1) on the top of the building, (2) at Marc's location, and (3) at Maria's location. Put your answers in a table like the one below.

	Mark	Maria
PE_1	?	?
PE_2	?	?
PE_3	?	?
KE_1	?	?
KE_2	?	?
KE_3	?	?

7. In Exercise 6, will Marc and Maria always agree on

   (a) The ball's potential energy?

   (b) The change in the ball's potential energy [from (1) to (2), (1) to (3), and (2) to (3)]?

   (c) The ball's kinetic energy?

8. A spring compresses 1.25 in. from its equilibrium position when a force of 8.4 lb is applied.

   (a) Calculate the spring constant of this spring.

   (b) How much work can the spring do if it is extended 0.85 in. from equilibrium?

9. A spring with a spring constant of 1800 N/m is attached to a wall. A 1.5-kg mass is attached to the free end of the spring. The mass can move right and left without friction.

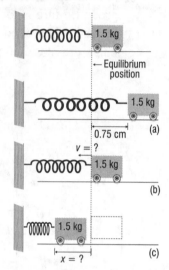

   (a) The mass is pulled to the right 0.75 cm from the equilibrium position. How much potential energy is stored in the spring relative to the equilibrium position?

   (b) The mass is released. When it reaches the equilibrium position, what is the kinetic energy of the mass? What is its speed?

   (c) How far to the left will the mass continue past the equilibrium position?

10. A tennis ball is dropped from a height of 1.6 m. The ball strikes the floor and rebounds to a height of 1.2 m. Has the collision with the floor changed the energy of the ball? Explain your answer.

11. Some satellites travel in elliptical orbits, like that shown here. As the satellite moves in the orbit, its PE and KE change but the total energy remains constant. At which point in the orbit, A, B, C, or D, does the satellite have the greatest PE? Greatest KE?

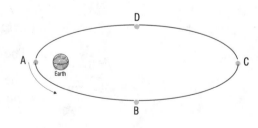

12. A hang-glider and his gear have a combined weight of 255 lb. With a running start, he leaves the edge of a cliff with an initial air speed of 14.6 ft/s.

   (a) What is the hang-glider's initial kinetic energy?

   (b) To gain air speed, the hang-glider immediately descends 250 ft. If you neglect air drag, what is the hang-glider's kinetic energy after the descent?

   (c) After descending 250 ft, the hang-glider's actual air speed is 105 ft/s. How much work is done on the hang-glider by drag forces during the descent?

13. An electric utility company uses electrical energy generated during the night (the low-demand hours) to pump water into a reservoir. During the day (the high-demand hours), the water is drained. As it runs out of the reservoir, the water turns hydroelectric turbines and generates additional peak-demand electricity for the company. The pump and piping system are 63% efficient. This means 63% of the energy supplied to the pump goes into increasing the water's gravitational potential energy.

   If the pump operates with a pressure difference of 250 psi and it pumps 366,000 ft³ of water, how much work is done by the pump? By how many foot-pounds is the potential energy of the water increased? How much energy is supplied to the pump?

14. A fire hose *straight-stream nozzle* increases the speed of water leaving the hose. The nozzle is 4.76 cm in diameter where it connects to the hose and 2.54 cm in diameter at the open end. Water enters the nozzle at a speed of 4 m/s and a pressure of 2.0×10^5 Pa.

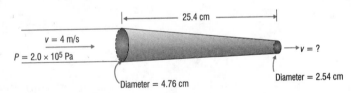

   (a) What is the speed of the water as it leaves the nozzle?

   (b) What is the pressure of the water as it leaves the nozzle?

15. Show that Bernoulli's equation includes the law of pressure change in a stationary fluid: In Figure 5.15, let $v_1 = v_2 = 0$. When the fluid is not moving, which should be greater, P_1 or P_2? Use Bernoulli's equation to complete the following for a stationary fluid.

$$P_1 = ?$$

   Explain why this equation makes sense. (Remember Pascal's law from Section 1.2.)

5.3 ENERGY IN ELECTRICAL SYSTEMS

Objectives

- Describe a capacitor. Explain how a capacitor stores energy.
- Define capacitance.
- Calculate the electrical energy stored in a capacitor.
- Describe an inductor. Explain how an inductor stores energy.
- Define inductance.
- Calculate the electrical energy stored in an inductor.

You learned in Section 2.3 that work must be done to create an electric field. Work is required because there is a coulomb force of attraction between positive and negative charges. A force must be applied to overcome the coulomb force and separate the charges. This force acts over a distance and does work. In an isolated electrical system where energy is conserved, what happens to this work? In mechanical and fluid systems, work can be stored as potential energy, and the same is true in electrical systems. The work is stored as potential energy in the electric field.

INTERNET *connection*

To find out more about energy in electrical systems, follow the links at **www.learningincontext.com**.

Capacitors

A **capacitor** is an electrical device that stores energy in an electric field. A pair of parallel metal plates, as illustrated in Figure 5.17, is a capacitor.

A power supply, or other source of potential difference, removes electrons from one plate and deposits electrons on the other plate. (We assume the process of moving electrons occurs slowly.) Thus, one plate becomes positively charged and the other becomes negatively charged. An electric field, and potential difference, is established between the plates. Charge separation and the buildup of electric field and voltage continue until the potential difference across the capacitor equals that of the power supply.

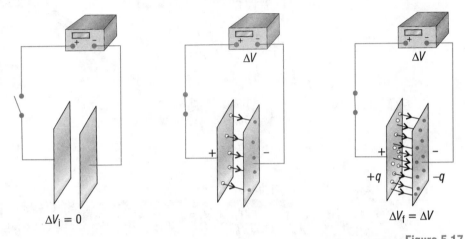

Figure 5.17

As a capacitor is charged, the electric field and potential difference between the plates increase. The work done to establish the electric field equals the potential energy stored in the field.

Before the switch in Figure 5.17 is closed, there is no potential difference between the plates, so $\Delta V_i = 0$. Right after the switch is closed, the work required to move charge is small because there is little existing charge on the plates opposing movement. But, as charge builds up, more work is needed. Let ΔV_f represent the final potential difference across the plates. The average potential difference $\Delta V_{average}$ during the charge transfer is

$$\Delta V_{average} = \frac{\Delta V_f + \Delta V_i}{2} = \frac{\Delta V_f + 0}{2} = \tfrac{1}{2}\Delta V_f$$

If the power supply voltage is ΔV, $\Delta V_f = \Delta V$.

You learned in Section 2.3 that the work W done in an electrical system is the product of the potential difference and charge moved q. But the potential difference is not constant while the capacitor is being charged. So use the average potential difference to calculate work.

$$W = q\Delta V_{average} = q(\tfrac{1}{2}\Delta V_f) = \tfrac{1}{2}q\Delta V$$

Therefore, the work done to separate an amount of charge q and to create a potential difference ΔV across a capacitor is one-half the product of q and ΔV. This work is the amount of potential energy stored in the electric field of the capacitor.

Every capacitor contains two conductors separated by an insulator. The capacitor in Figure 5.17 uses air as the insulator, but most capacitors use thin layers of plastic. The conductors are made of a metal foil. Because the materials are very thin and flexible, capacitors with large areas can be made into very compact shapes by rolling or folding the plates. Some examples are shown in Figure 5.18.

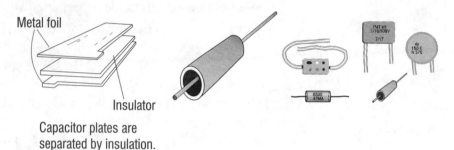

Metal foil

Insulator

Capacitor plates are separated by insulation.

Figure 5.18
Various types of capacitors

Refer to Appendix F for a career link to this concept.

Capacitance

If the charge deposited on a plate of a capacitor is doubled, the capacitor's voltage is doubled. If the charge is halved, the voltage is halved. In other words, the charge q on a capacitor is directly proportional to the potential difference ΔV across the capacitor. The proportionality constant between q and ΔV is called the **capacitance** of the capacitor. We use the symbol C to represent capacitance.

$$\text{Charge on either plate of a capacitor} = (\text{capacitance}) \begin{pmatrix} \text{potential difference} \\ \text{between the plates} \end{pmatrix}$$

$$q = C\Delta V$$

The SI and English unit of capacitance is the **farad** (F). Since $C = \dfrac{q}{\Delta V}$, 1 farad = 1 coulomb per volt, or 1 F = 1 C/V.

Remember, one coulomb is a very large amount of charge, so the farad is a very large unit. Most capacitors have capacitances measured in *microfarads* (µF) or *picofarads* (pF).

$$1 \ \mu F = 10^{-6} \ F \qquad\qquad 1 \ pF = 10^{-12} \ F$$

Capacitors like those shown in Figure 5.18 have fixed values of capacitance that are labeled on the outside of the capacitors.

Example 5.11 Charge on a Capacitor

A 240-volt motor has a 50-μF capacitor in its starting circuit. When the motor is started, the entire 240 V charges the capacitor. What is the charge on the capacitor after the voltage is applied?

Solution: $q = C\Delta V$

$$= (50 \times 10^{-6}\text{ F})(240\text{ V}) = 0.012\text{ C}$$

Notice that we have used the conversion 1 F = 1 C/V.

When connected to the 240-V potential difference, the capacitor stores 0.012 coulomb of charge.

Potential Energy in Capacitors

The potential energy stored in a capacitor equals the work done in establishing the electric field. At the beginning of the section, we derived the expression $\frac{1}{2}q\Delta V$ for this work.

$$PE = \tfrac{1}{2}q\Delta V$$

We can use the definition of capacitance to write another form for this equation. Substitute $C\Delta V$ for q:

$$PE = \tfrac{1}{2}(C\Delta V)\Delta V = \tfrac{1}{2}C\Delta V^2$$

$$\begin{matrix}\text{Potential energy stored} \\ \text{in a capacitor}\end{matrix} = \tfrac{1}{2}(\text{capitance})\left(\begin{matrix}\text{potential} \\ \text{difference}\end{matrix}\right)^2$$

$$PE = \tfrac{1}{2}C\Delta V^2$$

There is only one set of units for this equation. Capacitance is measured in farads, potential difference is measured in volts, and energy is measured in joules. $1\text{ J} = 1\text{ F·V}^2$.

Example 5.12 Energy of a Capacitor

How much potential energy is stored in the 50-μF capacitor of Example 5.11 after it is charged by the 240-V potential difference?

Solution: $PE = \tfrac{1}{2}C\Delta V^2$

$$= \tfrac{1}{2}(50 \times 10^{-6}\text{ F})(240\text{ V})^2 = 1.44\text{ J}$$

The capacitor stores 1.44 joules of energy.

Notice the symbol used to represent a capacitor in the circuit diagram in Example 5.13 below.

Example 5.13 Capacitors in Parallel

Capacitors of 3.6 µF and 6.3 µF are connected in parallel and charged with a single 16-V source of potential difference. Which capacitor has a greater charge? What is the energy stored in this capacitor?

$$16 \text{ V} \quad\quad C_1 = 3.6 \text{ µF} \quad\quad\quad C_2 = 6.3 \text{ µF}$$

Solution: Since they are connected in parallel, both capacitors have the same 16-V potential difference. Use the equation $q = C\Delta V$:

$$q_1 = C_1(16 \text{ V}) \quad \text{and} \quad q_2 = C_2(16 \text{ V})$$

Since $C_2 > C_1$, then $q_2 > q_1$.

The potential energy stored in this capacitor is PE_2:

$$PE_2 = \tfrac{1}{2}C_2\Delta V^2$$

$$= \tfrac{1}{2}(6.3 \times 10^{-6} \text{ F})(16 \text{ V})^2 = 8.1 \times 10^{-4} \text{ J}$$

Magnetic Fields and Induced EMF

An electric field exists around any set of electrical charges. The electric field can be measured using the force exerted on a test charge placed in the field. If the electric charges are moving, they create a **magnetic field** as well. A test charge will experience a force from the magnetic field only if the test charge is moving.

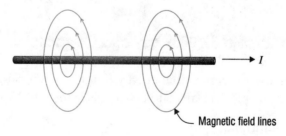

Magnetic field lines

Figure 5.19
Magnetic field lines around a
straight wire carrying a current

Figure 5.19 shows the magnetic field around a straight wire that carries a current I. The magnetic field lines are concentric circles with the current at the center. A charge placed in the magnetic field will not feel a force unless the charge moves. And, if the charge moves, it creates its own magnetic field. For example, suppose a second, parallel wire carrying a current is placed in the magnetic field. A force is exerted on the wire from the magnetic field of the first wire. The second wire creates its own magnetic field, which causes a force on the first wire. If the two currents are in the same direction, the wires are attracted. If the currents are in opposite directions, the wires are repelled. (See Figure 5.20.)

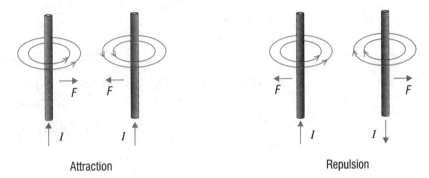

Attraction   Repulsion

Figure 5.20
Two parallel wires carrying currents create magnetic fields and forces.
There is a mutual force of attraction if the currents are in the same direction.
The mutual force is repulsion if the currents flow in opposite directions.

If a wire is formed into a loop, the magnetic field has the configuration shown in Figure 5.21(a). A *coil*, or *solenoid*, is a series of loops in the form of a helix. The magnetic field of a coil is shown in Figure 5.21(b). If the loops are close together and the coil is long relative to its diameter, the magnetic field inside the coil is uniform and parallel to its axis except near the ends.

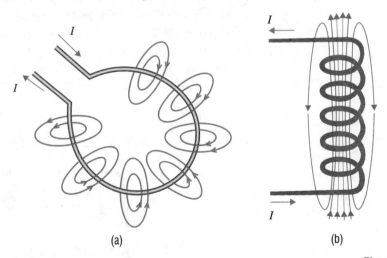

(a)   (b)

Figure 5.21
Magnetic fields of (a) a wire loop and (b) a coil

A permanent magnet has a magnetic field identical to a coil. This is because the electrons in the atoms of a permanent magnet form current loops and the loops are aligned. The Earth's magnetic field is also caused by current loops in the molten iron core at the center of the Earth. By convention, magnetic field lines point away from the north pole and toward the south pole. Notice the direction of the field lines in Figure 5.22. The Earth's geographic north pole is actually a magnetic south pole.

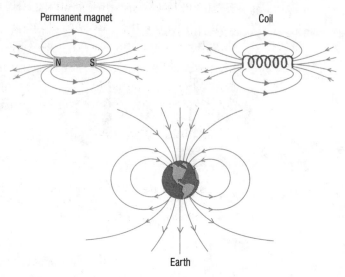

Figure 5.22
The magnetic fields of a permanent magnet, a coil, and the Earth are caused by current loops.

An electric field can cause current and therefore can produce a magnetic field. A magnetic field can also produce an electric field. The process is called **electromagnetic induction**, and it was discovered in 1831 independently by Michael Faraday in England and Joseph Henry in the United States. If a loop of wire moves through a magnetic field (or, equivalently, if a magnetic field moves past a wire), a current is produced in the wire.

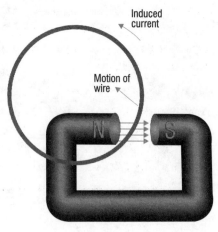

Figure 5.23
Electromagnetic induction

In the 1830s, it was known that a source of electrical energy, such as a battery, is needed to make electric charges flow through a wire. At that time, any source of electrical energy was called an **electromotive force**, or *EMF*. But EMF is not really a force—it is potential difference, or voltage. Even though the term EMF is misleading, it is still used to describe the induced voltage in a wire when a magnetic field moves past the wire or if a wire moves past a magnetic field. An EMF is induced in a wire any time it is in a magnetic field that changes magnitude or direction.

Electromagnetic induction is more important in loops or coils of wire. Figure 5.24 shows a permanent magnet not being moved, being moved toward a coil, and being moved away from a coil. A changing magnetic field inside the coil caused by the movement induces an EMF and current in the coil. You can increase the induced EMF by

- using a more intense magnetic field (larger magnet),

- using a coil with a larger diameter,

- using a coil with more turns of the wire, or

- moving the magnet faster.

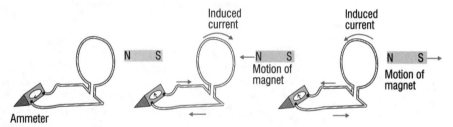

Figure 5.24
A changing magnetic field induces a current and EMF in a coil of wire.

The sign of the EMF and the direction of the current in Figure 5.24 must be consistent with conservation of energy. Energy must be supplied to electrons in the coil to create and increase the induced current. This energy comes from work done in moving the magnet and its magnetic field. Work is required to move the magnet because a force is acting on the magnet, opposing its motion. This force is caused by the magnetic field of the induced current in the coil.

The changing magnetic field caused by the moving magnet induces a current, and the direction of the induced current is such that its own magnetic field opposes the changes responsible for producing it. This statement is called **Lenz's law**, after the Estonian physicist Heinrich Lenz, who described the phenomenon in 1835.

Inductors

An **inductor** is an electrical device that stores energy in a magnetic field. A solenoid or coil of wire, as illustrated in Figure 5.25, is an inductor. Suppose a power supply or battery causes current to flow in the coil. The current generates a magnetic field, shown by magnetic-field lines. As the current increases, the magnetic field increases. The increasing magnetic field induces an EMF in the coil—the same coil whose current generated the field in the first place. By Lenz's law, this *self-induced EMF* opposes the change in magnetic field and current that created the EMF. The self-induced EMF is sometimes called the "back-EMF."

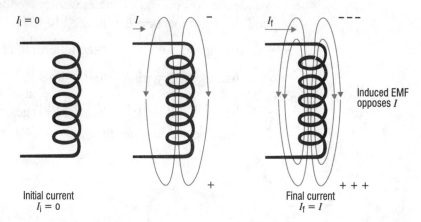

Figure 5.25
As the current in a coil builds up, the increasing magnetic field induces a back-EMF that opposes the buildup. Work must be done to push electrons through the induced EMF.

The back-EMF opposes the current through the coil. Therefore, the power supply or battery must do work to push electrons against the EMF to keep the current flowing. This work is in addition to the work required to push electrons through the wire coil's resistance. The work begins as soon as current begins to flow. Let the current increase steadily from an initial value of 0 A to a final value of I in a time interval Δt. The average current I_{average} during Δt is

$$I_{\text{average}} = \frac{I_{\text{f}} + I_{\text{i}}}{2} = \frac{I + 0}{2} = \tfrac{1}{2}I$$

The total charge q that flows in the coil while the current builds to the final value is

$$q = I_{\text{average}}\,\Delta t = \tfrac{1}{2}I\Delta t$$

The work done by the power supply or battery in moving this charge through the back-EMF is the product of the charge moved and the potential difference, which is the EMF.

$$W = q(\text{EMF}) = \tfrac{1}{2}I\Delta t(\text{EMF})$$

This product is the work done against an inductor's self-induced EMF to create a current I in the inductor. This work is the amount of potential energy stored in the magnetic field of the inductor.

What happens if a current I is flowing in the circuit and the power supply voltage is decreased? The drop in current causes the inductor to develop an EMF to oppose the change. Opposition to a decrease in voltage is an increase—the EMF *adds* voltage to the circuit. The potential energy stored in the inductor's magnetic field is released as work, pushing electrons and slowing the rate of decrease of current.

Inductance

When the current through an inductor changes by an amount ΔI in a time interval Δt, the *rate of change of current* in the inductor is the ratio $\frac{\Delta I}{\Delta t}$. The inductor produces an opposing EMF that is directly proportional to the rate of change of current. If the current changes twice as fast, the EMF is doubled. If the current changes half as fast, the EMF is halved. The proportionality constant between the EMF and $\frac{\Delta I}{\Delta t}$ is called the **inductance** of the inductor. We use the symbol L to represent inductance.

$$\text{EMF} = -(\text{inductance}) \begin{pmatrix} \text{rate of change} \\ \text{of current} \end{pmatrix}$$

$$\text{EMF} = -L \frac{\Delta I}{\Delta t}$$

The minus sign in the equation means that the EMF produced by an inductor is opposite in sign to ΔI. This is required by Lenz's law.

Notice that a steady-state current I does not change. If $\Delta I = 0$, EMF $= 0$. There is no back-EMF with a steady-state current.

The SI and English unit of inductance is the **henry** (H). Since $L = \dfrac{\text{EMF}}{-\Delta I / \Delta t}$, 1 henry = 1 volt per ampere per second, or 1 H $= 1\, \dfrac{\text{V·s}}{\text{A}}$.

The enhanced magnetic field formed by a loop or coil of wire creates an inductor. The central region of the coil is called the core. The amount of inductance depends on the diameter of the core, the number of turns of wire around the core, and the magnetic properties of the space inside the core. You can create large inductances with large-diameter cores, coils with large numbers of closely wound turns of wire, or cores filled with strongly magnetic substances like iron. By making adjustable the amount of iron core inserted into a coil, one can have a *variable* inductor. Resistors, capacitors, and inductors that are variable are essential in "tuning" electronic circuits.

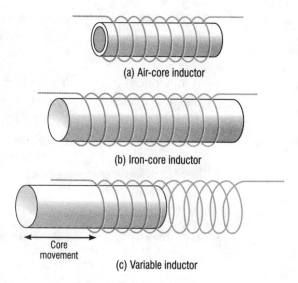

(a) Air-core inductor

(b) Iron-core inductor

Core
movement

(c) Variable inductor

Figure 5.26
Basic inductors

Example 5.14 Current Through an Inductor

A coil with an inductance of 45 mH produces an average opposing EMF of 1.15 V when the current in the coil drops to 0 A in 0.025 s. What is the initial current in the coil?

Solution: Let I_i represent the initial current. Since the current drops to 0, the final current is 0 A. The change in current is $\Delta I = 0 - I_i = -I_i$.

Substitute the given values into the inductance equation.

$$\text{EMF} = -L\frac{\Delta I}{\Delta t}$$

$$\text{EMF} = L\frac{I_i}{\Delta t}$$

$$I_i = \frac{\text{EMF }\Delta t}{L} = \frac{(1.15\ \text{V})(0.025\ \text{s})}{45 \times 10^{-3}\ \text{H}} = 0.64\ \text{A}$$

The initial current through the coil is 0.64 ampere.

Potential Energy in Inductors

The energy stored in an inductor equals the work done during a slow buildup of the current. Earlier in the section, we derived the expression $\frac{1}{2}I(\text{EMF})\Delta t$ for this work.

$$\text{PE} = \tfrac{1}{2}I(\text{EMF})\Delta t$$

We can use the definition of inductance to write another form for this equation. Substitute $L\dfrac{\Delta I}{\Delta t}$ for EMF. Since $I_i = 0$, $\Delta I = I_f = I$:

$$PE = \tfrac{1}{2}I(L\dfrac{I}{\Delta t})\Delta t = \tfrac{1}{2}LI^2$$

$$\boxed{\begin{array}{c} \text{Potential energy stored} \\ \text{in an inductor} \end{array} = \tfrac{1}{2}(\text{inductance})(\text{current})^2}$$

$$PE = \tfrac{1}{2}LI^2$$

There is only one set of units for this equation. Inductance is measured in henrys, current is measured in amperes, and energy is measured in joules. $1\ \text{J} = 1\ \text{H} \cdot \text{A}^2$.

Example 5.15 Energy of an Inductor

A coil has an inductance of 8 H and a resistance of 2 Ω. The coil is connected to a 30-V DC power source. What is the energy stored in the coil when the current is steady?

Solution: First find the steady current I that flows in the coil. From the definition of resistance:

$$I = \dfrac{\Delta V}{R} = \dfrac{30\ \text{V}}{2\ \Omega} = 15\ \text{A}$$

Now use the potential energy equation for an inductor.

$$PE = \tfrac{1}{2}LI^2$$
$$= \tfrac{1}{2}(8\ \text{H})(15\ \text{A})^2$$
$$= 900\ \text{J}$$

The energy stored in the coil is 900 joules.

Controlling Energy in Electrical Systems

A common application of capacitors and inductors is in electronic circuits where voltage changes or current changes need smoothing out. These types of circuits are called "filter circuits." (See Figure 5.27a.)

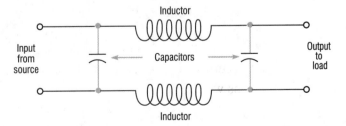

Figure 5.27a
Filter circuit

Frequently, electric motors are equipped with capacitors or inductors to help the motors start running. Motors equipped with capacitor starts (Figure 5-27b) are used to power devices such as air compressors. In this case, the motor must start running, develop enough torque to turn the compressor, and compress air—all at the same time. The energy stored in a capacitor can be used to help the motor do that.

Some electric motors use inductor-starting devices (Figure 5-27c). These types of motors are commonly used to power large machines such as punch presses. Here, the motor must start the rotating mass of the machine moving. This start-up time can be much longer, compared to the "instantaneous" (quick) start-up of an air compressor connected to a motor with a capacitor start.

(b) Capacitor-start motor   (c) Induction motor

Figure 5.27b,c
Uses of capacitors and inductors

Summary

- A capacitor is an electrical device that stores charge on metal plates separated by an insulator.

- Capacitance is the amount of stored charge per unit voltage across the plates. $C = q/\Delta V$. Capacitance is measured in farads.

- Potential energy is stored in the electric field of a capacitor. $PE = \frac{1}{2}C\Delta V^2$.

- An inductor is an electrical device that creates a magnetic field using a changing current in a loop or coil of wire.

- Inductance is the amount of voltage (or EMF) across the coil per unit rate of change of current through the coil. $L = \dfrac{EMF}{-\Delta I/\Delta t}$. Inductance is measured in henries.

- Potential energy is stored in the magnetic field of an inductor. $PE = \frac{1}{2}LI^2$.

Exercises

1. Where is energy stored in a capacitor? Where is energy stored in an inductor?

2. What SI units are used to measure the following?

   (a) Electric potential energy

   (b) Electric charge

   (c) Electric current

   (d) Electric potential difference

   (e) Electromotive force

   (f) Capacitance

   (g) Inductance

3. A capacitor contains two _____ separated by

   _____.

4. How much charge is deposited on either plate of a 1.5-mF capacitor when the voltage across the capacitor is 10 V?

5. A 10-μF capacitor is connected across a potential difference of ΔV, as in (a) below. A second 10-μF capacitor is connected across a potential difference of $2\Delta V$, as in (b). Which capacitor has a larger amount of charge? Explain the rationale for your answer.

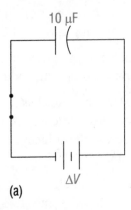

(a)

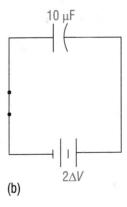

(b)

6. What voltage is required to deposit 2.0×10^{-3} C of charge on a 190-μF capacitor?

7. When a capacitor is connected to a 12-V source, it contains 40 μC of charge. What is the capacitance of the capacitor?

8. Energy is stored in a capacitor for the photoflash of a camera. If the capacitance is 12.5 μF and the capacitor is charged with 9.0 V, how much energy is stored?

9. In a circuit, if changes in voltage need to be smoothed out, would you insert a capacitor or an inductor? If changes in current need to be smoothed out, would you insert a capacitor or an inductor? Explain your answers.

10. In the circuit at the right:

    (a) What is the potential difference across capacitor C_1? across C_2?

    (b) Which capacitor stores less charge?

    (c) How much charge is stored on one plate in this capacitor?

    (d) How much potential energy is stored in this capacitor?

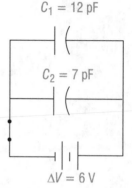

$C_1 = 12\ \text{pF}$

$C_2 = 7\ \text{pF}$

$\Delta V = 6\ \text{V}$

11. Scientists at Lawrence Livermore National Laboratory produce nuclear fusion with lasers. The lasers use short pulses of energy provided by very large capacitors. One capacitor provides 1.7 MJ of energy when charged with a potential difference of 10 kV. What is the capacitance?

12. Describe how you can use a coil of wire and a bar magnet to generate an electric current.

13. An inductor opposes changes in _____.

14. What is the voltage across a 15-mH inductor when the current through the inductor changes at a rate of 20 A/s?

15. The current through a coil increases from 1.8 A to 2.4 A in 0.56 s. If the average opposing EMF is 4.0 V, what is the inductance of the coil?

16. How much energy is stored in a 3-H inductor when a steady current of 1.8 A flows through the inductor?

17. A car's starting motor has a solenoid, or coil, that is an inductor. The resistance of the solenoid is 1.2 Ω. It stores 1200 J of energy when the voltage across the solenoid is 10.5 V and the current is steady. What is the inductance?

18. You can make an electromagnet by winding a wire around a nail and connecting the wire ends to a power supply. Which graph below represents a possible relationship between the current through the wire and the time after the power supply is turned on?

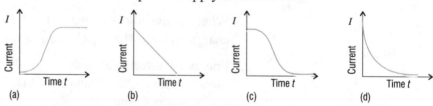

19. The resistance of the coil in a large electromagnet is measured with a multimeter. The multimeter uses a D-cell battery source of 1.5 V to measure resistance. The resistance of the coil is 3.8 Ω, and the inductance is 11.7 H. How much energy is stored in the coil as the resistance is measured?

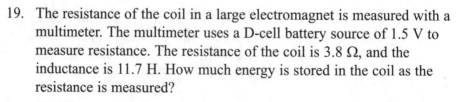

5.4 ENERGY IN THERMAL SYSTEMS

Objectives

- Define the internal energy of a system.

- Describe two ways you can change a system's internal energy.

- Explain the first law of thermodynamics. Use the first law to solve problems involving internal energy, heat, and work.

- Describe the operation of a heat engine and a refrigerator.

- Explain the second law of thermodynamics. Describe processes that are prohibited by the second law.

- Explain the differences between the Celsius and Kelvin temperature scales.

- Calculate the Carnot efficiency of a heat engine.

INTERNET *connection*

To find out more about energy in thermal systems, follow the links at **www.learningincontext.com**.

In Section 1.4 you learned that the temperature of a body is determined by its thermal energy. Thermal energy is the total kinetic energy of the random motion of the atoms or molecules that make up the body. This microscopic, random kinetic energy is not the same as the kinetic energy the body has as a whole. A moving body has a net velocity. The kinetic energy of this *ordered motion* is equal to $\frac{1}{2}mv^2$, where m and v are the mass and speed of the entire body.

Thermal energy is due to *random motion* of the atoms and molecules that make up the body. There is no net velocity of random motion. If you could "freeze" the particles' motion at one instant and count the number of particles moving in any given direction, you would count the same number moving in the opposite direction. Each particle in the body has a kinetic energy of random motion, equal to $\frac{1}{2}mv^2$, where m and v are the mass and speed of the particle. This speed changes frequently, as the particle interacts with other particles of the body.

In addition to moving in random translational motion, molecules of a gas can rotate and vibrate. All three modes are illustrated in Figure 5.28 for a diatomic gas. A molecule of a diatomic gas consists of two atoms bound together. Oxygen is a diatomic gas. A molecule of oxygen is written with the symbol O_2, to indicate that two oxygen atoms are bound together in a molecule. In a container of oxygen gas, the molecules have translational, rotational, and vibrational motion. But the temperature of the oxygen is determined by only the translational kinetic energy.

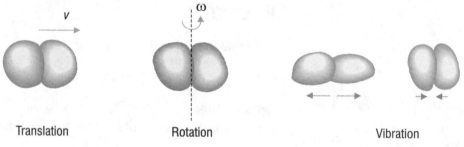

Translation Rotation Vibration

Figure 5.28
Gas molecules can translate, rotate, and vibrate.
But only the kinetic energy of translational motion
affects the temperature of the gas.

The particles of a liquid or solid are much closer together, and electrical forces limit their motions. In a solid, atoms and molecules are held in place by electrical forces and they vibrate about the fixed positions. In a liquid, the particles can slide past one another but their speeds are affected by electrical interactions with other particles. In any material, when atomic and molecular charge is moved in an electric field, the particles' energy can be stored as electric potential energy.

Internal Energy

On a microscopic scale, the particles of a body—whether it is a solid, liquid, gas, or plasma—are in constant random motion. As particles interact, the kinetic energy and potential energy of any given particle change. But, for an isolated body, the sum of the kinetic and potential energies of all the particles does not change. This total energy is called the **internal energy** of the body.

A body's internal energy depends on its material composition, its mass, its temperature, and its physical state (solid, liquid, gas, or plasma). Internal energy can be transferred from one body to another body if the bodies have different temperatures. Internal energy transferred because of a temperature difference is heat.

There is another way of changing a body's internal energy besides heat transfer. You can see this method with a simple demonstration. Place your hands together. If your right hand is the same temperature as your left hand, there is no heat transfer between them. So you cannot increase the internal energy of either hand with heat transfer. Now rub your hands together vigorously. You have increased the internal energy and temperature of your hands by doing work using the force of friction.

Figure 5.29
Work can be converted into internal energy.

Work done by frictional forces is converted into internal energy. Other forms of energy and work also can be converted into internal energy. For example, an electric stove uses resistance in its heating elements to convert electrical energy into internal energy. If you have ever used a hand pump to inflate a basketball, you have probably noticed that the pump gets hot. Some of this internal energy comes from friction, but most comes from work done by the piston on the air in the cylinder.

So a system's internal energy can be increased by adding heat or by doing work on the system. The reverse is also true—a system's internal energy can be decreased by removing heat or by the system doing work. The science dealing with the relationships between internal energy, heat, and work is called **thermodynamics**.

The First Law of Thermodynamics

The law of conservation of energy says that energy cannot be created or destroyed, but it can be changed into other forms. This law applied to thermal systems is called the **first law of thermodynamics**. In equation form, the first law says that a change in a system's internal energy is balanced by heat Q input to the system and work W done by the system. We use the variable U to represent internal energy.

$$\text{Change in internal energy of a system} = \text{net heat input to the system} - \text{work done by the system}$$

$$\Delta U = Q - W$$

When you use the first law to solve problems, you should first identify the system to which you are applying the law. The system should be a well-defined set of atoms, molecules, particles, or objects. For example, a system could be the air and fuel mixture in a car engine's cylinder, the cytoplasm inside a single biological cell, or the entire mass of an exploding star.

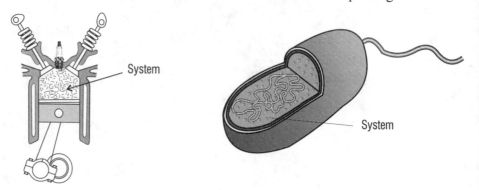

System

System

Figure 5.30
A system is a well-defined set of atoms, molecules, particles, or objects.

When you have defined the system, be careful to use the right sign for each term in the equation for the first law. Energy can enter or leave the system through heat and work. Heat is *positive* if it *enters* the system and negative if it leaves. But work is subtracted from heat. This is because, by convention, work is *positive* when the system *does* the work (energy *leaves* the system in this case, so you subtract energy). Work is *negative* when work *is done on* the system (energy *enters* the system in this case, so you add energy). These conventions arose at the beginning of the field of thermodynamics, when the laws were applied to engines. The goals of scientists and engineers were to maximize the work done by engines and to minimize the heat (and therefore cost) that must be provided.

The signs of internal energy, heat, and work are illustrated in Figure 5.31. The figure shows two ways of increasing the internal energy of air inside a cylinder—with heat transfer and with work. In each case, the system is the air inside the cylinder. An increase in internal energy means the change in internal energy is positive.

In Figure 5.31a, the cylinder is fitted with a lid. The lid does not move, so the system does not change volume, and can do no work. Suppose heat is added to the air, by placing the cylinder in contact with a high-temperature object like a stove burner. Heat enters the system, and is positive. The first law of thermodynamics for this case is

$$\Delta U = Q - 0 = Q$$

When heat is added to the system, Q is positive and the system's internal energy increases.

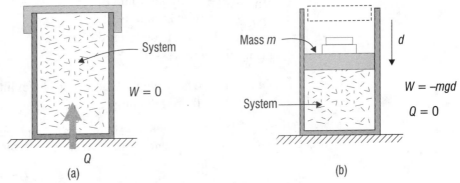

Figure 5.31
A system's internal energy can be increased by adding heat or by doing work on the system.

In Figure 5.31b, no heat is allowed to enter or leave the system. The cylinder is fitted with a movable, friction-free piston, which is forced downward by placing weights on top of the piston. In this case, the work done by the system is negative—work is done on the system. (If the total mass of the piston and added weights is m and the piston moves a distance d, the work done by gravity is mgd. The work done by the system is $-mgd$.)

A process in which there is no heat transfer to or from a system is called an **adiabatic** process. There are two ways of doing work adiabatically—you can isolate the system from its surroundings (with insulation), or you can do the work quickly enough that there is no time for heat transfer to take place. The first law of thermodynamics for an adiabatic process is

$$\Delta U = 0 - W = -W$$

When work is done on the system, as in Figure 5.31b, W is negative and the system's internal energy increases.

Can you explain how to *decrease* the internal energy of the system in Figure 5.31a, using only heat transfer? Can you explain how to *decrease* the internal energy of the system in Figure 5.31b, using only work?

Example 5.16 The First Law for a Compressor

A refrigerator's compressor has a cylinder fitted with a piston. The cylinder fills with refrigerant gas, and the piston compresses the gas to increase its temperature and pressure. During the compression process, 0.015 Btu of heat is removed from the gas. The internal energy increases by 0.036 Btu. How much work is done on the gas by the compressor?

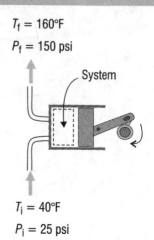

$T_f = 160°F$
$P_f = 150$ psi

System

$T_i = 40°F$
$P_i = 25$ psi

Solution: The system is the gas in the cylinder. Use the first law of thermodynamics.

$$\text{Change in internal energy of a system} = \text{net heat input to the system} - \text{work done by the system}$$

$$\Delta U = Q - W$$

Since the internal energy of the system increases, the change in internal energy is positive. Since heat is removed from the system, the net heat input is negative.

$$0.036 \text{ Btu} = -0.015 \text{ Btu} - W$$

$$W = (-0.036 - 0.015) \text{ Btu} = -0.051 \text{ Btu}$$

The work is negative because work is done on the system. The compressor does 0.051 Btu of work on the gas.

Heat Engines

A device that converts thermal energy into mechanical energy is called a **heat engine**. Examples are automobile and truck engines whose energy source is the burning of gasoline or diesel fuel, steam turbines whose energy source is the burning of fossil fuel (coal, oil, or natural gas) or nuclear reactions, the space shuttle main engine whose energy source is the chemical reaction between hydrogen and oxygen, and your own body whose energy source is the food you eat.

Every heat engine:

- Absorbs thermal energy from a high-temperature source.

- Converts some of the thermal energy into work.

- Discards the remaining thermal energy into a low-temperature "sink."

The sources and sinks of thermal energy are called reservoirs. The low-temperature reservoir is usually the Earth, the Earth's atmosphere, or a body of water on the Earth's surface.

The first law of thermodynamics applies to all heat engines. Many engines operate continuously or in a cycle, where the internal energy and temperature are constant. For example, your car's engine operates at a constant temperature after a "warm-up" period. When the internal energy does not change, the first law says:

$$\frac{\text{Net heat input}}{\text{to the system}} = \frac{\text{work done by}}{\text{the system}}$$

$$Q = W$$

The net heat input is the amount of heat the engine absorbs from the high-temperature reservoir minus the amount of heat the engine discards to the low-temperature reservoir. Figure 5.32 shows the balance of heat and work required by the first law.

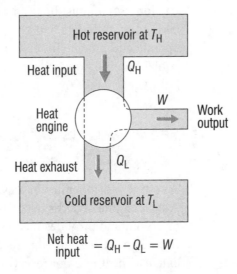

$$\frac{\text{Net heat}}{\text{input}} = Q_H - Q_L = W$$

Figure 5.32
When there is no change in internal energy, the **work done** by an engine is the difference between the amount of heat absorbed and the amount of heat discarded.

A four-stroke gasoline engine is an example of a heat engine that operates in a cycle. The cycle is illustrated in Figure 5.33 on the next page. The high-temperature reservoir is the burning fuel-air mixture. Heat is absorbed by the engine from this reservoir. Heat is discarded when hot exhaust gases are released to the atmosphere and also when heat is transferred to the cooling system. Coolant flows around the outside of each cylinder, where it is heated, and then flows to the radiator. In the radiator, heat is removed from the coolant and deposited into the atmosphere. The net heat input to the engine is the amount of heat absorbed minus the amount discarded. The work done by the engine equals the net heat input.

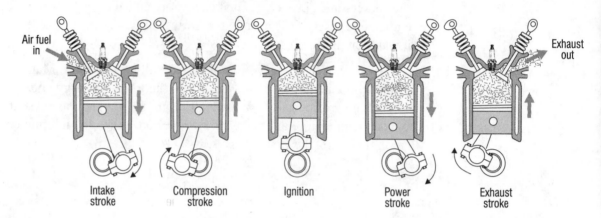

Figure 5.33
A cycle for one cylinder of a four-stroke gasoline engine. A car engine usually has four, six, or eight of these cylinders.

But in a car or truck, the work done by the engine is not the work done to turn the wheels. Some of the engine's work must be used to overcome friction. Some must be used to keep the engine operating (moving gas into and out of cylinders and compressing gas). And some must be used to operate equipment (for example, air-conditioning, electrical generator, coolant pump, power steering). Typically, 60%–70% of the engine work is left over to cause motion in a car's transmission.

Refrigerators and Heat Pumps

A refrigerator operates in a cycle that is the reverse of the heat engine. A heat engine absorbs heat from a hot reservoir, exhausts heat to a cold reservoir, and provides mechanical work output. A refrigerator absorbs heat from a cold reservoir (the inside storage volume of the refrigerator) and exhausts heat to a hot reservoir (the outside of the storage volume). Mechanical work must be done on a *working fluid* in the refrigerator as input energy to "push" the heat from a cold to a hot reservoir.

Figure 5.34 shows the balance of heat and work required by the first law of thermodynamics for a refrigerator. The net heat input ($Q_L - Q_H$) is negative because $Q_L < Q_H$. Therefore, the work done by the refrigerator is also negative.

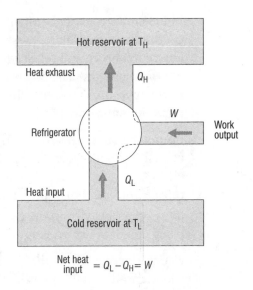

$$\text{Net heat} \atop \text{input} = Q_L - Q_H = W$$

Figure 5.34
A refrigerator absorbs heat from a low-temperature reservoir and exhausts heat to a high-temperature reservoir. The difference between the heat absorbed and the heat exhausted is negative. This is the energy that must be supplied, as mechanical work, to allow heat to flow in the reverse direction.

How does a refrigerator move heat from a cold region to a hot region? A refrigerator is a closed system that uses a working fluid called the *refrigerant* to absorb and release heat, and to absorb energy as work. The refrigerant is usually a material such as ammonia, methyl chloride, a chlorofluorocarbon (being phased out due to environmental concerns), or a hydrochlorofluorocarbon. A refrigerator cycle is shown schematically in Figure 5.35. At some points in the cycle the refrigerant is a gas, at others it is a liquid, and at some points it exists in both states.

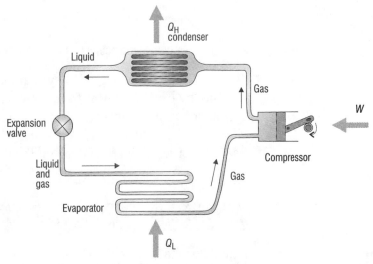

Figure 5.35
A refrigerator cycle. Heat enters and leaves the refrigerant when it changes phase in the condenser and evaporator. The compressor does work on the refrigerant.

There are four major components of a refrigerator. These components control the temperature, pressure, and volume of the refrigerant and its ability to absorb and release heat. The refrigerant enters the *compressor* as a low-pressure gas. The compressor has a piston that does work on the refrigerant in a cylinder. When the gas is compressed, its temperature and pressure increase.

From the compressor, the refrigerant flows into a *condenser*, where it is cooled and undergoes a change of phase, from gas to liquid. This phase change is called condensation, and it releases thermal energy equal to the refrigerant's heat of vaporization. The heat released is Q_H. This heat is transferred away from the condenser and to the high-temperature reservoir using air- or water-cooling of the condenser.

The refrigerant leaves the condenser as a high-pressure liquid. The pressure is decreased as the liquid flows through an *expansion valve*. On the low-pressure side of the expansion valve, some of the liquid becomes gas.

The remaining liquid is vaporized in an *evaporator*. To change phase from liquid to gas, the refrigerant absorbs thermal energy equal to the heat of vaporization. The heat absorbed is Q_L. This heat is transferred to the evaporator from the low-temperature reservoir, which is the refrigerated storage volume. From the evaporator, the refrigerant reenters the compressor.

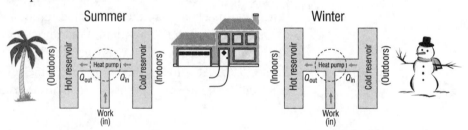

Figure 5.36
A heat pump acts as an air conditioner in the summer and a heater in the winter.

A *heat pump* is a refrigeration system that acts as an air conditioner in summer by extracting heat from the interior of a house and exhausting it to the outdoors. In winter, the system reverses and acts as a heater by taking heat from the outdoors and delivering it to the inside of the house. In both cases, mechanical work is done on the heat pump's refrigerant in order to satisfy the first law of thermodynamics.

Example 5.17 Heat Flow Rate Out of a Condenser

In a hospital's air-conditioning system, refrigerant is circulated through a refrigeration cycle at a rate of 110 kg/h. In the condenser, the refrigerant changes phase from gas to liquid at a constant temperature of 54°C. The heat of vaporization of the refrigerant at this temperature is 31.02 cal/g.

(a) Does the internal energy of the refrigerant in the condenser increase or decrease?

(b) At what rate is heat transferred out of the condenser in this air-conditioning system?

Solution: The system is the refrigerant in the condenser.

(a) Let Q_H represent the net heat input. Since no work is done in the condenser, the first law of thermodynamics is:

$$\Delta U = Q_H - W = Q_H$$

The heat of vaporization H_v is the amount of energy required to vaporize one gram of the refrigerant. This is also the amount of energy *released* when one gram of the refrigerant *condenses*. Since energy is released from the system, the net heat input is negative. If the mass of refrigerant is m, the net heat input is:

$$Q_H = -mH_v$$

Therefore, the change in internal energy is negative. The internal energy of refrigerant in the condenser decreases.

(b) In this problem, mass flow rate is given and heat flow rate is to be calculated. To obtain these rates, divide both sides of the equation above by a time interval Δt.

$$\frac{Q_H}{\Delta t} = -\frac{m}{\Delta t} H_v$$

Remember that the mass flow rate is $\dot{m} = \frac{m}{\Delta t}$ and the heat flow rate is $\dot{Q}_H = \frac{Q_H}{\Delta t}$. So you can write the equation as

$$\dot{Q}_H = -\dot{m} H_v$$

Substitute the given values for mass flow rate and heat of vaporization:

$$\dot{Q}_H = -\left(110\frac{kg}{h}\right)\left(31.02\frac{cal}{g}\right)\left(1000\frac{g}{kg}\right)$$

$$\dot{Q}_H = -3.41 \times 10^6 \text{ cal/h}$$

The heat transfer rate out of the condenser is 3.41×10^6 calories per hour.

The Second Law of Thermodynamics

Suppose you place an ice cube in the palm of your hand. The temperature of the ice is 0°C and your hand is 37°C. This temperature difference causes heat to flow from your palm to the ice. The internal energy transferred will begin to melt the ice and warm the resulting water. In accordance with the first law, the heat lost by your palm is gained by the ice and water.

Does it violate the first law for heat to flow in the opposite direction—from the ice cube to your palm—so the ice becomes colder and your palm warmer? Not if the internal energy lost by the ice equals that gained by your palm. But this process does violate the **second law of thermodynamics**. The second law can be stated in a number of equivalent ways. The simplest is a result of common observation:

> *The natural direction of heat flow is from a body (or reservoir) at a higher temperature to a body (or reservoir) at a lower temperature.*

Heat can be made to flow the other way, as in a heat pump, but only by doing work and adding energy to the system. In the absence of this work, heat flows in one direction, from hot to cold. When you place a potato in a hot oven, heat flows from the oven to the potato, not from the potato to the oven. The potato gets hot and the oven gets slightly cooler. You will never see the potato get cold and the oven get hotter.

The second law of thermodynamics also applies to engines. In a heat engine, thermal energy in a working fluid is converted into mechanical work of a piston or wheel. Remember, the thermal energy of the working fluid is the sum of the kinetic energies of the randomly moving atoms and molecules in the fluid. To convert thermal energy into a usable form, the random motion of atoms and molecules must be converted into ordered motion of a piston or a wheel. It is impossible to convert 100% of the random motion. After a fluid does work on a moving piston or wheel, there will always be leftover thermal energy in the atoms and molecules of the working fluid. The leftover energy is transferred out of the engine, as heat, to a low-temperature reservoir.

The second law of thermodynamics applied to heat engines can be stated as follows:

> *When work is done by an engine operating in a cycle, only some of the heat taken from a reservoir can be converted into work. The rest is rejected as heat at a lower temperature.*

Figure 5.37 illustrates the two statements of the second law.

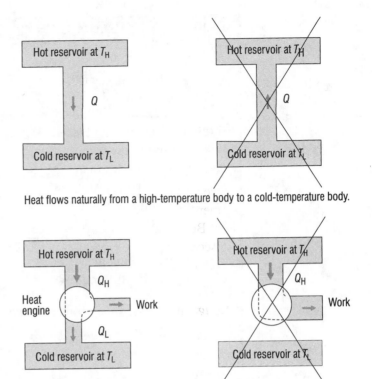

Heat flows naturally from a high-temperature body to a cold-temperature body.

A heat engine can convert only some of the heat taken from a reservoir.

Figure 5.37
Two statements of the second law of thermodynamics

The second law of thermodynamics says that a heat engine cannot be 100% efficient in turning heat into work. Even an ideal engine with no friction has an upper limit to its efficiency. This upper limit was first described by the French engineer Sadi Carnot in 1824. The maximum efficiency of a heat engine is called the **Carnot efficiency**; it depends on only the *absolute temperatures* of the hot and cold reservoirs, T_H and T_L.

$$\text{Carnot efficiency} = 1 - \frac{T_L}{T_H}$$

The absolute temperature scale is also called the **Kelvin scale**. The zero point of the Celsius scale is the freezing point of water. The zero point of the Kelvin scale is the lower limit of the temperature of any substance, where the thermal energy of the substance is zero. It is impossible to lower the temperature below this point, and it is therefore called **absolute zero**. The interval on this scale is the **kelvin** (K). The degree symbol is not used with the Kelvin scale. For example, the freezing point of water (0°C) is 273 K. The boiling point of water (100°C) is 373 K. The conversion between Celsius and Kelvin temperatures is:

$$T_{\text{Kelvin}} = T_{\text{Celsius}} + 273$$

Example 5.18 Carnot Efficiency of a Turbine

High-pressure steam enters a turbine at a temperature of 525°C. The steam expands in the turbine and pushes on the blades of the turbine shaft, causing the shaft to rotate and do work. The steam exits the turbine at a lower pressure and a temperature of 110°C. What is the maximum efficiency of the turbine?

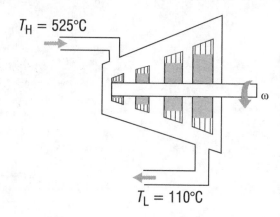

$T_H = 525°C$

$T_L = 110°C$

Solution: The steam transfers energy to the turbine at a high temperature of

$$T_H = 525°C$$
$$= 525 + 273 = 798 \text{ K}$$

The steam exits the turbine at a low temperature of

$$T_L = 110°C$$
$$= 110 + 273 = 383 \text{ K}$$

The Carnot efficiency of the turbine operating between these two absolute temperatures is

$$\text{Carnot efficiency} = 1 - \frac{383 \text{ K}}{798 \text{ K}}$$
$$= 0.52 \quad \text{or} \quad 52\%$$

The maximum efficiency of the turbine is 52%.

Energy Dissipation

The Carnot efficiency, like that calculated for the turbine in Example 5.17, is for an "ideal" process. An actual turbine will have a lower efficiency, probably less than 40%. This is because some of the steam's energy will go into overcoming friction in the turbine's bearings, turbulence in the steam flow, and heat transfer to the air surrounding the turbine. These are sometimes called energy "losses." But the energy is not really lost. It still exists, but it is *dissipated*, or no longer available to do work on the turbine.

Energy dissipation occurs in all processes. When electrical energy flows through a light bulb, some of the energy produces visible light and some is dissipated as thermal energy that heats the bulb. When gasoline is burned in a car engine, some of the energy produces motion and operates equipment and some of the energy is dissipated as thermal energy that heats the Earth's atmosphere. Energy is not "used up" in mechanical, fluid, electrical, or thermal systems. But energy is converted from usable forms to unusable forms. Energy dissipation means there may never be a shortage of energy on the Earth, but someday there may be a shortage of energy in usable forms.

Summary

- A system's internal energy can be changed by transferring heat to (or from) the system and by doing work on (or by) the system.

- The first law of thermodynamics is a statement that energy is conserved in a system. A system's change in internal energy is the net heat input minus the work done. Heat transferred to a system is positive. Work done by a system is positive.

- An adiabatic process is one in which there is no heat transfer.

- A heat engine is a device that converts thermal energy into work.

- A refrigerator reverses the cycle of a heat engine. It converts work into thermal energy and moves heat away from a cold reservoir to a hot reservoir.

- The second law of thermodynamics limits the number of possible processes. Without outside work, heat flows in only one direction—from a hot reservoir to a cold reservoir. Only some of the heat taken from a reservoir to operate an engine can be converted into work—the rest is rejected as waste heat.

- The Carnot efficiency is the maximum possible efficiency of a heat engine. Carnot efficiency $= 1 - \dfrac{T_L}{T_H}$, where T_L and T_H are absolute temperatures, measured in the Kelvin scale. $(T_{Kelvin} = T_{Celsius} + 273)$

1. The sum of the kinetic and potential energies of all the molecules that make up a system is called the system's _____.

2. (a) Describe two ways of increasing the internal energy of a system.

   (b) Describe two ways of decreasing the internal energy of a system.

3. By convention, when using the first law of thermodynamics to solve problems,

   (a) if heat enters a system, it is a _____ (positive or negative) quantity. In this case the internal energy of the system _____ (increases or decreases).

   (b) if work is done by the system, it is a _____ (positive or negative) quantity. In this case the internal energy of the system _____ (increases or decreases).

4. Suppose you compress the air in a bicycle air pump adiabatically. Which of the following is true?

   (a) The temperature of the air is constant.

   (b) The pressure of the air is constant.

   (c) No heat enters or leaves the air.

   (d) No work is done on or by the air.

5. Describe two ways you can compress the air in a bicycle air pump adiabatically.

6. A heat engine operates by taking in heat at one temperature, converting some of it into work, and exhausting the rest at _____ (a higher, a lower, or the same) temperature. The amount of heat exhausted is _____ (greater than, less than, or the same as) the amount of heat taken in.

7. A refrigerator operates by doing work on a fluid that absorbs heat at one temperature and exhausting heat at _____ (a higher, a lower, or the same) temperature. The amount of heat exhausted is _____ (greater than, less than, or the same as) the amount of heat taken in.

8. Match each component of a refrigerator with its function.

   Components: compressor, condenser, expansion valve, evaporator

   (a) decreases the pressure of the working fluid

   (b) changes the phase of the working fluid from gas to liquid

   (c) does work on the working fluid to increase its pressure and temperature

   (d) changes the phase of the working fluid from liquid to gas

9. The _____ (first or second) law of thermodynamics is a statement of the law of conservation of energy.

10. The _____ (first or second) law of thermodynamics says that not all the heat taken into an engine can be converted into work.

11. According to a magazine article, the temperature of the sun's core is approximately 1.5 million degrees. Does it matter whether this temperature is in degrees Kelvin or degrees Celsius? Explain.

12. Which of the following is possible?

    (a) The temperature of a superconductor is –2 K.

    (b) The efficiency of an ideal, friction-free engine is greater than the Carnot efficiency.

    (c) An engine that has attained the Carnot efficiency rejects no heat to a cold-temperature reservoir.

    (d) All of the above.

    (e) None of the above.

13. A cylinder contains a gas and a piston loaded with weights to maintain a constant pressure in the gas. The total weight of the piston and weights is 23.4 N. The side of the cylinder is insulated, but its bottom is not. When the cylinder is placed on a warm surface, heat flows into the gas and the gas expands. The piston rises a distance of 11.4 cm and then stops.

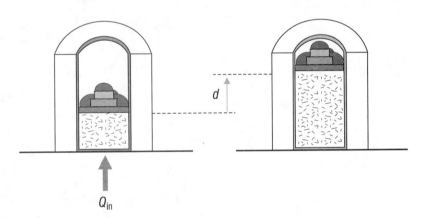

Q_{in}

    (a) How much work is done by the gas in the cylinder during the expansion?

    (b) If the internal energy of the gas increases by 9.50 J, how much heat is transferred to the gas?

14. A thermos bottle contains cold coffee. Suppose you shake the bottle vigorously. Does the internal energy of the coffee increase, decrease, or stay the same? Explain your answer, using the first law of thermodynamics.

15. The cylinders of a car's engine are 85 mm in diameter. The pistons travel a length of 105 mm during each stroke. The average pressure of the fuel-air mixture in the cylinder during the compression stroke is 8.5×10^5 Pa.

(a) What is the work done on the fuel-air mixture during the compression stroke of one piston? (The volume of a cylinder is $\pi r^2 h$, where r is the radius and h is the height.)

(b) The internal energy of the fuel-air mixture before the compression is 1440 J. What is the internal energy after the compression?

16. A 0.55-g hailstone falling at a terminal speed of 9.2 m/s strikes a concrete sidewalk. By how much does the internal energy of the hailstone change as it comes to a stop?

17. The Carnot efficiency of a heat engine is 65%. If heat is exhausted from the engine at a temperature of 113°C, at what temperature is heat absorbed by the engine?

18. A village in Iceland uses hot water from a geothermal well as a heat source for an electrical generation system. The system operates on a cycle and uses a working fluid that has a low boiling point, similar to the fluid used in a refrigeration system.

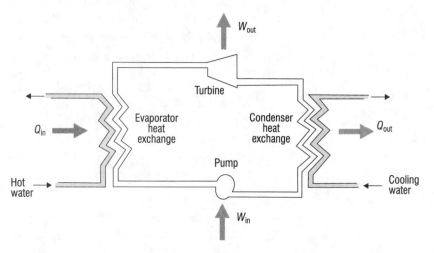

In the evaporator heat exchanger, 6.31×10^5 Btu per hour are absorbed by the working fluid from the hot water. In the condenser heat exchanger, 3.99×10^5 Btu per hour are removed from the working fluid. The pump does work at a rate of 3.16×10^5 Btu per hour.

(a) At what rate does the turbine in this system do work?

(b) The turbine drives an electrical generator. The efficiency of electrical energy generation is 85%. What is the electrical output, in kilowatts? (1 Btu = 1054 J and 1 J/s = 1 watt.)

CHAPTER FIVE
SUMMARY

Energy is the property of a system that enables it to do work. Energy can be in the form of kinetic or potential energy. The kinetic energy of an object or a fluid is proportional to its mass (or moment of inertia) and the square of its speed (or angular speed):

$$\text{KE}_{\text{translation}} = \tfrac{1}{2}mv^2 \qquad\qquad \text{KE}_{\text{rotation}} = \tfrac{1}{2}I\omega^2$$

The gravitational potential energy of an object or fluid depends on its mass and its distance from a reference height. Elastic potential energy is stored in an object as a result of its change in shape.

$$\text{PE}_{\text{g}} = mgh \qquad\qquad \text{PE}_{\text{elastic}} = \tfrac{1}{2}kx^2$$

Potential energy can be stored in the electric field of a capacitor and the magnetic field of an inductor.

$$\text{PE} = \tfrac{1}{2}C\Delta V^2 \qquad\qquad \text{PE} = \tfrac{1}{2}LI^2$$

The internal energy of a system is the sum of the microscopic kinetic and potential energies of the particles that make up the system. A system's internal energy increases if heat is added to the system or if work is done on the system.

$$\Delta U = Q - W$$

The total energy of a system is the sum of its kinetic, potential, and internal energies. Within a closed, isolated system, energy can change forms but the total energy is constant.

Unless work is done on a system, heat flows in only one direction—from a hot reservoir to a cold reservoir. Only a portion of the heat taken from a reservoir can be converted into work. The rest is discarded as waste heat.

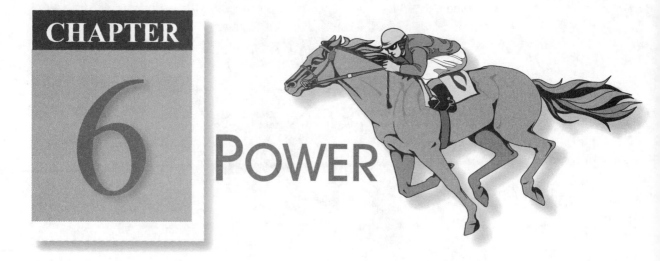

6 POWER

Mechanical, fluid, electrical, and thermal systems do work, or transfer energy from one form to another. Until this chapter, we have been concerned with only the amount of work done or energy transferred, not with the time required to do the work. For example, if a pump lifts 100 pounds of water through a height of 10 feet, the pump does 1000 ft-lb of work. It could take the pump one minute or one hour to lift the water, but in both cases the amount of work done is 1000 ft-lb.

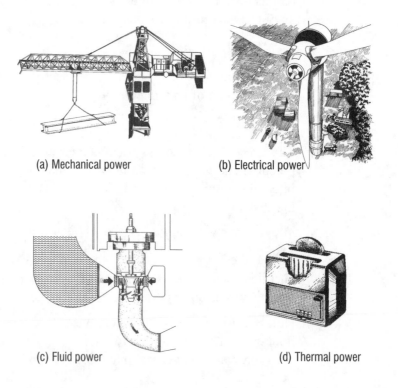

(a) Mechanical power

(b) Electrical power

(c) Fluid power

(d) Thermal power

The pump's *power* does depend on time. **Power** is the rate of doing work—the work done divided by the time required to do the work. Compare the power of two pumps. One pump can lift 100 lb of water 10 ft in one minute. The other pump can do the same work, but it takes one hour. The first pump is 60 times more powerful than the second. It does the work 60 times faster (or in 1/60 of the time) than the second pump.

In this chapter, you will calculate power by dividing work by the time interval. The expressions for work will be the same as those in Chapter 2. For example, in a mechanical system when a force is applied to an object in the direction of the object's movement, the work done on the object is the force times the distance moved ($W = F\Delta d$). The power is the work divided by the time interval ($\text{Pwr} = W/\Delta t = F\Delta d /\Delta t$).

You can use the equivalence of work and energy to solve some types of problems. Work can be calculated from an object's change in kinetic energy or from the amount of energy that changes from one type to another. So power is also the amount of energy changed or transferred per unit time.

In thermal systems, power is the same as heat flow rate, which you studied in Section 3.4. We will not repeat power in thermal systems in this chapter.

6.1 POWER IN MECHANICAL SYSTEMS

Objectives

- Explain the relationship between power and work.

- Explain the relationship between power, force, and speed for an object in translational motion.

- Calculate a device's efficiency in terms of the ratio of its output to input power.

- Explain the relationship between power, torque, and angular speed for an object in rotational motion.

- Solve problems involving power in mechanical systems.

Power in Translational Systems

INTERNET connection

To find out more about power in mechanical systems, follow the links at **www.learningincontext.com**.

Often the *time* it takes to complete an activity is as important as the work required. For example, when you run up a flight of stairs, you do the same amount of work as when you walk up the stairs. But these two activities are not the same, and you can feel the difference. When you run up the stairs, you are more tired than when you walk. When you run, you do the work *faster*. The rate of doing work or expending energy is **power**. It takes more power to run up the stairs than to walk.

Figure 6.1
When you run up a flight of stairs, you
do the same amount of work as when
you walk. But you do the work faster.
More power is required to run.

If an amount of work W is done in a time interval Δt, the power is the ratio
of W to Δt.

$$\text{Power} = \frac{\text{work done}}{\text{time interval}}$$

$$\text{Pwr} = \frac{W}{\Delta t}$$

We use the symbol Pwr as a variable instead of P to avoid confusion with
pressure P in the next section.

In the SI system, work and energy are measured in joules (J) and time is
measured in seconds (s), therefore, power is measured in joules per second
(J/s). One joule per second is called one **watt** (W). 1 watt = 1 W = 1 J/s.

The unit of power in the SI system was named after James Watt, the Scottish
engineer who made the steam engine an important power source during the
Industrial Revolution. Watt used the English system of measurement, in
which work is measured in foot pounds (ft·lb) and time is measured in
seconds (s). Therefore, power is measured in ft·lb/s. Steam engines were
invented to replace work done by horses and donkeys in pumping water out
of coal mines. Watt estimated that a horse could do work at a rate of about
550 ft·lb/s. So he called this rate one horsepower (hp). 1 hp = 550 ft·lb/s.

One horsepower is much larger than one watt. In fact, the watt is a rather
small quantity for many applications. The kilowatt (kW) is commonly used.
You can use the following factors for converting among units:

$$1 \text{ kW} = 1000 \text{ W}$$

$$1 \text{ hp} = 550 \text{ ft·lb/s}$$

$$1 \text{ hp} = 746 \text{ W}$$

Example 6.1 Power Required to Lift an Elevator

The total mass of a loaded elevator is 1200 kg. An electric motor raises the elevator three floors (15 m) at a constant speed in 12 seconds. What is the power output of the motor?

Solution: Since the elevator travels at a constant speed, no net force is acting on it. The force F_{motor} exerted upward equals the weight, or force of gravity F_g acting downward. The work W done by the motor in raising the elevator a height h is the force times the distance.

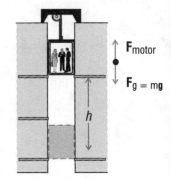

$$W = F_{motor}\, h = mgh$$

Substitute mgh for W in the equation for power:

$$\text{Pwr} = \frac{W}{\Delta t} = \frac{mgh}{\Delta t}$$

$$\text{Pwr} = \frac{(1200\ \text{kg})(9.80\ \text{m/s}^2)(15\ \text{m})}{12\ \text{s}} \qquad [\text{kg}\cdot\text{m/s}^2 = \text{N}]$$

$$= 14{,}700\ \frac{\text{N}\cdot\text{m}}{\text{s}} = 14.7 \times 10^3\ \frac{\text{J}}{\text{s}} \quad \text{or}\ \ 14.7\ \text{kW}$$

The power output of the motor is 14.7 kilowatts.

Suppose a constant force F does work on an object and the force acts in the direction in which the object moves. If the object moves a distance Δd while the force is applied, the work done is the product of force and distance: $W = F\Delta d$. The power delivered to the moving object is

$$\text{Pwr} = \frac{W}{\Delta t} = \frac{F\Delta d}{\Delta t}$$

But the speed v of the object is the distance traveled per unit time:

$$v = \frac{\Delta d}{\Delta t}$$

Therefore, when a constant force acts on an object in the direction of motion, the power delivered is the product of the force and speed.

$$\text{Power} = (\text{force})(\text{speed})$$

$$\text{Pwr} = Fv$$

The following example demonstrates this form of the power equation.

Refer to Appendix F for a career link to this concept.

Example 6.2 Drag Force on a Car

A car's drivetrain (engine, transmission, differential, drive shaft, and axle) delivers an average power of 50 hp to the rear wheels of the car when it travels at a constant velocity of 60 mph (88 ft/s). What is the total drag force exerted on the car?

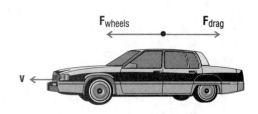

Solution: Since the car travels at a constant velocity, no net force is acting on it. The force F_{wheels} exerted by the wheels in the forward direction equals the force of drag F_{drag} in the opposite direction.

Solve the equation $\text{Pwr} = F_{wheels}v$ for F_{wheels} :

$$F_{wheels} = \frac{\text{Pwr}}{v}$$

$$= \frac{(50 \text{ hp})\left(550\dfrac{\text{ft}\cdot\text{lb/s}}{\text{hp}}\right)}{88 \text{ ft/s}}$$

$$= 313 \text{ lb}$$

The drag force on the car is 313 pounds.

Power and Efficiency

Resistive forces, such as drag and friction, act in the direction opposite a body's velocity. Therefore, they do negative work on the body. As discussed in Section 5.4, this is a *dissipation* of energy. Energy dissipation converts mechanical energy into thermal energy, and lowers the efficiency of engines and simple machines. The amount of energy dissipated per unit time is sometimes called a power "loss."

In Section 2.1, the efficiency of a machine was defined as the ratio of output work to input work.

$$\text{Efficiency} = \frac{\text{output work}}{\text{input work}}$$

You can also calculate efficiency using input and output power. Divide the numerator and denominator by a time interval Δt. Output work per unit time is output power, and input work per unit time is input power.

$$\text{Efficiency} = \frac{\text{output work}/\Delta t}{\text{input work}/\Delta t}$$

$$\text{Efficiency} = \frac{\text{output power}}{\text{input power}}$$

$$\text{Percent efficiency} = \frac{\text{output power}}{\text{input power}} \times 100\%$$

Friction, drag, or electrical resistance converts some of the input power of any real system into *thermal power*. Thermal power is the energy dissipation rate, or the rate of conversion of work or energy into thermal energy. Because of energy dissipation, the output power of a device or system is always less than the input power. The efficiency of a real system is less than 100%.

Example 6.3 Input Power of an Elevator Motor

The elevator motor in Example 6.1 has an efficiency of 89%. What is the electrical input power for the motor?

Solution: From Example 6.1, the output power of the motor is 14.7 kW. Let Pwr$_{\text{input}}$ represent the input power.

$$\text{Efficiency} = \frac{\text{output power}}{\text{input power}}$$

$$0.89 = \frac{14.7 \text{ kW}}{\text{Pwr}_{\text{input}}}$$

$$\text{Pwr}_{\text{input}} = \frac{14.7 \text{ kW}}{0.89} = 16.5 \text{ kW}$$

The electrical input power for the motor is 16.5 kilowatts.

Power in Rotational Systems

A torque applied to an object in rotation can also do work. In Section 2.1 you learned that work equals the product of the applied torque τ and the angle θ (in radians) through which the object moves.

$$W = \tau\theta$$

If you divide both sides of this equation by the time interval Δt over which the work is done, you get an equation for power.

$$\frac{W}{\Delta t} = \frac{\tau \theta}{\Delta t} = \tau \left(\frac{\theta}{\Delta t} \right)$$

The left side of the equation is the power (work done per unit time). In the right side, the ratio of angle moved through to time is the angular speed of the rotating object, $\frac{\theta}{\Delta t} = \omega$. Therefore, when a constant torque acts on an object in rotation, the power delivered to the object is the product of the torque and angular speed.

$$\text{Power} = \text{(torque)(angular speed)}$$

$$\text{Pwr} = \tau \omega$$

The following example demonstrates this form of the power equation.

Example 6.4 Torque Produced by a Spindle Motor

Data are stored magnetically in a computer hard drive on circular platters. A spindle motor rotates the platters so read/write heads (small electromagnets) can read, write, and search for data. If 8.1 W of power are delivered to the spindle motor for reading and writing and the motor rotates at a constant 7200 rpm, what torque is produced by the motor?

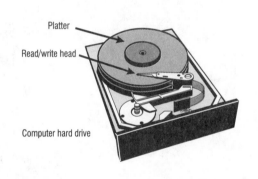

Platter

Read/write head

Computer hard drive

Solution: First convert the angular speed from rpm to radians per second.

$$\omega = \left(7200 \frac{\text{rev}}{\text{min}} \right) \left(\frac{1 \text{ min}}{60 \text{ s}} \right) \left(\frac{2 \pi \text{ rad}}{\text{rev}} \right) = 754 \text{ rad/s}$$

Solve the equation Pwr = $\tau \omega$ for τ.

Use Pwr = 8.1 W = 8.1 J/s.

$$\tau = \frac{\text{Pwr}}{\omega}$$

$$= \frac{8.1 \text{ J/s}}{754 \text{ rad/s}} \qquad \text{[Drop the unit } rad.\text{]}$$

$$= 0.011 \text{ N·m} \qquad \text{[J = N·m]}$$

The spindle motor produces a torque of 0.011 newton·meter.

- Power is the rate of doing work. Power is measured in watts (W) in the SI system and horsepower (hp) in the English system.

- If a constant force acts on an object in the direction of the object's velocity, the power delivered to the object is the product of the force and the speed. Pwr = Fv

- When a device converts input power to output power, the device's efficiency is the ratio of output to input power.

- If a constant torque acts on an object in rotation, the power delivered to the object is the product of torque and angular speed. Pwr = $\tau\omega$

Exercises

1. Which of the following is *not* a unit of power?

   (a) horsepower

   (b) watt

   (c) joule-second

   (d) newton-meter per second

2. How much power is required for you to hold a 1-kg book 1 m above the floor for 100 s?

3. How much power is required for you to run up a flight of stairs to a floor 5.0 m higher than where you start in 6.0 s, if your mass is 50 kg?

4. Which of the following equations for finding power is *incorrect*?

   (a) Pwr = $W/\Delta t$ (c) Pwr = $Fv/\Delta t$

   (b) Pwr = Fv (d) Pwr = $F\Delta d/\Delta t$

5. An electric motor is rated at ¼ hp. What is the power of the motor in ft-lb/s? In watts?

6. An elevator weighs 3500 pounds. It is pulled upward a distance of 30 feet at a constant speed in 10 seconds.

   (a) Find the work done in lifting the elevator.

   (b) Find the speed of the elevator.

   (c) How much power is required to lift the elevator? Write your answer in ft-lb/s and in horsepower.

7. A gas expands in a cylinder, exerting a force of 25 N on a piston. The piston moves at a constant speed of 0.4 m/s.

   (a) What is the power output of the expanding gas?

   (b) How much work does the gas do on the piston in 3 seconds?

8. An electric motor has a shaft torque of 0.55 lb-ft when it turns at a rotational speed of 800 rpm. What is the shaft horsepower of the motor?

9. What is the efficiency of a machine that requires 1200 watts of input power to raise a 900-newton load a distance of 1.5 meters in 11 seconds?

10. To remove a flat tire, you use a hand jack to lift the back of the car 0.5 foot off the ground. The jack lifts 850 pounds.

    (a) What is the power output of the jack if the car is lifted in 10 seconds?

    (b) What is the power output if the car is lifted in 1 minute?

    (c) How much work is done by the jack in part (a)?

    (d) How much work is done in part (b)?

11. A triathlete swims 2.4 miles in 65 minutes with an average power output of 0.22 hp. What is the average drag force exerted on the triathlete during the swim?

12. The bilge pump of a sailboat can lift 7.5 liters of water per minute through a height of 1.5 meters. If the pump is 70% efficient, how much power must be supplied to the pump? (The mass of 1 L of water is 1 kg.)

13. Three equations for power in translational systems are shown below. What are the corresponding analogous equations for power in rotational systems?

Translational Systems	Rotational Systems
$Pwr = \dfrac{W}{\Delta t}$	$Pwr = ?$
$Pwr = \dfrac{F\Delta d}{\Delta t}$	$Pwr = ?$
$Pwr = Fv$	$Pwr = ?$

14. A dynamometer measures the power output of a car's engine as 185 hp at 4500 rpm. What is the torque output of the engine?

15. A flywheel isolates torque pulsations between a gas compressor and its drive motor. The moment of inertia of the flywheel is 8640 kg·m². The flywheel is accelerated from rest to its operating speed of 441 rpm in 20 seconds.

    (a) What is the change in kinetic energy of the flywheel during its acceleration?

    (b) What is the power input to the flywheel?

16. Prior to production, new car designs are tested for wind drag. The results of a test are shown below. How many horsepower must be delivered to the drive wheels of this car to keep it moving on a level horizontal road at a constant speed of 30 mph? at a constant 60 mph?

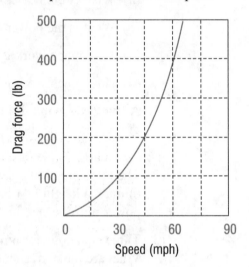

17. The tires of the car in exercise 16 have a radius of 16 inches. How much torque must be applied to the drive wheels to maintain a constant 60 mph? Assume the torque is equally divided between two drive wheels.
[Hint: You can find the tire's angular speed (in rev/s) by dividing the car's speed (in ft/s) by the distance the car moves per revolution (in ft/rev). This distance is the circumference of the tire.]

6.2 POWER IN FLUID SYSTEMS

Objectives

- Explain the relationship between power and work in a fluid system.

- Explain the relationship between a fluid's power, pressure, and change in volume for a constant-pressure process.

- Explain the relationship between a fluid's power, volume, and change in pressure for a steady-flow process.

- Solve problems involving power in fluid systems.

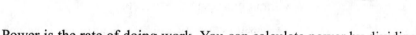

Power is the rate of doing work. You can calculate power by dividing the amount of work W done by the time interval Δt it takes to do the work.

$$\text{Pwr} = \frac{W}{\Delta t}$$

To find out more about power in fluid systems, follow the links at **www.learningincontext.com.**

Suppose you slide a book across a table at a constant speed. You exert a constant force F on the book for a distance Δd in the direction of the force. The work you do on the book is $F\Delta d$. Your power can be written as follows.

$$\text{Pwr} = \frac{F\Delta d}{\Delta t} = Fv$$

Thus, for a mechanical system, power can be written as the product of the prime mover (force) and a rate (speed). In fluid systems, we can write a similar equation for power, but we can have *either* a changing pressure *or* a changing volume. Therefore, we must examine both of these possibilities.

Fluid Power

Fluids do work when they move objects. The work done is calculated using the fluid pressure and volume. As in Section 2.2, we will consider the work done by fluids, and fluid power, in constant-pressure and steady-flow processes.

Constant-Pressure Processes. A fluid in a cylinder does work on a moving piston. If the fluid pressure P is constant and the volume changes by an amount ΔV, the work done by the fluid is the product $P\Delta V$. Let Δt represent the time interval over which the work is done. The fluid power is the ratio of work to time.

$$\text{Pwr} = \frac{P\Delta V}{\Delta t}$$

The pressure P and time interval Δt are always positive quantities. But volume change ΔV can be positive or negative. If ΔV is positive, work and power are positive—the fluid does work. If ΔV is negative, work and power are negative—work is done on the fluid.

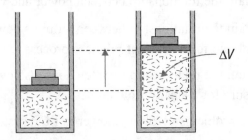

Figure 6.2
An expanding fluid does work on a moving piston. A gas expands at constant pressure if heat is added or if gas is added to the cylinder.

If the fluid in a cylinder is a *gas*, there are two ways to change the volume without changing the pressure:

- Heat transfer—you can heat or cool the gas. The gas expands as the temperature increases and contracts as the temperature decreases.

- Fluid flow—you can add gas to the cylinder or remove gas from the cylinder.

If the fluid in a cylinder is a *liquid*, the change in volume caused by heat transfer is very small unless the liquid changes phase. You can usually neglect the volume change of a liquid caused by heat transfer, unless you are told there is a phase change. Otherwise, there is only one way to change the volume of a liquid without changing the pressure:

- Fluid flow—you can add liquid to the cylinder or remove liquid from the cylinder.

The ratio $\frac{\Delta V}{\Delta t}$ is the rate of change of volume. As in Section 3.2, we write this rate with the symbol $\dot{V}$. If heat is transferred to a gas at constant pressure, $\dot{V}$ is the expansion rate of the gas. If a gas or liquid flows into or out of a region, $\dot{V}$ is the volume flow rate. In SI units, $\dot{V}$ is measured in m³/s. Substituting this variable into the power equation gives the following.

$$\text{Pwr} = P\dot{V}$$

This form of the power equation is similar to the equation for mechanical power—the product of the prime mover (pressure) and a rate (rate of change of volume).

Example 6.5 Power Required to Fill a Balloon

A tank of compressed air is used to fill balloons. A balloon that is initially flat has a final volume of 1.25 ft³. The atmospheric pressure is 14.2 psi. What is the power, in horsepower, from the compressed air that is required to fill the balloon in 1.5 s? (1 hp = 550 ft·lb/s)

Solution: The air inflating the balloon does work by pushing against atmospheric pressure. This pressure is constant, so use $\text{Pwr} = P\dot{V}$. Convert the pressure to lb/ft².

$$\text{Pwr} = P\dot{V} = P\frac{\Delta V}{\Delta t}$$

$$\text{Pwr} = \left(14.2\frac{\text{lb}}{\text{in}^2}\right)\left(\frac{1.25 \text{ ft}^3}{1.5 \text{ s}}\right)\left(\frac{144 \text{ in}^2}{1 \text{ ft}^2}\right) = 1704 \text{ ft·lb/s}$$

Convert to horsepower:

$$\text{Pwr} = (1704 \text{ ft·lb/s})\left(\frac{1 \text{ hp}}{550 \text{ ft·lb/s}}\right) = 3.1 \text{ hp}$$

The output of the air is 3.1 horsepower.

Steady-Flow Processes. Fluids flowing through pumps and turbines are examples of steady-flow processes. In a steady-flow process, the mass flow rate is constant. The mass flow rate entering a pump or turbine equals the mass flow rate exiting the pump or turbine. You learned in Section 3.2 that volume flow rate $\dot{V}$ is related to density ρ and mass flow rate $\dot{m}$ as follows:

$$\dot{V} = \frac{\dot{m}}{\rho}$$

If ρ and $\dot{m}$ are both constant, the volume flow rate is constant.

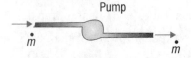

Pump

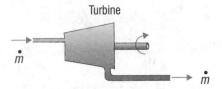

Turbine

Figure 6.3
A pump does work on a fluid. A fluid does work on a turbine. In each device, the mass flow rate is constant.

Suppose a volume of fluid V moves through a device in a steady-flow process and the fluid pressure changes by an amount ΔP. From Section 2.2, the work done by the fluid is $-V\Delta P$. Let Δt represent the time interval over which the work is done. The fluid power is the ratio of work to time.

$$\text{Pwr} = -\frac{V\Delta P}{\Delta t}$$

The volume V and time interval Δt are always positive quantities. But pressure change ΔP can be positive or negative. If ΔP is positive, work and power are negative—work is done on the fluid (as in a pump). If ΔP is negative, work and power are positive—the fluid does work (as in a turbine).

The ratio $\dfrac{V}{\Delta t}$ is the volume of fluid moving through a system per unit time. This is the volume flow rate $\dot{V}$. Substituting this variable into the power equation gives the following.

$$\text{Pwr} = -\dot{V}\Delta P$$

Thus, for problems involving steady flow and constant fluid density, the power equation is similar to the equation for mechanical power. But this time it is the product of the change in the prime mover (pressure) and a rate (volume flow rate).

Example 6.6 Power Output of a Pump

A pump transfers jet fuel from a storage tank into an airliner's wing tank through an 8.5-cm-diameter pipe. The fuel travels at an average speed of 3.8 m/s through the pipe. The pump increases the fuel pressure from 150 kPa to 250 kPa. What is the power output of the pump?

Solution: From Section 3.2, the volume flow rate is the product of the pipe cross-sectional area and the fuel speed through the pipe.

$$\dot{V} = Av = \pi r^2 v = \pi \left(\frac{0.085}{2} \text{m}\right)^2 \left(3.8\frac{\text{m}}{\text{s}}\right)$$

$$\dot{V} = 0.0216 \text{ m}^3/\text{s}$$

The power output of the pump equals the power input to the jet fuel.

$$\text{Pwr} = -\dot{V}\Delta P \qquad\qquad\qquad [\text{Pa} = \text{N/m}^2]$$

$$= -\left(0.0216 \frac{\text{m}^3}{\text{s}}\right)(250\times10^3 - 150\times10^3)\frac{\text{N}}{\text{m}^2}$$

$$= -2160 \text{ W} \quad \text{or} \quad -2.16 \text{ kW} \quad [\text{N}\cdot\text{m} = \text{J and W} = \text{J/s}]$$

The negative signs mean that work is done on the fuel. The pump power output is 2.16 kilowatts.

Power in Hydraulic and Pneumatic Systems

Hydraulic and pneumatic systems convert power in moving liquids or gases into mechanical power. Figure 6.4 shows a partial hydraulic system. A pump increases the pressure of a working fluid. The fluid moves a piston and load to the right. (A second control valve and additional tubing, not shown in Figure 6.4, reverse the direction of fluid flow. This moves the piston to the left.) In a pneumatic system, air is used as the working fluid. An air compressor replaces the pump, and a pressurized tank replaces the reservoir. The air is usually not recycled.

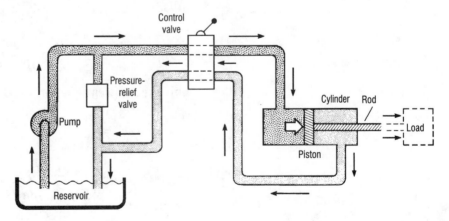

Figure 6.4
A partial hydraulic power system

Example 6.7 Pressure in a Hydraulic System

In a robotic hydraulic power system, a piston moves a 980-N load a distance of 15 cm in 1.2 s. The system's pump delivers high-pressure fluid at a rate of 150 cm³/s. What is the output mechanical power of the piston? What is the pressure of the fluid?

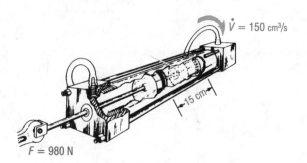

$\dot{V} = 150$ cm³/s

←15 cm→

$F = 980$ N

Solution: The output mechanical power is the work done by the piston per unit time.

$$\text{Power} = \frac{W}{\Delta t} = \frac{Fd}{\Delta t} = \frac{(980 \text{ N})(0.15 \text{ m})}{1.2 \text{ s}} = 122.5 \text{ W}$$

The output mechanical power is 122.5 watts. This is also the fluid power, assuming there is no friction between the piston and cylinder and the fluid is nonviscous.

The hydraulic fluid moves the piston at constant pressure. To find the pressure, use the power equation in the form $\text{Pwr} = P\dot{V}$. But first convert the units of volume flow rate to m³/s.

$$\dot{V} = 150 \ \frac{\text{cm}^3}{\text{s}} \cdot \frac{1 \text{ m}^3}{10^6 \text{ cm}^3} = 1.5 \times 10^{-4} \text{ m}^3/\text{s}$$

Solve the power equation for the pressure P.

$$P = \frac{\text{Pwr}}{\dot{V}}$$

$$= \frac{122.5 \text{ J/s}}{1.5 \times 10^{-4} \text{ m}^3/\text{s}} \qquad [\text{W} = \text{J/s}]$$

$$= 8.17 \times 10^5 \ \frac{\text{N}}{\text{m}^2} \qquad [\text{J} = \text{N} \cdot \text{m}]$$

The fluid pressure is 8.17×10^5 Pa, or 817 kPa.

Power from Heat of Combustion

Internal-combustion engines burn gasoline or diesel fuel to power cars and trucks. In gas turbines, hot gases from burning fuel pass through sets of blades to power airplanes, ships, and electrical generators. Rocket motors burn solid or liquid fuel—and accelerate the hot exhaust gases through nozzles— to provide lifting power for the rocket.

Table 6.1 Heat of Combustion
(MJ = 10^6 J)

Liquids	MJ/kg
Diesel fuel	44
Gasoline	46

Gases	MJ/m^3
Hydrogen	10
Natural gas	33-71
Acetylene	54
Propane	86

The *heat of combustion* of a fuel is the amount of heat released when one kilogram or one cubic meter of the fuel is completely burned. Table 6.1 lists heats of combustion for several fuels. If you know an engine's power output and rate of combustion of fuel, you can use the heat of combustion to calculate the engine's efficiency.

Example 6.8 Efficiency of a Car Engine

A dynamometer measures the power output of a car's engine as 140 hp. The engine consumes 20.8 kg/h of gasoline. What is the efficiency of the engine?

Solution: The power input to the engine comes from burning gasoline.

$$\text{Input power} = \left(20.8 \frac{\text{kg}}{\text{h}} \right) \left(46 \times 10^6 \frac{\text{J}}{\text{kg}} \right) \left(\frac{1 \text{ h}}{3600 \text{ s}} \right) = 2.66 \times 10^5 \text{ W}$$

Convert the output power to watts:

$$\text{Output power} = (140 \text{ hp}) \left(\frac{746 \text{ W}}{1 \text{ hp}} \right) 1.04 \times 10^5 \text{ W}$$

The efficiency of the engine is the ratio of output to input power.

$$\text{Efficiency} = \frac{\text{output power}}{\text{input power}} = \frac{1.04 \times 10^5 \text{ W}}{2.66 \times 10^5 \text{ W}} = 0.39 \text{ or } 39\%$$

The engine's efficiency is 39%.

Summary

- In a fluid system, power is the rate of work done by the fluid.

- When a fluid expands or contracts at constant pressure, the power output of the fluid is $\text{Pwr} = \dfrac{P\Delta V}{\Delta t}$.

- In a steady-flow process, a volume of fluid moves through a pressure difference. The power output of the fluid is $\text{Pwr} = -\dfrac{V\Delta P}{\Delta t}$.

- Fluid power can be positive or negative.

Exercises

1. What fluid conditions are necessary for you to use the following equation for calculating power?

$$\text{Pwr} = P\dot{V}$$

2. What fluid conditions are necessary for you to use the following equation for calculating power?

$$\text{Pwr} = -\dot{V}\Delta P$$

3. If fluid power is positive in a process, work is done _____ (on or by) the fluid. If fluid power is negative, work is done _____ (on or by) the fluid.

4. You are selecting a pump for a laser cooling system that uses water. The pump must provide a pressure difference of 42 psi and a volume flow rate of 3.5 ft³/min. You have three pumps from which to choose: ¼ hp, ½ hp, and ¾ hp. Which pump would you select?

5. What flow rate can be expected from a 1-hp pump that produces a pressure difference of 250 kPa?

6. A piston in a hydraulic cylinder has a power output of 7500 watts when it applies a force of 2000 newtons to a load.

   (a) At what speed does the piston move?

   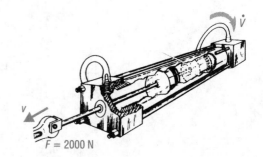

   $F = 2000$ N

   (b) The area of the piston is 40 cm². What is the volume flow rate into

7. The inlet to a hydroelectric turbine is located 61 m below the surface of a lake. Water from the lake flows through and turns the turbine. The turbine turns a generator, which produces 50 megawatts of electrical power.

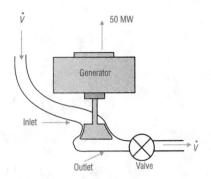

(a) What is the water pressure at the inlet to the turbine? (The density of water is 1000 kg/m³.)

(b) The water pressure at the outlet of the turbine is 87.2 kPa. If the turbine-generator system is 90% efficient, what is the flow rate of water through the turbine?

8. In a steam engine, a cylinder fitted with a piston has a volume of 2.0 ft³ and is filled with steam at 50 psi. Heat is transferred to the steam. In 60 s, the steam expands, pushing the piston at constant pressure until the volume increases to 2.6 ft³.

(a) What power is developed by the steam during the expansion? Write your answer in units of Btu/s. (1 Btu = 778 ft-lb)

(b) During the expansion, heat is added at a rate of 0.38 Btu/s. At what rate does the internal energy of the steam increase?

9. An in-floor radiant heating system uses warm water to heat a room. The water is circulated by a pump through a tube embedded in the room's sub-floor. The radius and length of the tube are shown in the diagram.

(a) If the volume flow rate of water through the tube is 500 cm³/s (5×10^{-4} m³/s), how much does the pressure drop as the water flows through the length of tubing in the room? The viscosity of the water is 6.5×10^{-4} Pa·s. (Remember Poiseuille's law from Section 4.2.)

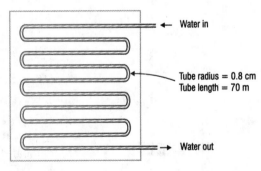

(b) How much power is needed from the pump to move water through the room?

10. An earthmover's diesel engine consumes 36.6 kg/h of fuel.

(a) What is the power input to the engine?

(b) What is the power output if the power conversion efficiency is 32%?

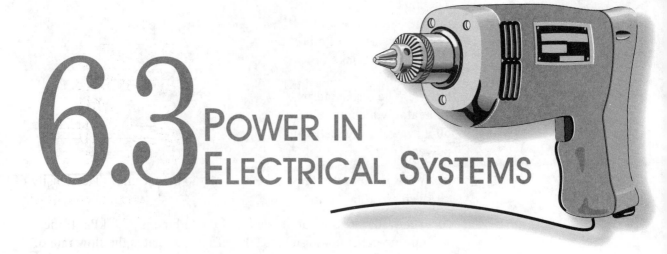

6.3 POWER IN ELECTRICAL SYSTEMS

Objectives

- Explain the relationship between power, current, and voltage in electrical systems.

- Explain the relationship between power, current, and resistance in electrical systems.

- Calculate energy usage in kilowatt-hours.

- Solve problems involving power in electrical systems.

To find out more about power in electrical systems, follow the links at **www.learningincontext.com.**

Electrical systems convert electric work or energy into other forms of work or energy. For example, in a laser electric energy is converted into light. In a radio, electric energy is converted into sound. A sewing machine converts electric energy into motion. An oven converts electric energy into thermal energy. In an electric circuit, a device that converts electric energy into mechanical, thermal, or other electric or magnetic forms is called the *load*. Power is the rate of energy conversion in the load.

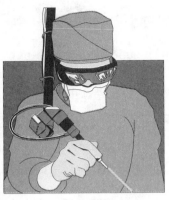

A laser converts electric energy into light.

A sewing machine converts electric energy into motion.

Electric Power

A potential difference causes charge to move in the electric circuit of the laser, radio, sewing machine, or oven. A battery, or other source of potential difference for each circuit, creates an electric field. The field is the source of a driving force that does work in pushing charge through the load in the circuit. Then the charge does work as it moves through the load. You learned in Section 2.3 that work done is the product of the charge moved q and the potential difference ΔV through which the charge moves.

$$\text{Work} = q\Delta V$$

Electric power is the rate at which work is done by charge flowing in a circuit.

$$\text{Pwr} = \frac{\text{work done}}{\text{time interval}} = \frac{q\Delta V}{\Delta t}$$

Remember, current I is the rate of charge flow in the circuit.

$$I = \frac{q}{\Delta t}$$

Therefore, the equation for electric power can be written as the product of the prime mover (potential difference) and a rate (current).

$$\text{Pwr} = I\Delta V$$

In electrical systems, power is measured in watts (W), current is measured in amperes (A), and potential difference is measured in volts (V).

$$1 \text{ watt} = 1 \text{ ampere} \times 1 \text{ volt}$$

$$1 \text{ W} = 1 \text{ A·V}$$

Example 6.9 Current Through a Laser Power Supply

A circuit in the power supply for a high-power laser produces 1.5 kW when the potential difference across the circuit is 110 V. What is the current flowing in the power supply circuit?

Solution: Solve the power equation for current:

$$I = \frac{\text{Pwr}}{\Delta V}$$

$$= \frac{1500 \text{ W}}{110 \text{ V}} \qquad [1.5 \text{ kW} = 1500 \text{ W}]$$

$$= 13.6 \text{ A} \qquad\qquad [\text{W} = \text{A} \cdot \text{V}]$$

The current is 13.6 amps.

Power in a Resistance

Refer to Appendix F for a career link to this concept.

An electric mixer, a television, a microwave oven, and a hair dryer are loads in a household circuit. As they convert electric energy, they resist charge flow. The resistance R of a load was defined in Section 4.3 as the ratio of the potential difference across the load to the current through the load.

$$R = \frac{\Delta V}{I} \quad \text{or} \quad \Delta V = IR$$

Substitute this expression for ΔV into the power equation.

$$\text{Pwr} = I\Delta V = I(IR)$$

$$\text{Pwr} = I^2 R$$

You can also write an equation for power using voltage and resistance. From the definition of resistance, $I = \dfrac{\Delta V}{R}$. Substitute this expression I into the power equation.

$$\text{Pwr} = I\Delta V = \left(\frac{\Delta V}{R}\right)\Delta V$$

$$\text{Pwr} = \frac{\Delta V^2}{R}$$

All three forms of the power equation are often used in solving problems.

$$\text{Pwr} = I\Delta V$$

$$\text{Pwr} = I^2 R$$

$$\text{Pwr} = \frac{\Delta V^2}{R}$$

Example 6.10 Power Dissipated by a Resistor

A 5.0-Ω resistor is connected across a battery. If 2.2 A of current flow through the resistor,

(a) what power is dissipated by the resistor?

(b) how much energy is dissipated in 12 seconds?

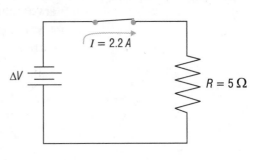

Solution: (a) $\quad$ Pwr $= I^2R$

$$= (2.2\text{ A})^2(5.0\ \Omega) \qquad [\Omega = \text{V/A}]$$

$$= 24.2\text{ W} \qquad\qquad [\text{W} = \text{A}\cdot\text{V}]$$

The resistor dissipates 24.2 watts of power.

(b) Remember, *energy dissipation* means the resistor converts electric energy into thermal energy. The rate of energy dissipation is power. In a time interval Δt of 12 seconds, the energy E dissipated is:

$$E = \text{Pwr} \times \Delta t$$

$$= (24.2\text{ J/s})(12\text{ s}) \qquad [\text{W} = \text{J/s}]$$

$$= 290.4\text{ J}$$

In 12 seconds, the resistor dissipates 290.4 joules.

Kilowatt-Hours

Electric utility companies are often called "power companies." But they really sell energy, not power. When you use an electrical device you pay for the energy used by the device. This energy equals the rate of energy consumption (the power of the device, in watts) times the number of seconds the device is used.

Remember the relationship between the units of power and energy, $\text{W} = \text{J/s}$. So a joule is also a watt-second. The electric company could charge you for the number of joules, or watt-seconds, of energy used. But a watt-second is a small amount of energy. For energy sales, electric companies use a larger unit, called a **kilowatt-hour** (kWh). A kilowatt-hour is the energy consumed by a 1-kW (1000-J/s) device operated continuously for 1 hour (3600 s).

$$1\text{ kWh} = (1000\text{ J/s})(3600\text{ s}) = 3.6 \times 10^6\text{ J} \quad \text{or} \quad 3.6\text{ MJ}$$

Figure 6.6 shows a typical meter that measures household electric energy use in kilowatt-hours. This meter has a small electric motor whose speed of rotation depends on the energy being delivered to the house's circuit. As the motor rotates, it turns a system of gears. The gears rotate pointers on dials, or registers.

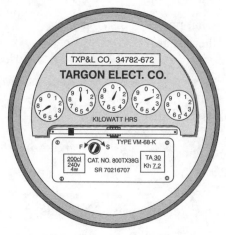

Once per month the electric company reads the meter to determine the number of kilowatt-hours of energy used since the last reading. The registers are read from left to right. Each register represents a decimal-place value. For example, the right-most register is the one's place, the next register is the ten's place, and so on. The electric company subtracts the reading for last month from the reading for this month, and the difference is the energy used for the month.

Example 6.11 The Cost of Operating a Television

An electric company charges $0.085 per kWh of electric energy consumption. What is the cost of operating a television set for one month (30 days) if the set is operated an average of 7.5 hours per day? The television set draws 1.5 A when connected to a house's 120-V circuit.

Solution: Find the energy used in kWh. Energy equals the power times the time interval.

$$E = \text{Pwr} \times \Delta t$$

$$\text{Pwr} = I\Delta V = (1.5 \text{ A})(120 \text{ V}) = 180 \text{ W} \quad \text{or} \quad 0.18 \text{ kW}$$

$$\Delta t = (30 \text{ d})(7.5 \text{ h/d}) = 225 \text{ h}$$

$$E = (0.18 \text{ kW})(225 \text{ h}) = 40.5 \text{ kWh}$$

$$\text{Cost} = (\$0.085/\text{kWh})(40.5 \text{ kWh}) = \$3.44$$

The cost of operating the TV for one month is $3.44.

Summary

- Power is the rate of doing work. In electrical systems, power can be calculated by multiplying current by voltage: $Pwr = I\Delta V$.

- In terms of a circuit's resistance, power can be calculated using $Pwr = I^2 R$ or $Pwr = \Delta V^2 / R$.

- In a device (or load) that converts electrical work or energy into another form, the energy converted is the product of the power and the time interval: $E = Pwr \times \Delta t$.

- A kilowatt-hour (kWh) is an energy unit used by electric companies.

Exercises

1. Which of the following equations can be used to calculate power in an electric circuit?

   (a) $Pwr = q\Delta V$

   (b) $Pwr = \dfrac{(\Delta V)^2}{R}$

   (c) $Pwr = I^2 R$

   (d) $Pwr = \dfrac{q\Delta V}{\Delta t}$

   (e) $Pwr = \dfrac{\Delta V}{I}$

   (f) $Pwr = W\Delta t$

   (g) $Pwr = I\Delta V$

   (h) $Pwr = IR$

2. A simple circuit consists of a power source, a resistor, and connecting wires.

   (a) Draw a schematic diagram of the circuit.

   (b) If the resistance is kept constant and the voltage from the power supply is doubled, how does the power dissipated by the resistor change? Explain.

   (c) If the voltage from the power supply is kept constant and the resistance is doubled, how does the power dissipated by the resistor change? Explain.

   (d) If both the voltage and resistance are doubled, how does the power dissipated change? Explain.

3. One watt is equal to one volt times one ampere, or $1\ W = 1\ V{\cdot}A$. Which of the following are also equal to 1 W?

   (a) $1\ V^2/\Omega^2$

   (b) $1\ A^2{\cdot}\Omega$

   (c) $1\ V^2/\Omega$

   (d) $1\ J/s$

   (e) $1.34 \times 10^{-3}\ hp$

   (f) $^{1}/_{1000}$ of a kilowatt

   (g) $1\ cal/s$

   (h) $1\ N{\cdot}m$

4. A 60-W light bulb and a 100-W light bulb work on a 120-V circuit. Which bulb has a higher resistance? Explain your answer.

5. When an electric toaster works on a potential difference of 110 volts, it draws a current of 9.09 amps. How much power does the toaster use?

6. How much current flows through a 75-watt light bulb when it operates at 110 volts?

7. A 50-Ω resistor is guaranteed to operate according to Ohm's law up to a maximum power level of 100 W. What is the maximum voltage that should be applied across this resistor?

8. The voltage drop across a 15-Ω resistor is 12 V. How much energy is dissipated by the resistor in 5 minutes?

9. Which uses more energy: a 1-kW electric heater operated for 1 hour or ten 100-W light bulbs left on for 1 hour? Explain.

10. The efficiency of a light bulb is approximately 15%. This means that about 15% of the energy used by a bulb is converted into light energy. How many joules of energy are emitted as light by a 100-W light bulb in one minute? How many joules are converted into thermal energy in one minute?

11. An electric iron draws 3.2 A of current when connected to a 110-V circuit. How much heat does the iron give off in one hour?

12. An electrical engineer designs a lighting system for an office building. She groups lights into circuits, each protected by a circuit breaker. The maximum current allowed by a breaker in a circuit is 20 amps. Each circuit operates at 277 volts. How many 160-watt florescent lights can be grouped in one circuit?

13. A 5-hp electric motor operates for 20 hours.

    (a) How much energy, in kWh, is consumed?

    (b) At $0.085 per kWh, how much does it cost to run the motor for 20 hours?

14. A fire department's water boost pump provides a pressure difference of 50 psi at a flow rate of 1200 gal/min. The pump is driven by an electric motor that operates on 600 V. The pump and motor combination is 80% efficient. How much current does the motor draw? (7.48 gal = 1 ft^3)

15. The heating element of a 55-gal electric water heater operates on 220 V and draws 25 A of current. How long will it take to increase the water's temperature from 20°C to 60°C? The specific heat of water is 1 $\dfrac{\text{cal}}{\text{g°C}}$ and the density is 1000 kg/m³. (1 cal = 4.18 J and 1 m³ = 264 gal)

CHAPTER SIX
SUMMARY

Power is the rate of doing work (or transferring energy), or the ratio of work done to the time interval required to do the work. You can also calculate power using the product of the prime mover and a rate. The equations for calculating power in mechanical, fluid, and electrical systems are listed in the table below.

$$\text{Power} = \frac{\text{work done}}{\text{time interval}}$$

Energy System	Prime Mover	Work Done	Power
Mechanical			
Linear	Force (F)	$W = F\Delta d$	$\text{Pwr} = \dfrac{F\Delta d}{\Delta t} = Fv$
Rotational	Torque (τ)	$W = \tau\,\theta$	$\text{Pwr} = \dfrac{\tau\theta}{\Delta t} = \tau\omega$
Fluid	Pressure (P) or Pressure Difference (ΔP)	Constant pressure: $W = P\Delta V$ Steady state, constant density: $W = -V\Delta P$	$\text{Pwr} = \dfrac{P\Delta V}{\Delta t} = P\dot{V}$ $\text{Pwr} = \dfrac{V\Delta P}{\Delta t} = \dot{V}\Delta P$
Electrical	Potential Difference (ΔV)	$W = q\Delta V$	$\text{Pwr} = \dfrac{q\Delta V}{\Delta t} = I\Delta V$

(Note: In fluid systems, ΔV is the change in volume. In electrical systems, ΔV is the potential difference or voltage.)

In thermal systems, power is the same as heat flow rate, $\dot{Q}$. Although we did not use the term *power*, you studied heat flow rate in Section 3.4.

MOMENTUM

To stop an object that is moving, you must exert a force on the object over a time interval. For example, to stop a 2500-kg boat drifting at a speed of 0.1 m/s, you can apply a force of 250 N for 1.0 s in the direction opposite the boat's motion. This combined force and time interval describe the difficulty involved in stopping the boat.

The boat's *momentum* also describes the difficulty. **Momentum** is defined as the mass of the boat times its velocity. Notice that the momentum of the boat equals that of a 50-kg skater coasting at a speed of 5 m/s. (2500 kg·0.1 m/s = 50 kg·5 m/s) Therefore, a force of 250 N exerted for 1.0 s also stops the skater.

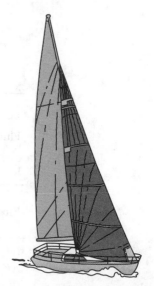

A 2500-kg boat drifting at a speed of 0.1 m/s has the same momentum as a 50-kg skater coasting at 5 m/s.

Momentum is a property that you will find useful in solving problems where objects interact. For example, when a batter hits a softball, you can use the change in the ball's momentum to calculate the *impulse* exerted by the bat. **Impulse** is the force applied by the bat times the time interval during which the force is applied.

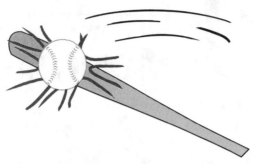

Impulse exerted by a bat changes a softball's momentum.

In addition, you can consider the ball and the bat as a system. If the interaction force between the ball and bat is the only force acting on the system, the total momentum of the system is constant. A property that remains constant during an interaction is said to be *conserved*. In this example, conservation of momentum means that the total momentum of the ball plus the bat before the impact equals the total momentum after the impact.

7.1 LINEAR MOMENTUM

Objectives

- Define linear momentum.

- Explain the relationship between force and rate of change of momentum.

- Define impulse.

- Explain the relationship between impulse and change in momentum.

- Explain Newton's third law of motion.

- Explain the law of conservation of momentum.

- Use linear momentum, impulse, and conservation of momentum to solve problems.

INTERNET *connection*

To find out more about linear momentum, follow the links at **www.learningincontext.com.**

You learned in Chapter 1 that inertia is the tendency of an object to resist changes in motion. Newton's first law of motion describes inertia:

> *An object at rest will remain at rest, and an object in motion will continue to move in a straight line, unless the object is acted on by a net force.*

An object's mass tells you how much inertia it has.

Objects in motion have *momentum* also. An object's momentum tells you how difficult it is to stop the object. Some problems involving motion are easier to solve using momentum instead of work, energy, and acceleration.

Refer to Appendix F
for a career link
to this concept.

Momentum

Have you ever caught a softball that was tossed gently and then caught the same softball thrown at high speed? For each catch, the ball has the same *mass*, but the *speeds* are different. The fast-moving softball is harder to stop—it has more momentum (see Figure 7.1a).

Now compare catching a softball to catching a heavy iron shot, when both objects are tossed at the same *speed*. (An iron shot is used in shot-put competitions.) The *masses* are different, and the more massive shot is harder to stop—it has more momentum (see Figure 7.1b).

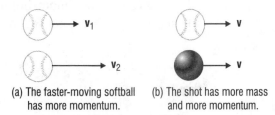

(a) The faster-moving softball
has more momentum.

(b) The shot has more mass
and more momentum.

Figure 7.1
Objects with higher speeds and higher mass have more momentum.

So, to compare the momentum of two softballs, or a softball and an iron shot, you need to consider both the mass and the velocity. The momentum of an object increases as the mass increases and as the speed increases. For this reason, **linear momentum** is defined as the product of an object's mass *m* and its velocity **v**. We use the symbol **p** to represent linear momentum.

$$\text{Linear momentum} = \text{mass} \times \text{velocity}$$
$$\mathbf{p} = m\mathbf{v}$$

Linear momentum is a vector quantity. The direction of **p** is the same as the direction of the velocity **v**. In SI, the units of linear momentum are kg·m/s. The English units of linear momentum are slug·ft/s.

We call the product *m***v** *linear* momentum because it is directed along a straight *line*. The direction of an object's linear momentum is the same as the direction of the object's velocity. In the next section you will learn about *angular* momentum—a property of an object moving in rotation. There is usually no question as to which momentum is involved in a situation. For this reason, *linear momentum* is usually referred to simply as *momentum*.

Example 7.1 Momenta of a Softball and an Iron Shot

A 9.5-ounce softball has a mass of 0.018 slug. A 16-pound shot has a mass of 0.50 slug. Suppose a softball is thrown at a speed of 60 ft/s. At what speed must a shot be tossed to have the same momentum as the softball?

Solution: The momentum of the shot equals the momentum of the softball.

$$p_{shot} = p_{softball}$$

$$m_{shot}\ v_{shot} = m_{softball}\ v_{softball}$$

$$v_{shot} = \frac{(0.018 \text{ slug})(60 \text{ ft/s})}{0.50 \text{ slug}}$$

$$= 2.16 \text{ ft/s}$$

To have the same momentum as the softball, the shot must be tossed at a speed of 2.16 feet per second.

Momentum and Newton's Second Law

Consider what happens when a bat strikes a softball (see Figure 7.2). The bat exerts a force on the ball and changes its direction and speed. In other words, the force accelerates the softball.

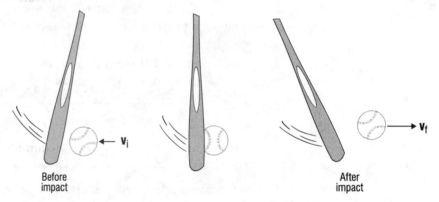

Before impact

After impact

Figure 7.2
When a bat strikes a softball, it changes the momentum of the ball.

In Chapter 4 you learned the relationship between the net force exerted on an object, the mass of the object, and the object's acceleration. This relationship is expressed in Newton's second law.

$$\mathbf{F} = m\mathbf{a}$$

The acceleration of the softball is its rate of change of velocity.

If the velocity changes by an amount $\Delta\mathbf{v}$ in a time interval Δt, the acceleration is the ratio of $\Delta\mathbf{v}$ to Δt.

$$\mathbf{a} = \frac{\Delta\mathbf{v}}{\Delta t}$$

Substitute this expression for $\mathbf{a}$ into the equation for Newton's second law.

$$\mathbf{F} = m\frac{\Delta\mathbf{v}}{\Delta t} = \frac{m\Delta\mathbf{v}}{\Delta t}$$

Let $\mathbf{v}_i$ represent the softball's initial velocity and $\mathbf{v}_f$ represent the final velocity. Then you can write the numerator of the equation above as follows:

$$m\Delta\mathbf{v} = m\left(\mathbf{v}_f - \mathbf{v}_i\right) = m\mathbf{v}_f - m\mathbf{v}_i$$
$$m\Delta\mathbf{v} = \mathbf{p}_f - \mathbf{p}_i$$
$$m\Delta\mathbf{v} = \Delta\mathbf{p}$$

In this equation, the ball's initial momentum is $\mathbf{p}_i \; (= m\mathbf{v}_i)$ and the final momentum is $\mathbf{p}_f \; (= m\mathbf{v}_f)$.

Therefore, the equation for Newton's second law can be written as the following ratio:

$$\mathbf{F} = \frac{\Delta\mathbf{p}}{\Delta t}$$

This equation states an alternative, equivalent form of Newton's second law.

A net force exerted on an object equals the rate of change of the object's linear momentum.

Example 7.2 Braking Force and Momentum Change

A loaded tractor-trailer has a mass of 21,000 kg. If it is moving at a speed of 90 km/h, what braking force is required to stop the tractor-trailer in 30 seconds?

Solution: Let **F** represent the braking force, and let $\mathbf{v}_i$ and $\mathbf{v}_f$ represent the tractor-trailer's initial and final velocities. Since motion is in one dimension, solve the equations using magnitudes of the vector quantities.

$$\Delta p = p_f - p_i = mv_f - mv_i$$

Since the tractor-trailer stops, $v_f = 0$. Convert v_i to meters per second.

$$v_i = \left(90\frac{\text{km}}{\text{h}}\right)\left(1000\frac{\text{m}}{\text{km}}\right)\left(\frac{1\text{ h}}{3600\text{ s}}\right) = 25\text{ m/s}$$

$$\Delta p = 0 - (21,000\text{ kg})(25\text{ m/s}) = -5.25 \times 10^5\text{ kg·m/s}$$

$$F = \frac{\Delta p}{\Delta t} = \frac{-5.25 \times 10^5\text{ kg·m/s}}{30\text{ s}}$$

$$= -1.75 \times 10^4\text{ N} \qquad \left[\text{kg·m/s}^2 = \text{N}\right]$$

The force is negative because it acts opposite the direction of the forward motion. The required braking force is 17,500 newtons.

Impulse

To change the speed and momentum of an object, a force must be applied for a period of time. For example, to accelerate a car from rest, the engine and drivetrain apply a force **F** for a time interval Δt. The greater the force and the longer it is applied, the greater the car's final speed and momentum. This idea leads to a quantity called *impulse*. **Impulse** is the product of force **F** and the time interval Δt over which the force acts.

$$\text{Impulse} = \mathbf{F}\Delta t$$

Impulse is a vector quantity. Its direction is the same as the direction of the force.

The impulse applied to a car determines the car's momentum change. To see why, write Newton's second law as rate of change of momentum and multiply both sides by Δt:

$$\mathbf{F} = \frac{\Delta \mathbf{p}}{\Delta t}$$

$$\mathbf{F}\Delta t = \frac{\Delta \mathbf{p}}{\Delta t}\Delta t$$

$$\mathbf{F}\Delta t = \Delta \mathbf{p}$$

Or in words,

$$\text{Impulse} = \text{momentum change}$$

Impulse is *force* times *time*. Therefore, the SI units of impulse are newton·seconds (N·s). These are equivalent to momentum units (kg·m/s). (Can you prove this?) But impulse units are written as N·s to distinguish impulse from momentum. The English units of impulse and momentum are also equivalent (see Table 7.1).

Table 7.1
Units of Force, Momentum, and Impulse

	SI Units	English Units
Force	N	lb
Momentum	kg·m/s	slug·ft/s
Impulse	N·s	lb·s

Impulse explains the importance of "follow-through" in many sports. A baseball or softball batter, a tennis player, or a golfer strikes a ball with a large force, but follows through with the swing to extend the time of contact of the force on the ball. A large force times a large time interval is a greater impulse, which results in a greater momentum change of the ball.

Figure 7.3
The change in momentum can be increased by increasing the force and/or the time interval over which the force acts. $\Delta p = F\Delta t$.

When calculating impulse using the product $F\Delta t$, we assume that F is constant. But the force can vary during the time interval Δt in many applications. For example, a bat exerts a force on a softball that varies in time. The force starts at zero, reaches a maximum value, and then decreases back to zero. The time-varying force of a bat striking a softball is graphed in Figure 7.4. In this type of impulse problem, we use the *average value* of the force to calculate $F\Delta t$.

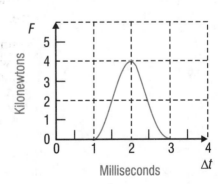

Figure 7.4
Force exerted by a bat on a softball as a function of time

Example 7.3 Impulse and Force on a Soccer Ball

In a penalty kick, a soccer player increases the speed of a ball from zero to 35 m/s. The mass of a soccer ball is 0.45 kg.

(a) What impulse does the soccer player give the ball?

(b) If the player's foot is in contact with the ball for 0.12 s, what is the average force exerted on the ball?

Solution: (a) The impulse equals the momentum change. The ball's initial speed is zero, so $v_i = 0$.

$$\text{Impulse} = \Delta p = p_f - p_i$$

$$\text{Impulse} = mv_f - mv_i = (0.45 \text{ kg})(35 \text{ m/s}) - 0$$

$$\text{Impulse} = 15.75 \text{ N·s}$$

(b) The impulse equals the average force times the time interval.

$$\text{Impulse} = F\Delta t$$

$$F = \frac{\text{Impulse}}{\Delta t} = \frac{15.75 \text{ N·s}}{0.12 \text{ s}} = 131 \text{ N}$$

The soccer player exerts an average force of 131 newtons on the ball.

Newton's Third Law of Motion

Refer to Appendix F for a career link to this concept.

In Example 7.3, we stated that the soccer player exerts a force on the ball. But isn't it also true that the ball exerts a force on the soccer player? A force is simply a push or a pull. But a force cannot be exerted on one object unless a second object exerts the force. Therefore, a force is an *interaction* between two objects. Newton stated this interaction in his **third law of motion:**

Whenever one body exerts a force on another body, the second body exerts an equal and opposite force on the first.

Newton's third law says that forces always come in pairs, sometimes called *action* and *reaction* forces. Each force in a pair acts on a different object, and the two forces are equal in magnitude and opposite in direction. If the objects are labeled A and B, then $\mathbf{F}_{A \text{ on } B} = -\mathbf{F}_{B \text{ on } A}$.

For example, when a soccer player kicks a ball, his foot exerts a force on the ball. The ball exerts an equal and opposite force on the player's foot. When a flower vase is placed on a table, the vase exerts a force on the table (its weight). The table exerts an equal and opposite force on the vase. When fuel is burned in a rocket motor, the motor exerts a force on the expanding gas causing the gas to accelerate through a nozzle. The gas exerts an equal and opposite force on the rocket motor causing the rocket to accelerate.

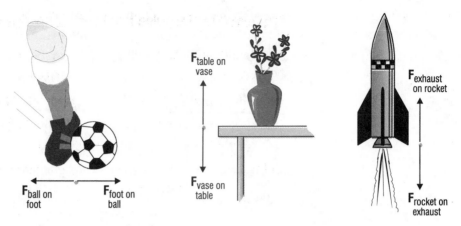

Figure 7.5
Forces always occur in pairs.

You can use Newton's laws and energy conservation to analyze the motion of objects such as those in Figure 7.5. But first you must define the "system." If the system is the soccer ball, a net force is acting on the system and it accelerates. But, suppose you enlarge the system to include the ball, the player, and the ground on which the player is standing. Now the only forces are action-reaction pairs, which are equal and opposite and cancel each other. There is no net force on this larger system. But you can still get important information about the motion of objects in this system if you use linear momentum.

Conservation of Linear Momentum

Consider the motion of two balls in a collision, as shown in Figure 7.6. The balls have different masses and initial velocities, and therefore different momenta before and after the collision. Let the system consist of both balls. In this case, the system does not lose or gain mass. This is called a **closed system**. The only forces involved in the closed system of Figure 7.6 are internal forces. A closed system on which no net external forces act is called an **isolated system**.

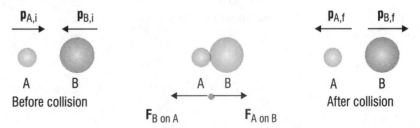

Figure 7.6
The momentum of each ball in a collision changes, but the total momentum of the system does not change.

Apply the impulse-momentum equation to the isolated system. Since the net external force is zero, the impulse applied to the system is zero and the system's momentum change is zero.

$$\mathbf{F}\Delta t = 0 = \Delta \mathbf{p}$$

If $\Delta \mathbf{p} = 0$, then $\mathbf{p}_f - \mathbf{p}_i = 0$, or $\mathbf{p}_f = \mathbf{p}_i$. The system's linear momentum does not change.

You can prove that the total momentum of the system in Figure 7.6 does not change as follows. Write the impulse-momentum equation for each ball.

$$\text{Ball A: } \mathbf{F}_{\text{B on A}}\Delta t = \mathbf{p}_{A,f} - \mathbf{p}_{A,i}$$

$$\text{Ball B: } \mathbf{F}_{\text{A on B}}\Delta t = \mathbf{p}_{B,f} - \mathbf{p}_{B,i}$$

The forces are action-reaction forces, internal to the system. From Newton's third law, they are equal and opposite. $\mathbf{F}_{\text{A on B}} = -\mathbf{F}_{\text{B on A}}$. The forces are applied over the same time interval Δt. Therefore, the impulses are equal and opposite.

$$\mathbf{F}_{\text{A on B}}\Delta t = -\mathbf{F}_{\text{B on A}}\Delta t$$

Substitute the impulse-momentum equations for ball A and ball B from above and simplify.

$$\mathbf{p}_{B,f} - \mathbf{p}_{B,i} = -(\mathbf{p}_{A,f} - \mathbf{p}_{A,i})$$

$$\mathbf{p}_{B,f} - \mathbf{p}_{B,i} = -\mathbf{p}_{A,f} + \mathbf{p}_{A,i}$$

You can rearrange this result, with the final values on one side and initial values on the other.

$$\mathbf{p}_{A,f} + \mathbf{p}_{B,f} = \mathbf{p}_{A,i} + \mathbf{p}_{B,i}$$

$$\frac{\text{total final}}{\text{momentum}} = \frac{\text{total initial}}{\text{momentum}}$$

$$\mathbf{p}_f = \mathbf{p}_i$$

No matter what internal interactions take place in a closed isolated system, its linear momentum never changes. This is called the **law of conservation of linear momentum**.

> *When no net external forces act on a closed system, the total linear momentum of the system remains constant.*

When you use conservation of linear momentum to solve a problem, the first step is to define the closed isolated system. Define the system boundary so: (1) no mass enters or leaves the system (no mass crosses the boundary), and (2) no *external* force acts on the system (all forces are *internal* to the system).

Example 7.4 Conservation of Momentum for a Spaceship

A 670-kg spaceship is traveling at 1200 m/s. The ship's rocket motor burns 120 kg of fuel. After the burn, the fuel exhaust is traveling at 2800 m/s in the direction opposite the spaceship. What is the final speed of the spaceship?

Solution: Define the system as the spaceship (including unburned fuel) and the fuel exhaust. This is a closed system since no mass enters or leaves. No external force is acting on the system, so it is isolated. Therefore, the linear momentum of the system is conserved.

Let m and $\mathbf{v}$ represent the mass and velocity of the spaceship, and m_{fuel} and $\mathbf{v}_{\text{fuel}}$ represent the mass and velocity of the fuel exhaust.

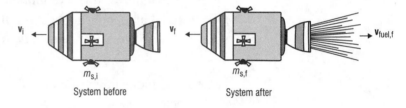

$$\mathbf{p}_f = \mathbf{p}_i$$

$$m_f\,\mathbf{v}_f + m_{\text{fuel},f}\,\mathbf{v}_{\text{fuel},f} = m_i\,\mathbf{v}_i$$

The velocities act along a line, so we can use speeds. Let the positive direction be in the direction of the spaceship's velocity. Then $v_{\text{fuel},f}$ is a negative quantity.

$$m_f\,v_f - m_{\text{fuel},f}\,v_{\text{fuel},f} = m_i\,v_i$$

Before the fuel burns, the mass of the spaceship m_i includes the mass of fuel. So $m_i = 670$ kg.

Initially, the fuel and spaceship travel together at the same speed. $v_i = 1200$ m/s.

After the fuel burns, the spaceship mass is 120 kg less.

$$m_f = 670 - 120 = 550 \text{ kg}$$

Substitute the known values into the equation.

$$(550 \text{ kg})(v_f) - (120 \text{ kg})(2800 \text{ m/s}) = (670 \text{ kg})(1200 \text{ m/s})$$

$$v_f = \frac{(670)(1200) + (120)(2800)}{550} \text{ m/s} = 2073 \text{ m/s}$$

The final speed of the spaceship is 2073 m/s.

Summary

- Linear momentum is the product of an object's mass and its velocity. $\mathbf{p} = m\mathbf{v}$.

- According to Newton's second law of motion, if a net force is exerted on an object, the force equals the object's rate of change of momentum. $\mathbf{F} = \dfrac{\Delta \mathbf{p}}{\Delta t}$.

- When a force is exerted on an object, the impulse is the applied force times the time interval over which it is applied.

- When an impulse is applied to an object, the impulse equals the object's change in momentum. $\mathbf{F}\Delta t = \Delta \mathbf{p}$.

- Newton's third law of motion says that for every action there is an equal and opposite reaction. *Whenever one body exerts a force on another body, the second body exerts an equal and opposite force on the first.*

- The momentum of a closed system is constant if no net external force acts on the system.

Exercises

1. An object that moves in a straight line has linear momentum equal to the product of the object's_____ and _____.

2. Newton's second law can be written in the form $\mathbf{F} = \Delta\mathbf{p}/\Delta t$. Prove that the SI units for the left side equal those for the right side.

3. The impulse-momentum equation is $\mathbf{F}\Delta t = \Delta\mathbf{p}$. Prove that the English units for the left side equal those for the right side.

4. Find the linear momentum of an 18,000-lb aircraft traveling at 180 mph due west.

5. A car with a mass of 1250 kg moves at a speed of 90 km/h to the north.

   (a) Draw the car's momentum vector. Write the magnitude next to the vector.

   (b) A second car with a mass of 800 kg has the same momentum. What is its velocity?

6. A net force accelerates a 75-kg skier from 1.0 m/s to 6.5 m/s over a time interval of 20 s.

   (a) Sketch the skier's initial and final momentum vectors. What is the skier's change in momentum?

   (b) What is the magnitude of the average net force acting on the skier?

7. An empty truck of mass m_o moves at a speed v_o. Suppose the truck is loaded, so that its mass is doubled, and the speed is reduced by one-half. The truck's new momentum is

   (a) $m_o v_o$.

   (b) $\frac{1}{2} m_o v_o$.

   (c) $2 m_o v_o$.

   (d) $4 m_o v_o$.

8. Someone kicks a 0.44-kg soccer ball traveling at 8.0 m/s. After the kick, the ball travels at the same speed but in the opposite direction.

   (a) Draw vectors representing the soccer ball's momentum before and after it is kicked.

   (b) Choose a positive direction for momentum. What is the change in momentum of the soccer ball?

   (c) If the ball is in contact with the kicker's foot for 0.75 s, what is the average force exerted on the ball?

9. The law of conservation of linear momentum applies to closed, isolated systems. What two conditions must be true for a system to be closed and isolated?

10. A hockey puck weighs 0.25 lb. A 180-lb goalie catches a puck traveling at 9.5 ft/s. The goalie is initially at rest. At what speed does the goalie slide across the ice after catching the puck?

11. Coal is transported to electrical generating plants in railroad cars. An empty coal car with a mass of 9000 kg coasts at a speed of 2.5 m/s. An 18,000-kg load of coal with no horizontal velocity is dropped into the car. At what speed does the car-coal combination coast?

12. When a 160-lb man steps from a 16-ton commercial fishing boat onto a dock, the only apparent movement is the man's—the boat hardly moves at all. But when the same man steps from a 160-lb fiberglass fishing boat onto a dock, he may fall into the water if the boat isn't tied securely to the dock. Explain why these two situations are different, using the law of conservation of linear momentum.

13. The anvil of a pneumatic nail driver has a mass of 0.30 kg. Air pressure accelerates the anvil from zero to 33.9 m/s in 0.21 s. What average force does the air exert on the anvil?

14. Water flows through a pipe with a 90° elbow, as shown below. The mass flow rate is constant and equals 10 kilograms per second. The speed is also constant and equals 3 meters per second.

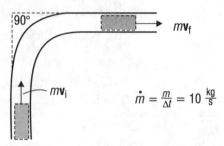

$$\dot{m} = \frac{m}{\Delta t} = 10 \ \frac{\text{kg}}{\text{s}}$$

Notice that, if you isolate a parcel of water of mass m, the momentum of the parcel before the turn has the same *magnitude* as the momentum after the turn ($mv_i = mv_f$). But the vector momentum changes ($m\mathbf{v}_i \neq m\mathbf{v}_f$) because the direction of the parcel's velocity changes.

(a) Use a parcel of mass $m = 10$ kg. On graph paper, plot the vector momentum $m\mathbf{v}_i$ with a convenient scale.

(b) Plot the vector $m\mathbf{v}_f$ using the same scale. Use the "head-to-tail" method of vector addition to find $m\mathbf{v}_f - m\mathbf{v}_i$. What are the magnitude and direction of the resultant?

(c) The pipe exerts a force on the water to make it turn. What are the magnitude and direction of the force?

15. Two designs for a car bumper are tested for their ability to absorb shock in low-speed collisions. Each bumper is mounted on a 3050-lb car, and the car is rolled into a wall at a speed of 5 mph. Bumper A stops the car in 0.35 s. Bumper B stops the car in 0.78 s.

(a) What is the average force exerted on the car by bumper A?

(b) What is the average force exerted by bumper B?

(c) Below, the magnitude of the force exerted by each bumper is plotted as a function of time. Which graph is bumper A, and which is bumper B?

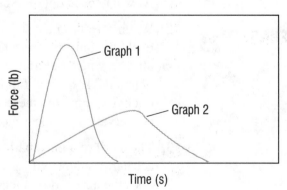

7.2 ANGULAR MOMENTUM

Objectives

- Define angular momentum.

- Explain the relationship between torque and rate of change of angular momentum.

- Define angular impulse.

- Explain the relationship between angular impulse and change in angular momentum.

- Explain the law of conservation of angular momentum.

- Solve problems using angular momentum, angular impulse, and conservation of angular momentum.

INTERNET *connection*

To find out more about angular momentum, follow the links at **www.learningincontext.com**.

When we say an object is in *translation*, we imply that it moves in a straight line. When we say an object is in *rotation*, we imply that it spins or rotates around an axis. In Section 5.1 you learned the analogy between the equations for the kinetic energy of bodies in translation and rotation.

$$\text{KE}_{\text{translation}} = \tfrac{1}{2}\,mv^2$$

$$\text{KE}_{\text{rotation}} = \tfrac{1}{2}\,I\omega^2$$

In rotation, the moment of inertia I is analogous to mass, and angular velocity ω is analogous to velocity. The analogy is true also for momentum.

Linear momentum tells you how difficult it is to stop an object moving in a straight line. *Angular momentum* tells you how difficult it is to stop a rotating object. The linear momentum of an object is the product of its mass and velocity. **Angular momentum** is the product of an object's moment of inertia and its angular velocity. We use the symbol L to represent angular momentum.

$$p = mv$$

$$L = I\omega$$

Remember that objects of equal mass but different shapes can have different moments of inertia. Formulas for calculating I were given in Section 5.1 for several common shapes. These formulas are repeated in Figure 7.7.

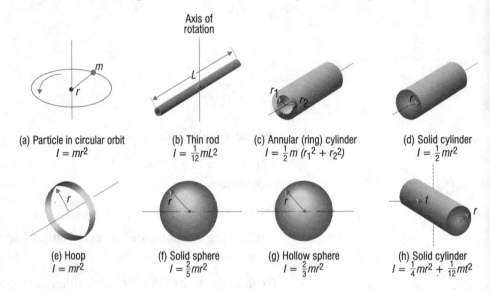

(a) Particle in circular orbit
$I = mr^2$

(b) Thin rod
$I = \frac{1}{12}mL^2$

(c) Annular (ring) cylinder
$I = \frac{1}{2}m\,(r_1^2 + r_2^2)$

(d) Solid cylinder
$I = \frac{1}{2}mr^2$

(e) Hoop
$I = mr^2$

(f) Solid sphere
$I = \frac{2}{5}mr^2$

(g) Hollow sphere
$I = \frac{2}{3}mr^2$

(h) Solid cylinder
$I = \frac{1}{4}mr^2 + \frac{1}{12}mt^2$

Figure 7.7
Moment of inertia formulas for different-shaped objects. In each formula, m is the mass of the object.

The SI and English units for moment of inertia, angular velocity, and angular momentum are listed in Table 7.2

Table 7.2
Units Needed to Calculate Angular Momentum

$L = I\omega$	
SI Units	**English Units**
$I = \text{kg} \cdot \text{m}^2$	$I = \text{slug} \cdot \text{ft}^2$
$\omega = \text{rad/s}$	$\omega = \text{rad/s}$
$L = \text{kg} \cdot \text{m}^2/\text{s}$	$L = \text{slug} \cdot \text{ft}^2/\text{s}$

Angular momentum and angular velocity are vector quantities. But in this book we will work with only the magnitudes of these quantities.

Example 7.5 Linear and Angular Momenta of a Basketball

A basketball free-throw shooter gives the ball an initial velocity of 12 feet per second toward a point above the basket. (This is the velocity of the ball's center of mass.) The shooter also spins the ball at a rate of 4.5 revolutions per second. What are the magnitudes of the initial linear momentum and angular momentum of the basketball? A basketball weighs 21 ounces and has a radius of 0.40 foot.

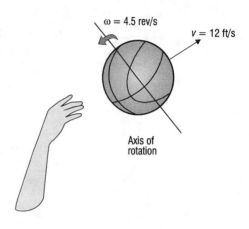

Solution: Find the mass of the basketball in slugs. (1 lb = 16 oz)

$$m = \frac{(21 \text{ oz})\left(\dfrac{1 \text{ lb}}{16 \text{ oz}}\right)}{32.2 \text{ ft/s}^2} = 0.0408 \text{ slug} \qquad \left[\text{slug} = \text{lb} \cdot \text{s}^2/\text{ft}\right]$$

A basketball is a hollow sphere. From Figure 7.7, the formula for the moment of inertia of a hollow sphere is:

$$I = \tfrac{2}{3}mr^2 = \tfrac{2}{3}(0.0408 \text{ slug})(0.40 \text{ ft})^2 = 4.35 \times 10^{-3} \text{ slug} \cdot \text{ft}^2$$

The angular speed must be in radians per second.

$$\omega = \left(4.5 \ \frac{\text{rev}}{\text{s}}\right)\left(\frac{2\pi \text{ rad}}{\text{rev}}\right) = 28.3 \text{ rad/s}$$

Now calculate the linear and angular momenta.

$$p = mv \qquad\qquad\qquad L = I\omega$$
$$p = (0.0408 \text{ slug})(12 \text{ ft/s}) \quad L = (4.35 \times 10^{-3} \text{ slug} \cdot \text{ft}^2/\text{s})(28.3 \text{ rad/s})$$
$$p = 0.49 \text{ slug} \cdot \text{ft/s} \qquad\qquad L = 0.12 \text{ slug} \cdot \text{ft}^2/\text{s}$$

Newton's Second Law for Rotation

A net force is required to start (or stop) an object moving in translation. A net torque is required to start (or stop) an object moving around an axis of rotation. Torque in rotational motion is analogous to force in translational motion. Newton's second law relating force and linear momentum can be rewritten for torque and angular momentum.

Translation	**Rotation**
A net force exerted on an object equals the rate of change of the object's linear momentum.	*A net torque exerted on an object equals the rate of change of the object's angular momentum.*

$$F = \frac{\Delta p}{\Delta t}$$

$$\tau = \frac{\Delta L}{\Delta t}$$

Example 7.6 Force and Torque Required to Stop a Satellite

In an on-orbit repair mission, an astronaut volunteers to attempt to grab a satellite to stop its spin. The satellite's mass is 900 kg, and it is spinning at a rate of 10 rpm. The shape of the satellite can be modeled as a solid cylinder of radius 0.7 m.

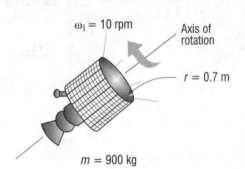

ω_i = 10 rpm
Axis of rotation
r = 0.7 m
m = 900 kg

The astronaut's boots will be firmly fixed to the space shuttle's robot arm. The shuttle will maintain a fixed attitude (will not rotate) in orbit by using its thrusters during the recovery. If the astronaut can grab a point on the outside surface of the satellite and hold on for 0.5 second, what force will be required to stop the spin?

Solution: Use the equation $\tau = \frac{\Delta L}{\Delta t}$ to calculate the torque required to stop the rotation. The torque is caused by a force F applied at a distance r from the center of rotation. When τ is known, you can calculate F from the equation $\tau = Fr$.

From Figure 7.7 for a solid cylinder, $I = \frac{1}{2}mr^2$.

$$I = \frac{1}{2}(900 \text{ kg})(0.7 \text{ m})^2 = 220.5 \text{ kg} \cdot \text{m}^2$$

The initial angular velocity ω_i must be converted to radians per second.

$$\omega_i = \left(10\frac{\text{rev}}{\text{min}}\right)\left(\frac{1 \text{ min}}{60 \text{ s}}\right)\left(\frac{2\pi \text{ rad}}{\text{rev}}\right) = 1.05 \text{ rad/s}$$

If the satellite stops, its final angular velocity ω_f is zero. The moment of inertia does not change. $(I_f = I_i = I)$

$$\tau = \frac{\Delta L}{\Delta t} = \frac{I\omega_f - I\omega_i}{\Delta t}$$

$$\tau = \frac{0 - (220.5 \text{ kg·m}^2)(1.05 \text{ rad/s})}{0.5 \text{ s}}$$

$$\tau = -463 \text{ N·m} \qquad\qquad [\text{kg·m/s}^2 = \text{N}]$$

$$F = \frac{\tau}{r} = \frac{-463 \text{ N·m}}{0.7 \text{ m}} = -661 \text{ N}$$

The negative sign means the torque and force must be applied in the direction opposite the satellite's motion.

The force required to stop the satellite in 0.5 s is 661 N.

Angular Impulse

To change the angular speed of a rotating object, such as the satellite in Example 7.6, a torque must be applied over a time interval. *Angular impulse* in rotational motion is analogous to linear impulse in translational motion. **Angular impulse** is the product of the torque τ and the time interval Δt over which the torque acts.

Linear impulse $= F\Delta t$ Angular impulse $= \tau\Delta t$

A potter's wheel is a massive disk that rotates about an axis through its center. The potter uses angular impulse when she sets the wheel in motion, or accelerates a wheel that is already rotating. By pushing on the outside edge of the wheel, she applies a torque that equals the force times the lever arm. As shown in Figure 7.8, the lever arm is the distance from the applied force to the center of rotation.

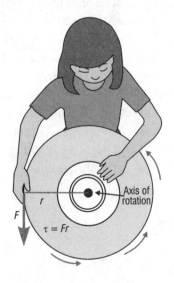

Figure 7.8
An angular impulse increases the momentum of a potter's wheel.

The greater the torque and the longer it is applied, the greater the angular impulse. The angular impulse determines the change in angular speed and momentum. This relationship is analogous to the relationship between linear impulse and momentum.

Translation	*Rotation*

$$\frac{\text{Linear}}{\text{impulse}} = \frac{\text{change in}}{\text{linear momentum}} \qquad \frac{\text{Angular}}{\text{impulse}} = \frac{\text{change in}}{\text{angular momentum}}$$

$$F\Delta t = \Delta p \qquad\qquad \tau\Delta t = \Delta L$$

Example 7.7 Torque on a Potter's Wheel

A 100-pound potter's wheel is 2 feet in radius. A cylinder of clay 6 inches in radius is fixed at the axis of rotation of the wheel. The rotational inertia of the wheel keeps the clay turning at a nearly constant rate while the potter forms the clay into a shape.

The wheel spins at an initial rate of 3.5 rev/s. The potter applies a frictional force of 2 lb on the outside surface of the clay cylinder. The force is applied over a time interval of 10 s. The clay weighs 3.8 lb and does not slip on the wheel as it is formed.

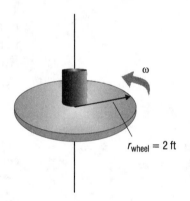

What torque is applied to the clay and wheel?

Solution: The torque is the applied force times the lever arm. In this case the lever arm is the radius of the clay cylinder. The force is frictional, so it opposes the rotation. (It slows the angular speed.) Therefore, it is a negative quantity and so is the torque.

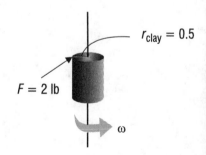

$$\tau = Fr = -(2.0 \text{ lb})(0.5 \text{ ft})$$

$$\tau = -1.0 \text{ lb·ft}$$

Example 7.8 Angular Speed of a Potter's Wheel

What is the angular speed of the potter's wheel in Example 7.7, after the torque is applied for 10 s? The radius of the clay does not change significantly over this time interval. Write the answer in rev/s.

Solution: Use the angular impulse-momentum equation. The combined moment of inertia I of the wheel and clay doesn't change. $(I_f = I_i = I)$

$$\tau \Delta t = \Delta L = I\omega_f - I\omega_i = I(\omega_f - \omega_i)$$

The moment of inertia of the combined shapes is the sum of the individual shapes. Both the wheel and clay are solid cylinders. From Figure 7.6, the moment of inertia of a solid cylinder is $\frac{1}{2}mr^2$.

$$I = I_{wheel} + I_{clay}$$

$$I = \frac{1}{2}m_{wheel}r_{wheel}^2 + \frac{1}{2}m_{clay}r_{clay}^2 \qquad \left[m = \frac{Weight}{g}\right]$$

$$I = \frac{1}{2}\left(\frac{100 \text{ lb}}{32.2 \text{ ft/s}^2}\right)(2 \text{ ft})^2 + \frac{1}{2}\left(\frac{3.8 \text{ lb}}{32.2 \text{ ft/s}^2}\right)(0.5 \text{ ft})^2$$

$$I = 6.23 \text{ slug} \cdot \text{ft}^2 \qquad \left[\text{lb} = \text{slug} \cdot \text{ft/s}^2\right]$$

Angular speed must be in units of rad/s.

$$\omega_i = \left(3.5\frac{\text{rev}}{\text{s}}\right)\left(2\pi\frac{\text{rad}}{\text{rev}}\right) = 22.0 \text{ rad/s}$$

Substitute the values into the angular impulse-momentum equation.

$$\tau \Delta t = I(\omega_f - \omega_i)$$

$$-(1.0 \text{ lb} \cdot \text{ft})(10 \text{ s}) = (6.23 \text{ slug} \cdot \text{ft}^2)(\omega_f - 22.0 \text{ rad/s})$$

$$-\frac{(1.0)(10)}{6.23}\frac{\text{rad}}{\text{s}} + 22.0\frac{\text{rad}}{\text{s}} = \omega_f \qquad \left[\text{slug} = \text{lb} \cdot \text{s}^2/\text{ft}\right]$$

$$\omega_f = 20.4 \text{ rad/s}$$

Convert to rev/s.

$$\omega_f = \left(20.4\frac{\text{rad}}{\text{s}}\right)\left(\frac{1 \text{ rev}}{2\pi \text{ rad}}\right) = 3.25 \text{ rev/s}$$

The potter's wheel slows to 3.25 revolutions per second.

In the last section, we derived the law of conservation of linear momentum by applying Newton's laws of motion to a closed system. The impulse applied to a closed system equals the change in the system's linear momentum. If no net force is applied to a system, the impulse is zero and there is no change in the system's linear momentum.

The same logic applies to a rotational system. Torque is analogous to force, and angular momentum is analogous to linear momentum.

Translation	*Rotation*
Linear impulse $=$ change in linear momentum	Angular impulse $=$ change in angular momentum
$F\Delta t = \Delta p$	$\tau\Delta t = \Delta L$
If $F = 0$, then $\Delta p = 0$ and $p_f = p_i$.	If $\tau = 0$, then $\Delta L = 0$ and $L_f = L_i$.

The result for rotational motion is called the **law of conservation of angular momentum**.

> *When no net external torque acts on a closed system, the total angular momentum of the system does not change.*

Skaters, gymnasts, dancers, and divers use conservation of angular momentum. For example, a diver changes from a pike position to an extended position at the end of a flip. This extension of mass away from the center of rotation increases the diver's moment of inertia I. There is no net external torque on the diver, angular momentum is conserved, and the product $I\omega$ is constant. When I is increased, ω is decreased. As the diver enters the water, her angular velocity is so small that it appears to be zero.

$L_i = I_i\omega_i$
Small I_i, large ω_i

$L_i = L_f$
$I_i\,\omega_i = I_f\omega_f$

Large I_f, small ω_f
$L_f = I_f\omega_f$

Figure 7.9
A diver's angular momentum is conserved. If $I\omega$ is constant, as I increases, ω decreases.

The diver in Figure 7.9 extends mass away from her center of rotation, and increases her moment of inertia. The skater in Example 7.9 below moves mass inward, toward his center of rotation. This decreases his moment of inertia. Will the skater's angular velocity increase or decrease?

Example 7.9 A Skater's Angular Momentum

A skater begins a spin with his arms outstretched. In this position, his moment of inertia is 4.6 kg·m² and he spins at a rate of 1.5 revolutions per second. The skater brings his arms close to his body to increase his spin rate. In this position, his moment of inertia is 1.4 kg·m². What is the skater's final angular speed?

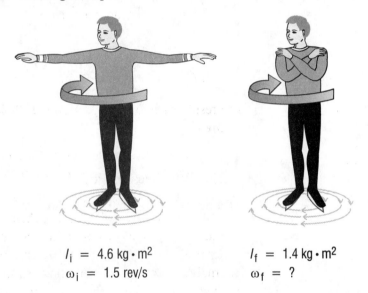

$$I_i = 4.6 \text{ kg} \cdot \text{m}^2 \qquad I_f = 1.4 \text{ kg} \cdot \text{m}^2$$
$$\omega_i = 1.5 \text{ rev/s} \qquad \omega_f = ?$$

Solution: The force and torque caused by friction between the skates and ice are very small. If this torque can be ignored, angular momentum is conserved.

$$L_f = L_i$$

$$I_f \omega_f = I_i \omega_i$$

$$\omega_f = \frac{I_i}{I_f} \omega_i = \left(\frac{4.6 \text{ kg} \cdot \text{m}^2}{1.4 \text{ kg} \cdot \text{m}^2} \right) (1.5 \text{ rev/s}) = 4.9 \text{ rev/s}$$

In this calculation, you do not need to convert angular speed to rad/s since the conversion factors would cancel.

The skater's final speed is 4.9 revolutions per second.

Example 7.10 Work Done by a Skater

How much work does the skater in Example 7.9 do when he pulls his arms in to his body?

Solution: From the work-energy theorem, the work done by the skater equals the change in kinetic energy.

$$W = \Delta KE = KE_f - KE_i$$

The kinetic energy of an object in rotation is $\frac{1}{2}I\omega^2$.

$$KE_i = \frac{1}{2}I_i\omega_i^2$$

$$= \frac{1}{2}(4.6 \text{ kg·m}^2)\left(1.5\frac{\text{rev}}{\text{s}} \cdot \frac{2\pi \text{ rad}}{\text{rev}}\right)^2 = 204 \text{ J}$$

$$KE_f = \frac{1}{2}I_f\omega_f^2$$

$$= \frac{1}{2}(1.4 \text{ kg·m}^2)\left(4.9\frac{\text{rev}}{\text{s}} \cdot \frac{2\pi \text{ rad}}{\text{rev}}\right)^2 = 664 \text{ J}$$

$$W = 664 \text{ J} - 204 \text{ J} = 460 \text{ J}$$

The skater does 460 joules of work.

Use dimensional analysis to show that the units in Example 7.10 are correct.

Summary

- Angular momentum is the product of an object's moment of inertia and its angular velocity. $L = I\omega$

- If a net torque is applied to an object, the torque equals the object's rate of change of angular momentum. $\tau = \dfrac{\Delta L}{\Delta t}$

- If a torque is applied to an object, the angular impulse is the torque times the time interval over which the torque is applied.

- When an angular impulse is applied to an object, the angular impulse equals the change in angular momentum. $\tau\Delta t = \Delta L$

- The angular momentum of a closed system is constant if no net external torque acts on the system.

Exercises

1. A spinning object has angular momentum equal to the product of the object's _____ and _____.

2. When a torque acts on a rotating object over an interval of time, the product of the torque and the time interval is called _____.

3. Write an equation for Newton's second law for an object in translation, using force and momentum. Write an analogous equation for an object in rotation. What two pairs of variables in the equations are analogous?

4. Match the units on the left to the descriptions on the right.

   ____ $(lb \cdot ft) \cdot s$ a. Angular momentum in SI units

   ____ $(N \cdot m) \cdot s$ b. Angular momentum in English units

   ____ $kg \cdot m/s^2$ c. Same as a slug

   ____ $slug \cdot ft^2/s$ d. Angular impulse in SI units

   ____ $lb \cdot s^2/ft$ e. Same as a newton

   ____ $kg \cdot m^2/s$ f. Angular impulse in English units

5. Newton's second law for rotation can be written in the form $\tau = \Delta L/\Delta t$. Prove that the English units for the left side equal those for the right side.

6. The angular impulse-momentum equation can be written $\tau \Delta t = \Delta L$. Prove that the SI units for the left side equal those for the right side.

7. A pitcher throws a curve ball at an initial velocity of 75 mph (33.5 m/s) toward the plate. The pitcher also spins the ball at a rate of 30 revolutions per second. What are the magnitudes of the baseball's initial linear momentum and angular momentum? A baseball has a mass of 0.14 kg and a radius of 3.6 cm.

8. The mass of the Earth is 5.98×10^{24} kg and its radius is 6.37×10^6 m. What is the angular momentum of the Earth's spin about its polar axis?

9. A 300-kg flywheel is used to store energy in a punch press. The flywheel is in the shape of a solid cylinder of radius 0.8 m. When the operator engages the press, the flywheel slows from 250 rpm to 150 rpm in 6 seconds. What torque is applied to the flywheel?

10. A turbine rotates at an initial angular speed of 200 rad/s. A torque of 400 N·m causes the angular speed to double in 30 s. What is the moment of inertia of the turbine?

11. The moment of inertia of a complicated shape is difficult to calculate directly. Describe how you could measure the moment of inertia experimentally.

12. The 229,000-lb space shuttle orbiter is in a circular orbit 147 miles above the surface of the Earth. It completes an orbit every 89 minutes.

    (a) What is the angular speed of the orbiter in rpm? In rad/s?

    (b) What is the linear speed of the orbiter in mi/h? In ft/s? (The Earth's radius is 3960 miles.)

    (c) What is the moment of inertia of the orbiter?

    (d) What is the orbiter's angular momentum?

13. An ice skater begins a spin with her arms outstretched and then pulls them inward. Tell whether each of the following increases, decreases, or stays the same.

    (a) moment of inertia

    (b) spin rate

    (c) angular momentum

    (d) kinetic energy

14. Neutron stars are believed to be formed from the cores of larger stars that collapse under their own forces of gravity. The collapse can cause a supernova explosion. Prior to a collapse, suppose a large star has a core of radius 150,000 km. The core is a solid sphere that rotates once every 16 hours.

    (a) What is the angular speed of rotation in rad/s?

    (b) During the collapse, the outer layers of the star are blown off and the core shrinks to a radius of 15 km. There are no external forces to produce torques on the core, and the mass stays approximately the same. What is the new angular speed in rad/s? In rpm?

CHAPTER SEVEN SUMMARY

Momentum is a property of an object in motion. An object in translation has linear momentum equal to the product of its mass and velocity. An object in rotation has angular momentum equal to the product of its moment of inertia and angular velocity. $\mathbf{p} = m\mathbf{v}$; $L = I\omega$

Newton's second law of motion can be written as an equation using momentum. If a net force is exerted on an object, the force equals the rate of change of the object's linear momentum. If a net torque is exerted on an object, the torque equals the rate of change of the object's angular momentum. $\mathbf{F} = \dfrac{\Delta \mathbf{p}}{\Delta t}$; $\tau = \dfrac{\Delta L}{\Delta t}$

The impulse (or angular impulse) given an object is the average force (or torque) exerted on the object multiplied by the time interval over which the force (or torque) acts. The impulse (or angular impulse) given an object equals the object's change in linear momentum (or angular momentum). $\mathbf{F}\Delta t = \Delta \mathbf{p}$; $\tau \Delta t = \Delta L$

By Newton's third law of motion, when two objects interact, they exert forces on each other that are equal in magnitude and opposite in direction. Since the forces act over the same time interval, the impulses are equal and opposite. This means the total momentum change of the combined system is zero. This is the law of conservation of momentum.

When working momentum problems, first define the system. Then examine the system before and after the event. If the system is closed and isolated, its momentum and angular momentum are conserved. If $\mathbf{F}_{net} = 0$, then $\Delta \mathbf{p} = 0$ or $\mathbf{p}_i = \mathbf{p}_f$. If $\tau_{net} = 0$, then $\Delta L = 0$ or $L_i = L_f$.

CHAPTER 8

WAVES AND VIBRATION

Waves transfer energy from one place to another. For example, when you toss a rock into a lake, some of the rock's energy creates water waves. A *water wave* is a disturbance in the height of the surface of the water. The disturbance travels outward in all directions through the water. When the wave reaches a floating model boat, the wave raises the boat, increasing the boat's gravitational potential energy. Work is required to lift the boat. This work is done by the wave. The wave gets the energy to do the work from the rock entering the water. Therefore, the wave transfers energy from the point at which the rock enters the water to the boat.

Sound waves also transfer energy. When someone plucks a guitar string, some of the string's energy creates sound waves. A *sound wave* is a disturbance in the pressure of the air. The disturbance travels outward in all directions through the air. When the wave reaches your ear, it does work in moving your eardrum. The wave gets the energy to do this work from the moving guitar string. Therefore, the sound wave transfers energy from the guitar string to your ear.

When rocks inside the Earth slip or fracture suddenly, energy stored as gravitational or elastic potential energy is converted into kinetic energy. This sudden movement is an earthquake. The disturbance travels outward in all directions through the Earth, and is called a *seismic wave*. When a seismic wave reaches a building, it does work in moving the building vertically and horizontally. The seismic wave transfers energy from the point of origin of the earthquake to the building. A seismograph is a device that measures earthquakes by recording the motion of the ground as a seismic wave passes by.

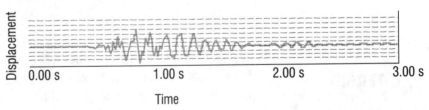

A recording from a seismograph shows ground motion of a seismic wave.

8.1 PROPERTIES OF WAVES

Objectives

- Describe how a mechanical wave transfers energy through a medium.

- Explain the difference between a transverse wave and a longitudinal wave.

- Define amplitude and wavelength.

- Define frequency and period, and the relationship between them.

- Define wave speed.

- Solve problems using amplitude, wavelength, frequency, period, and speed.

- Describe the properties of sound.

INTERNET connection

To find out more about properties of waves, follow the links at **www.learningincontext.com**.

In previous chapters you have studied various ways of transferring energy and converting it from one form to another. Driving a nail with a hammer, using high-pressure steam to turn a turbine, and using a battery to force current to flow in a circuit all involve transfers of energy. Each of these also involves a transfer of matter.

Wave motion is another way to transfer energy, but without a transfer of matter. Figure 8.1 illustrates the difference. In 8.1a, energy is transferred when someone throws a football. Matter is also transferred—the ball carries energy and mass from the person on the left to the person on the right.

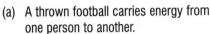

(a) A thrown football carries energy from one person to another.

(b) A wave pulse in a rope carries energy from one person to another.

Figure 8.1
Two ways of transferring energy:
(a) by transferring matter, and (b) by using a wave pulse

In Figure 8.1b, the same two people hold the ends of a rope. The person on the left gives the rope a sudden up-and-down shake. This single disturbance of the rope is called a *wave pulse*. The pulse carries energy down the rope to the person on the right. In this case, energy is transferred from one person to another but no mass is transferred between the two.

Mechanical Waves

The wave pulse in Figure 8.1b is an example of a **mechanical wave**. A mechanical wave requires a medium—such as a rope, air, water, or soil—to transfer the energy of the wave from one place to another. The wave motion begins at a source. The source causes molecules in the medium to move up and down, right and left, or in and out around their undisturbed (equilibrium) positions. Because of the electrical forces between molecules, vibrating molecules cause adjacent molecules to vibrate also. A wave is formed as the vibration is passed along, from molecule to molecule, in the medium. The molecules always return to their original, equilibrium positions—mass is not transferred as a wave passes through a medium.

In the next chapter you will learn about *electromagnetic waves*. These are not the same as mechanical waves. Electromagnetic waves also transfer energy, and they have many properties in common with mechanical waves, but they do not require media. They travel through a vacuum.

Transverse and Longitudinal Waves

A **wave pulse** is produced if the source makes a single disturbance that travels through the medium. If the source vibrates repeatedly, it produces a **periodic wave**. The person in Figure 8.1b can transfer energy with a periodic wave by moving the end of the rope repeatedly up and down (see

Figure 8.2a.) Notice that the waves in the rope travel horizontally but the particles in the rope move vertically. These are called *transverse waves*. In a **transverse wave**, the particles in the medium move in a direction perpendicular to the direction of wave motion.

(a) A transverse wave. The wave moves to the right. Particles in the rope move up and down.

(b) A longitudinal wave. The wave moves to the right. Particles in the spring move right and left.

Figure 8.2
A transverse wave in a rope and a longitudinal wave in a Slinky. Both are periodic waves.

In a **longitudinal wave**, the particles in the medium move in the same direction as (or parallel to) the wave propagation. You can generate a longitudinal wave in a coiled spring Slinky, as shown in Figure 8.2b. The end of the spring can be pushed or pulled quickly one time to generate a wave pulse or repeatedly pushed and pulled to generate a periodic wave. In Figure 8.2b, the particles in the Slinky vibrate right and left and the wave propagates from left to right. Particles in the Slinky move parallel to the direction of the wave.

In periodic waves, such as those illustrated in Figure 8.2, the smallest section of the wave that repeats at regular intervals is called the *waveform*. Most periodic waves have *sinusoidal* waveforms because they have exactly the same appearance as the graph of a sine (or cosine) function. You will investigate these functions in the exercises.

Amplitude

Suppose one end of a long rope is attached to a distant wall and the rope is stretched tightly. (We choose a distant wall so we don't have to worry about reflected waves coming back from the wall. We will deal with reflections later.) The other end of the rope is moved up and down repeatedly in a direction perpendicular to the rope's length. (Are the waves produced transverse or longitudinal?) Figure 8.3a on the next page is a "snapshot" of the rope showing the outward-traveling wave. It is called a snapshot because it is what you would record on film with a high-speed camera. Figure 8.3b is a snapshot of the same rope when the displacement from equilibrium is less.

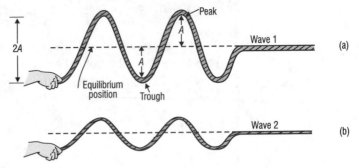

Each of the highest points on the rope is called a *peak*, or *crest*. Each of the
lowest points is called a *trough*. The distance from the rope's equilibrium
position to the crest is called the **amplitude** of the wave. (The amplitude is
also the distance from the equilibrium position to the trough.) A wave's
amplitude usually is determined by the source of the wave. The larger the
displacement of the source, the larger the amplitude. Which wave in
Figure 8.3 has a larger amplitude? Notice that it takes more work (in a given
medium) to generate a wave with a larger amplitude—the force at the wave's
source must be moved through a longer distance. Therefore, the amplitude of
a wave determines how much energy the wave transfers.

Wavelength

The length of the repeating pattern is another important characteristic of a
periodic wave. This length is called the **wavelength**. We use the Greek letter
lambda λ to represent wavelength. You can measure the wavelength from a
snapshot of a wave by measuring the shortest distance between two points
where the pattern repeats. For example, λ is shown in Figure 8.4 as
measured from peak to peak, from trough to trough, and from equilibrium
point to equilibrium point.

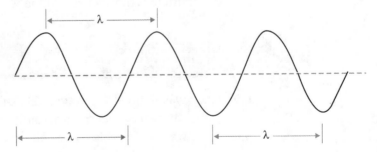

Figure 8.4
The wavelength can be measured between any
two points where the wave pattern repeats.

Example 8.1 Amplitude and Wavelength of Water Waves

Water waves pass by a 16-ft fishing boat. There are exactly 12 crests from front to back of the boat. The vertical distance between a crest and a trough is 7 inches. What are the amplitude and wavelength of the water waves?

Solution:

The wave amplitude is one-half the distance from crest to trough.

$$\text{Amplitude} = \tfrac{1}{2} \, (7 \text{ in}) = 3.5 \text{ in}$$

Since exactly 12 crests extend horizontally between the front and back of the boat, there are 11 crest-to-crest distances. The wavelength λ is one crest-to-crest distance.

$$11\lambda = 16 \text{ ft}$$

$$\lambda = \frac{16 \text{ ft}}{11} = 1.45 \text{ ft}$$

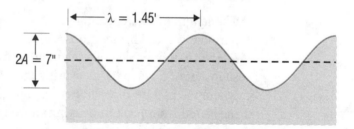

The amplitude is 3.5 inches and the wavelength is 1.45 feet.

Frequency and Period

Frequency was defined in Section 3.3 as the rate of occurrence of events, or the number of events occurring per unit time. For waves, **frequency** is the number of waves (or cycles) per unit time that pass a point in the medium. Frequency is measured in hertz (Hz). One hertz is one cycle per second.

The **period** of a wave is the amount of time it takes for one complete wavelength to pass a point in the medium. The frequency f and period T of a wave are reciprocals:

$$f = \frac{1}{T} \quad \text{and} \quad T = \frac{1}{f}$$

Frequency and period apply to periodic waves only, not wave pulses. They depend only on the source of the wave, not on the medium or the speed of the wave.

Example 8.2 Frequency and Period of Water Waves

Using a stopwatch for the water waves in Example 8.1, you determine that 3 wave crests pass the bow of the boat in 2.6 seconds. What are the frequency and period of the water waves?

Solution:

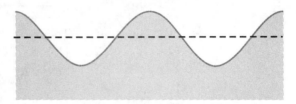

There are 2 wave cycles between 3 crests.

$$f = \frac{\text{number of cycles}}{\text{time interval}}$$

$$= \frac{2 \text{ cycles}}{2.6 \text{ s}}$$

$$= 0.77 \text{ cycle/s} \quad \text{or} \quad 0.77 \text{ Hz}$$

The wave period is the reciprocal of the frequency.

$$T = \frac{1}{f}$$

$$= \frac{1}{0.77 \text{ cycle/s}}$$

$$= 1.3 \text{ s/cycle}$$

By convention, the unit "cycle" is dropped when reporting the period of a wave. The wave frequency is 0.77 hertz and the period is 1.3 seconds.

Example 8.3 Frequency and Period of a Wave Trace

A voltage signal is displayed on an oscilloscope screen as shown in the illustration below. The display is called a *trace*. The vertical scale is the voltage, and the horizontal scale is time. The *time/division* setting on the oscilloscope is 0.05 s/div. What are the frequency and period of the signal?

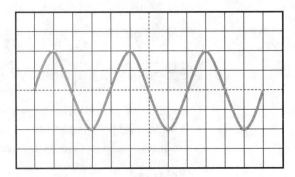

Solution: The trace shows that 3 complete wavelengths, or cycles, span 12 time divisions. Each time division is 0.05 second. Thus, the time interval is the product:

$$\text{Time interval} = (12 \text{ div})(0.05 \text{ s/div}) = 0.6 \text{ s}$$

$$f = \frac{\text{number of cycles}}{\text{time interval}} = \frac{3 \text{ cycles}}{0.6 \text{ s}} = 5.0 \text{ cycles/s}$$

$$= 5.0 \text{ Hz}$$

The wave period is the reciprocal of the frequency.

$$T = \frac{1}{f} = \frac{1}{5.0 \text{ cycle/s}} = 0.2 \text{ s/cycle}$$

The signal frequency is 5.0 hertz and the period is 0.2 second.

Speed

You can measure the speed of a wave pulse or periodic wave the same way you measure the speed of a moving object. If a point on the wave (for example, a peak or a trough) moves a distance Δx in a time interval Δt, the wave speed is $v = \dfrac{\Delta x}{\Delta t}$. Note that v is the speed of a point traveling with the wave, not the speed of the medium.

The wave travels a distance of one wavelength in a time interval of one period. Therefore, the speed v of a wave can be calculated if you know the wavelength λ and period T (or frequency f).

$$v = \frac{\text{distance traveled}}{\text{time interval}} = \frac{\lambda}{T}$$

Since $T = \dfrac{1}{f}$,

$$v = \lambda f$$

The speed of a mechanical wave depends on the medium through which the wave travels. For example, sound waves travel faster through denser media. Sound travels through air (at 20°C) at 343 m/s, through water (at 25°C) at 1490 m/s, and through steel at 5700 m/s. As a comparison, the speed of an electromagnetic wave (a nonmechanical wave) in vacuum is 3×10^8 m/s.

Example 8.4 Speed of Water Waves

What is the speed of the water waves in Examples 8.1 and 8.2?

Solution: From Example 8.1, the wavelength λ is 1.45 feet. From Example 8.2, the frequency f is 5.0 Hz.

$$
\begin{aligned}
v &= \lambda f \\
&= (1.45 \text{ ft})(5.0 \text{ cycles/s}) \qquad \text{[Drop "cycles"]} \\
&= 7.25 \text{ ft/s}
\end{aligned}
$$

The speed of the water waves is 7.25 feet per second.

Refer to Appendix F for a career link to this concept.

Sound

Sound is a longitudinal mechanical wave. The source of a sound wave vibrates rapidly, causing *pressure variations* in the medium. A guitar string, a drumhead, and your vocal cords are sources of sound waves. Their vibrations cause sound to propagate through air.

Figure 8.5 on the next page illustrates how a portion of a vibrating membrane, such as a stereo speaker, causes sound. When the membrane moves forward, air molecules next to it are pushed forward. This creates a region of increased air density and pressure. This region is called a *compression*. When the membrane moves backward, the air in front of it expands, decreasing the air density and pressure. This region is called a *rarefaction*.

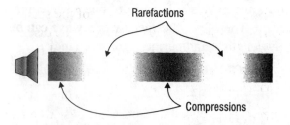

Figure 8.5
A sound wave is a pattern of
compressions and rarefactions.

If the membrane vibrates regularly, a pattern of pressure variation is created. The pattern is a sound wave. The sound wave is shown in Figure 8.6 as a series of snapshots and graphs for three instants in time. Each graph shows how the air pressure varies as a function of distance in front of the source. This kind of graph shows the *spatial variation* of air pressure at one instant in time caused by the sound wave. Each graph is a sinusoidal waveform.

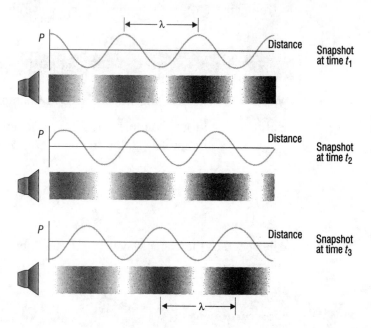

Figure 8.6
Sound is a longitudinal wave consisting of compressions and rarefactions in the air.

You also can measure air pressure at a given location over a time interval. Figure 8.7 shows a graph of the measurement. This graph is also a sinusoidal, showing the *time*, or *temporal variation*, of air pressure at one location caused by the sound wave.

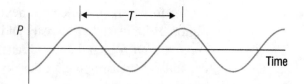

Figure 8.7
The time variation of pressure at one location caused by a sound wave.
The pressure-versus-time plot is sinusoidal.

You can measure the wavelength of the sound (or pressure) wave from the spatial variation. The wavelength is the distance required to complete one wave cycle. You can measure the period from the temporal variation. The period is the time required to complete one wave cycle. The amplitude can be measured from either graph.

When you hear sound, energy is transferred from a source to your ears. The pressure variations in the sound wave cause your eardrum to vibrate at the same frequency as the wave. Your brain interprets the vibrations detected by your ears. The loudness of the sound depends on the amplitude of the pressure wave. The human ear is sensitive to extremely small amplitudes—less than one billionth of normal atmospheric pressure. But our ears are not sensitive to a large frequency range. Most people can hear sounds between approximately 20 Hz and 16,000 Hz. We lose sensitivity, especially to higher frequencies, with long-term exposure to loud sounds and as we age.

Example 8.5 The Wavelength of Middle C

On a piano, middle C has a frequency of 262 Hz. If the speed of sound in air is 343 m/s, what is the wavelength of the sound wave produced by the piano's middle C?

Solution: Solve the wave-speed equation for λ:

$$v = \lambda f$$

$$\lambda = \frac{v}{f}$$

$$= \frac{343 \text{ m/s}}{262 \text{ cycles/s}}$$

$$= 1.31 \text{ m}$$

The wavelength is 1.31 meters.

Summary

- In a transverse mechanical wave, particles oscillate in a direction perpendicular to the direction of the wave motion.

- In a longitudinal wave, particles oscillate parallel to the direction of wave motion.

- The amplitude of a mechanical wave is the maximum displacement of particles in the medium from their equilibrium positions.

- The wavelength is the shortest distance between two points on the wave where the pattern repeats.

- Frequency is the number of complete cycles or oscillations per unit time.

- Period is the time required for one complete cycle, or oscillation. Period is the reciprocal of frequency.

- The speed of a wave is how fast the wave travels along the direction of propagation. The wave speed equals the product of its wavelength and its frequency. $v = \lambda f$

- Sound is a longitudinal wave that propagates through a medium as pressure variations.

Exercises

1. What are two ways of transferring energy from one place to another?

2. A _____ (mechanical or electromagnetic) wave requires a medium containing matter for propagation. A _____ (mechanical or electromagnetic) wave does not require a medium.

3. What is the primary difference between a transverse wave and a longitudinal wave?

4. In a periodic wave traveling down a stretched string, the vertical distance between a crest and a trough is 1.0 cm. What is the amplitude of the wave?

5. Match the following definitions to the words at the right.

____ The distance between two adjacent crests on a transverse wave

____ The distance from the peak of a transverse wave to the equilibrium, or average, position of the wave

____ The distance between two adjacent high-pressure regions in a sound wave

____ The time one cycle of a wave takes to pass by a fixed location

____ The rate at which complete cycles in a wave pass by a fixed location

____ The product of wavelength and frequency

a. frequency

b. period

c. wavelength

d. amplitude

e. wave speed

6. A snapshot of a transverse wave traveling down a stretched string is shown below. The horizontal axis shows the distance along the string, in millimeters. The vertical axis shows the displacement of the string, in millimeters.

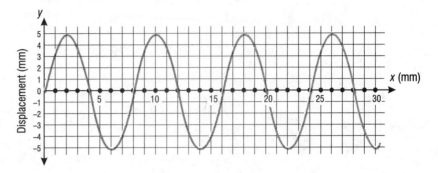

(a) What is the amplitude of the wave?

(b) What is the wavelength?

7. The graph below shows the displacement (in millimeters) as a function of time (in milliseconds) for a point on the string of Exercise 6.

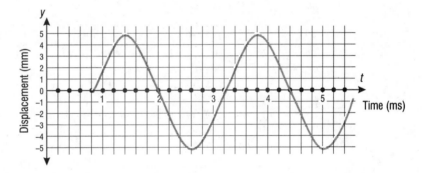

(a) What is the period of the wave?

(b) What is the frequency?

(c) What is the wave speed?

8. When you hear sound, the pressure wave moves your eardrum back and forth between maximum and minimum displacements d_{max} and d_{min}. Sketch a graph of your eardrum's displacement in response to each of the following single-frequency tones. Use axes similar to those below.

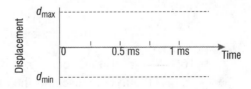

(a) A 1-kHz (1000 Hz) tone. Show one complete cycle.

(b) A 2-kHz tone. Show two complete cycles.

9. While waiting to catch a wave, a surfer estimates that 20 meters separate the crests of adjacent waves. A wave passes the surfer every 8 seconds. What is the approximate speed of the water waves?

10. The wavelength of blue light is 470 nm. (1 nm = 10^{-9} m) The speed of light is 3×10^8 m/s.

    (a) Find the frequency of blue light.

    (b) Find the period.

11. What property of a sound wave (or pressure wave) changes when the loudness, or intensity, of the sound increases?

12. The speed of sound in steel is 5700 m/s. How far apart are the compressions caused by a sound wave that has a frequency of 8400 Hz?

13. A bat emits short pulses of high-frequency sound waves (called ultrasound). By listening to echoes of the emitted ultrasound, the bat can detect and catch flying insects. What is the frequency of the sound emitted by the bat if its wavelength is 3.2 mm? The speed of sound in air is 343 m/s.

14. A radio station broadcasts an FM electromagnetic wave at a frequency of 92.5 MHz. The speed of electromagnetic waves is 3×10^8 m/s.

    (a) What is the period of the wave in seconds?

    (b) What is the wavelength in meters?

15. The oscilloscope trace below is for an alternating voltage signal. The volts/division (vertical scale) control is set at 2 volts/div. The time/division (horizontal scale) control is set at 0.2 msec/div.

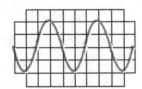

    (a) What is the amplitude of the voltage signal?

    (b) What is the period?

    (c) What is the frequency?

16. A right triangle contains one 90° angle. The side opposite the right angle is the hypotenuse and the other two sides are called the legs. The hypotenuse is the longest side of a right triangle.

Let h represent the length of the hypotenuse, and let x and y represent the lengths of the legs, as shown at the right. h is related to x and y by the Pythagorean theorem:

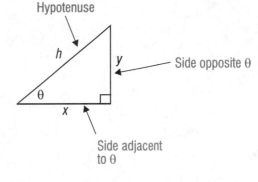

$$h^2 = x^2 + y^2$$

The *sine*, *cosine*, and *tangent* of an angle in a right triangle are defined with ratios involving the lengths of the sides of the triangle. These ratios are abbreviated *sin*, *cos*, and *tan*. For the angle θ shown above, y is the length of the opposite side and x is the length of the adjacent side.

$$\sin\,\theta = \frac{y}{h} = \frac{\text{opposite}}{\text{hypotenuse}}$$

$$\cos\,\theta = \frac{x}{h} = \frac{\text{adjacent}}{\text{hypotenuse}}$$

$$\tan\,\theta = \frac{y}{x} = \frac{\text{opposite}}{\text{adjacent}}$$

For the triangle at the right, calculate:

(a) The length of the hypotenuse.

(b) $\sin\,\theta$

(c) $\cos\,\theta$

(d) $\tan\,\theta$

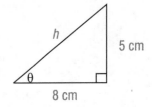

17. You can use your calculator to find values for the sine, cosine, and tangent of an angle. Most calculators will work with either degrees or radians. We will work with degrees, so make sure your calculator is in **DEG** mode. To find the sine of 60°, press **60**, then **sin**. Your calculator should read 0.866025403. Rounded to three significant figures, $\sin 60° = 0.866$.

For the triangle at the right, calculate:

(a) $\sin 42°$, $\cos 42°$, and $\tan 42°$.

(b) y. (Use the ratio for $\sin \theta$ given in Exercise 16.)

(c) x. (Use the ratio for $\cos \theta$ given in Exercise 16.)

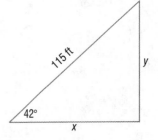

18. (a) Make a table of values for sin θ, for values of θ from 0° to 360°, similar to the one below. Use increments of 30°, and round your values to two significant figures.

θ	sin θ	θ	sin θ	θ	sin θ
0°		120°		240°	
30°		150°		270°	
60°		180°		300°	
90°		210°		330°	
				360°	

(b) Plot the data from your table, using coordinate axes as shown below and graph paper. The result is a sine wave. How many cycles of a sine wave are between 0° and 360°?

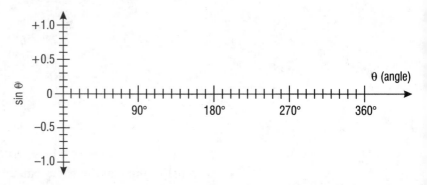

(c) How would you change the horizontal axis of your graph to show the sine wave with units of radians instead of degrees?

19. A *wave function* can be written in the form

$$y = A \sin \omega t$$

where A is the amplitude of the wave, ω is the angular frequency, and t is time. In this formula, the angle θ is the product ωt. This is called the *phase* of the wave. In a wave function, the phase has units of radians, not degrees.

Let y represent the time-varying voltage output of a signal generator. The maximum value of y is 5 volts, and the minimum value is −5 volts. The signal has a frequency of 10 Hz. (Remember, $\omega = 2\pi f$.)

Plot the wave function, with y on the vertical axis and t on the horizontal axis. Show one cycle of the wave, from $\omega t = 0$ (or $t = 0$ s) to $\omega t = 2\pi$ (or $t = 2\pi/\omega$). Compare your plot to the one from Exercise 18. How are they alike? How are they different?

8.2 WAVE INTERACTIONS

Objectives

- Describe what's meant by interference of waves.

- Distinguish between constructive and destructive interference.

- Use the superposition principle to find the resultant wave produced by two interfering waves.

- Explain how a standing wave is formed.

- Define natural frequency.

- Explain how forced vibrations or oscillations can produce resonance.

To find out more about wave interactions, follow the links at **www.learningincontext.com**.

When two or more waves *of the same type* are combined at the same place at the same time, the result is called **interference**. You can see wave interference if you drop two stones into water. The water waves produced by the stones spread and eventually overlap. A two-dimensional **interference pattern** is produced when the two periodic water waves occupy the same region at the same time.

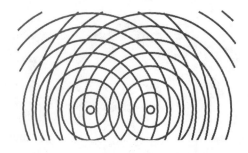

Figure 8.8
Overlapping water waves produce an interference pattern.

Suppose each end of a stretched rope is given a single up-and-down shake, producing identical wave pulses. The pulses travel toward each other, and when they meet they interfere (see Figure 8.9.) At the moment when the peaks of the pulses coincide, the amplitude of the resultant pulse is the sum of the amplitudes of the individual pulses. The displacement of the rope is greater than the displacement caused by either individual pulse. This effect is called **constructive interference**. Notice that each pulse reappears and continues moving in its original direction as if the other pulse did not exist. The properties of a pulse (amplitude, wavelength, speed, and frequency) are unaffected by the presence of another pulse.

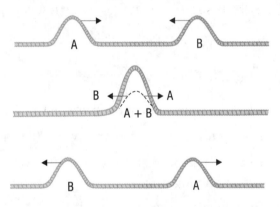

Figure 8.9
Constructive interference of
two wave pulses in a stretched rope

Now suppose one of the pulses is inverted, as in Figure 8.10. (One person gives the rope a down-and-up shake.) When these pulse amplitudes coincide, the resultant is still the sum of the amplitudes of the individual pulses. But this time the sum is zero. The displacement of the rope is less than the displacement caused by either individual pulse. This effect is called **destructive interference**. Once again, each pulse reappears and continues moving in its original direction as if the other pulse did not exist.

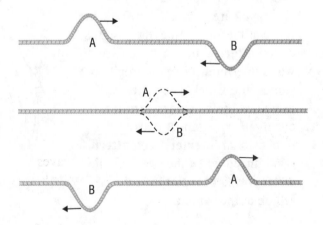

Figure 8.10
Destructive interference of
two wave pulses

When waves interfere as in Figures 8.9 and 8.10, you can add the displacements produced by the individual waves to find the displacement of any point in the rope at any given time. The principle of adding displacements of overlapping waves is called the **principle of superposition**. The principle holds for most types of waves, including wave pulses and periodic waves in a stretched rope, water waves, sound waves, and electromagnetic waves. The principle can be used whenever the properties of wave pulses or periodic waves are not affected by the presence of other waves.

Example 8.6 Constructive Interference of Two Sine Waves

At one instant in time, two sound waves, A and B, of the same wavelength interfere as shown below. Sketch the resultant wave.

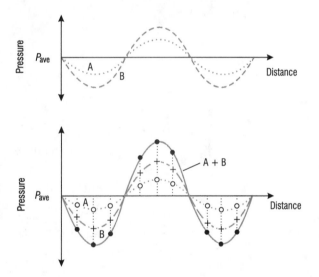

Solution: Using the superposition principle, add A and B. Draw several vertical guidelines from the average pressure line to each wave, as shown above. For each guideline, use segment addition: The segment length to wave A plus the segment length to wave B equals the segment length to the resultant wave (A + B). Make a dot to show the endpoint of each segment. Sketch a sine wave through the dots.

In Example 8.6, notice that the pressure in the resultant wave (A + B) is greater than the pressure in either wave A or wave B. These two waves interfere constructively.

In the example on the next page, two waves interfere destructively. In this case, the resultant wave has an amplitude between the amplitudes of the original waves.

Example 8.7 Destructive Interference of Two Sine Waves

Two voltage signals, A and B, exist simultaneously across a resistor. The signals have the same wavelength but different amplitudes. As shown below, the signals are *out of phase*—one increases while the other decreases. What is the amplitude of the resultant wave?

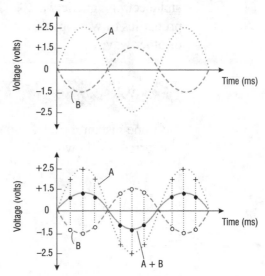

Solution: Add the two waves using superposition and the same procedure as in Example 8.6. The voltage in wave B is always opposite in sign to the voltage in wave A. Therefore, the amplitude of the resultant is the difference between the amplitude of A and the amplitude of B.

$$\text{Amplitude of (A + B)} = \text{amplitude of A} - \text{amplitude of B}$$
$$= 2.5 \text{ V} - 1.5 \text{ V}$$
$$= 1.0 \text{ V}$$

The amplitude of the resultant wave is 1.0 volt.

Wave Reflections

When a wave is reflected, it changes direction. A wave traveling on a stretched rope can be reflected if the end of the rope is tied securely to a wall. Figure 8.11 shows a reflection of a wave pulse. An incident wave I travels to the right, the wave is reflected at a wall, and the reflected wave R travels to the left.

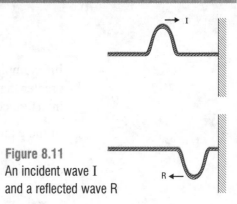

Figure 8.11
An incident wave I and a reflected wave R

Notice that the reflected wave changes direction but the wavelength does not change. Notice also that the reflected wave is inverted. A crest becomes a trough, and a trough becomes a crest.

Suppose the incident wave is periodic instead of a pulse. The reflected wave will be periodic also. In this case, the incident and reflected waves will be present in the rope at the same time, and they interfere. This interference can form a *standing wave* in the rope.

Standing Waves

Sound from a guitar or violin string is created by **standing waves** in the string. These waves are a result of reflections at the fixed ends of the string. Waves travel back and forth between the ends of the string, constantly being reflected and interfering with each other. But the string cannot move at the fixed ends. Therefore, destructive interference must always occur at the ends.

Figure 8.12 shows a standing wave in a string at three instants in time. This standing wave has a wavelength equal to the length of the string. For this wavelength, there is one point in the string (in addition to the ends) that is stationary. This point is called a **node**. The first illustration is at a time when the incident and reflected waves have their crests and troughs overlapping. We say these incident and reflected waves are **in phase**. When two waves are in phase, they constructively interfere. The second illustration is at a time when the incident wave crest overlaps the reflected wave trough, and vice versa. We say these two waves are **out of phase**. Two waves that are out of phase interfere destructively. Are the incident and reflected waves in phase or out of phase in the third illustration?

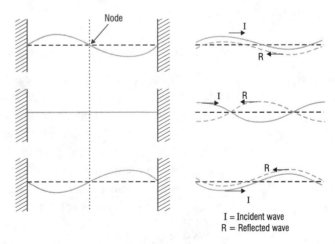

I = Incident wave
R = Reflected wave

Figure 8.12
A standing wave is produced by interference between incident and reflected waves.

You can make standing waves in a stretched rope or length of flexible tubing. Tie one end of the rope securely to a support. Shake the other end at a low frequency until you see a standing wave with the length of the rope equal to one-half wavelength (see Figure 8.13a). If you double the frequency, you will create a standing wave whose wavelength equals the length of the rope (see Figure 8.13b). If you triple the original frequency, the standing wave will have a wavelength of 2/3 the length of the rope (see Figure 8.13c).

Suppose a rope has length L. A standing wave exists in the rope if incident and reflected waves cause destructive interference at both ends of the rope. This happens only for certain wavelengths λ. As shown in Figure 8.13, a standing wave can exist only if the length of the rope is a multiple of $\lambda/2$. In other words $L = \lambda/2$, λ, $3\lambda/2$, 2λ, and so on. If you solve for the possible wavelengths of a standing wave, $\lambda = 2L$, L, $2L/3$, $L/2$, and so on.

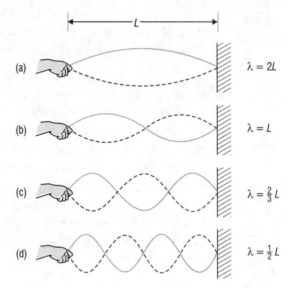

Figure 8.13
The first four possible wavelengths
of a standing wave in a stretched rope of length L

Other types of waves also can occur as standing waves when there are reflectors at appropriate distances. A drumhead supports standing waves because it is fixed around its perimeter. Displacement travels as a wave in two dimensions through the drumhead, and the wave is reflected at the perimeter. Vibrating air columns in flutes, organ pipes, and other musical instruments are standing sound waves. Sound waves are reflected at the ends of each musical instrument. Laser light is produced from standing light waves. In a laser, light is reflected by mirrors. Microwave ovens use standing microwaves to deposit energy in food (mostly water) molecules. The inner walls of the oven reflect microwaves. You will learn more about light, microwaves, and other electromagnetic waves in the next chapter.

Applications of Wave Interference

Interference is especially useful in light-wave technology (optics) and sound-wave technology (acoustics).

When light waves of similar frequency and wavelength interfere, they produce a series of bright and dark regions called an *interference pattern*. The bright regions, or *bands*, are a result of constructive interference. The dark bands are a result of destructive interference. One application of interference patterns is the use of optical flats to determine the flatness of machined parts. An optical flat is a piece of perfectly flat glass about ¾ inch thick. It is placed on the machined surface to be checked, and light is directed toward the surface (see Figure 8.14). Some of the light is reflected by the machined surface; some is reflected by the glass.

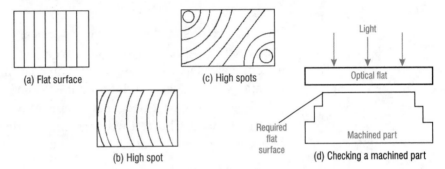

(a) Flat surface (c) High spots (b) High spot (d) Checking a machined part

Figure 8.14
Interference patterns indicate the flatness of machined parts.

Since the light from the work surface travels a little farther, the waves are reflected out of step—that is, out of phase. This out-of-phase condition creates an interference pattern. The interference pattern is seen by the machinist, looking down at the surface of the part under the flat. By properly interpreting the interference pattern, the machinist can infer the relative flatness of a machined surface. The drawings in Figure 8.14 give you a sample of some results seen by a machinist checking for flatness.

The interference pattern in Figure 8.14a indicates to the machinist that the part is flat within a wavelength of light. Figure 8.14b (where the bands are curved) indicates that a part is high in the middle. Figure 8.14c (where the bands have swirls in them) indicates that the part has several high spots. Because the wavelength of light is very short (less than 1/1000 of a millimeter), accurate measurements of high or low spots on the surface of the machined part can be made. Then the machinist knows how much more grinding or polishing is needed to make the part flat.

The interference of sound waves also produces patterns that can be controlled. In concert halls and recording studios, reflections (or echoes) interfere with the original sound. Interference is reduced by using heavy drapes, foam, or other absorbing material to eliminate reflections.

Figure 8.15
Controlling sound waves in a studio

Two sources of sound waves that are at nearly the same frequency (or wavelength) will interfere constructively and destructively in a regular pattern, just as in a standing wave. You hear this pattern as pulsations, or variations in loudness, of the combined sound. The variations in loudness are called **beats**. The beat frequency is much lower than the frequency of either source of sound. The beat frequency equals the difference between the frequencies of the two interfering waves.

For example, suppose a violinist bows a single string, creating a standing wave of frequency 440 Hz (this is the concert pitch of A above middle C). A second violinist bows a note at a frequency of 442 Hz. The combined sound heard by the violinists will have a frequency equal to the *average* of the two frequencies, or 441 Hz. The violinists will also hear a beat, with a frequency equal to the *difference*, or 2 Hz (2 beats per second). If the second violinist slowly reduces the tension in his violin string, the beats will get farther apart, and finally disappear when the two frequencies are the same.

**Refer to Appendix F
for a career link
to this concept.**

Natural Frequency

The **natural frequency** of an object is a single frequency at which the object vibrates or oscillates when it does so on its own. Think about a simple pendulum, like a grandfather clock or a child's swing. If the swing is set in motion, it moves back and forth at a certain frequency. If you stop the swing and then start it again, it moves back and forth at the same frequency. As long as you don't change the length, every time you start a pendulum swinging, it oscillates at the same frequency. That's its natural frequency.

Or think about a vibrating spring. One end of the spring is attached to a ceiling. A weight is hung on the other end. The spring is pulled down and let go. It then bobs up and down. It does so at a single frequency—its natural frequency. As long as you don't change the weight, every time you pull the spring down and let it go, it oscillates at the same frequency.

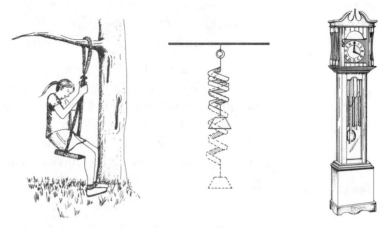

Figure 8.16
All oscillating objects have natural frequencies.

Resonance

The Tacoma Narrows bridge disaster is a historic example of what can happen when an outside force sets up a motion that matches the natural frequency of an object. On November 7, 1940, an intense wind caused the bridge to begin *twisting* along its entire length. The back-and-forth twisting motion matched the natural twisting frequency of the suspended bridge. As the blowing wind gave more and more energy to the torsional motion of the bridge, the bridge twisted back and forth with larger and larger amplitude. Finally, at approximately 11:00 A.M. the bridge tore itself apart.

Figure 8.17
Tacoma Narrows bridge undergoing a twisting motion

A force can be applied to any object like the Tacoma Narrows bridge at regular intervals. The object is forced to oscillate at the frequency of the applied force. The motion of the object is called **forced vibration**. When the frequency of a forced vibration matches the natural frequency of an object, the object vibrates with increasing amplitude. This condition is called **resonance**. Resonance happens because the source of forced vibrations transfers energy to the object as work—a force is applied to the object in the direction of its motion during each oscillation.

You can demonstrate resonance with a swing. A swing is a pendulum with a natural frequency of oscillation. You "pump" a swing by leaning back and pushing your legs forward at the same point in each oscillation. You can also push someone else in the swing by applying forces repeatedly at just the right time. In either case, you are the source of forced vibration. If the frequency at which you apply forces equals the natural frequency of the swing, the swing's amplitude increases. This is resonance.

On the other hand, when the frequency of a forced vibration does not match the natural frequency of an object or mechanical system, the object's amplitude does not increase substantially. You can prove this by trying to "pump" a swing by pushing it at a frequency of forced vibration that's different from the natural frequency of the swing. You'll find that you can't build up much amplitude in the swing. That's because your successive *pushes* are *out of phase* with the natural frequency of the swing.

Resonance is very important in mechanical systems. Engineers, architects, and technicians purposely match forced oscillations and natural frequency when resonance is desired. Alternatively, they work to avoid or dampen undesired resonance. (Shock absorbers are used to dampen oscillation. These devices convert the kinetic energy of the oscillation into internal energy of a fluid inside the shock absorber.) Vibrations are almost always produced in machines when they operate. Structures also vibrate when forced vibrations are present. Vibrating machines, earthquakes, passing trucks, and sonic booms are a few examples of forced vibrations that can affect structures and machines. These vibrations don't usually represent a major problem—unless they coincide with a natural frequency of the machine or structure.

When they do coincide, however, resonance occurs. Then the amplitude of the vibration increases dramatically. The result is excessive wear and shortened life expectancy of the machine or structure or—in the case of an earthquake—instant damage. Vibration-isolation pads are used to isolate vibration caused by heavy, high-speed machines. Special shock absorbers are built into the structures of tall buildings to damp out vibrations (swaying) caused by wind forces.

Vibrations produced in internal-combustion engines are controlled to avoid resonance. During design, engines can have cylinders added, subtracted, or repositioned. The V-angle in a V-8 or V-6 can be adjusted. Or the firing order of the engine can be changed. Within the engine itself, a flywheel is added on the rear of the crankshaft and a vibration damper (harmonic balancer) is added to the front. Both help reduce and damp out engine vibrations. Engine mounts made of springs or rubber bushings are designed to eliminate vibrations that might cause resonance in the frame or body of the car (see Figure 8.18).

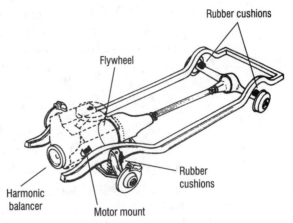

Figure 8.18
Vibration-reducing devices in an automobile

Resonance of a nonmechanical form is important in electrical systems. When a capacitor and an inductor are connected in parallel across an AC source, as shown in Figure 8.19, they form an *LC circuit*. This is also called a *resonant circuit*. Electrical energy flows back and forth (oscillates) between the inductor and the capacitor. It does so at a rate that depends on the natural frequency of oscillation of the LC circuit. Resonant LC circuits are used in many types of electronic equipment, such as radios, amplifiers, tuners, and television sets. If you take a course in electronics, you'll learn a lot more about resonant circuits.

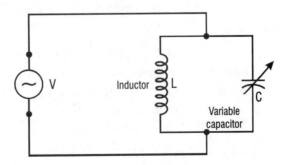

Figure 8.19
Resonant LC circuit in an electrical system

Summary

- When two or more waves in a medium pass through the same place at the same time, the waves overlap and interfere with each other.

- When two or more waves in a medium interfere, the overall wave displacement is equal to the sum of the displacements caused by the individual waves. This is called the principle of superposition.

- When two waves of equal frequency are in phase and interfere, the resultant wave has the same frequency but the amplitude is the sum of the individual amplitudes. This is called constructive interference.

- When two waves of equal frequency are out of phase and interfere, the resultant wave has the same frequency but the amplitude is the difference between the individual amplitudes. This is destructive interference.

- The natural frequency of an object or system is that frequency at which the object will vibrate on its own when set into motion.

- Resonance between a source of vibration and another object or system exists when the frequency of the vibrating source matches the natural frequency of the object. In resonance, the amplitude of vibration increases rapidly.

Exercises

1. What is the general term used to describe what happens when two or more waves of the same type overlap in the same medium?

2. When two waves of equal frequency are in phase and interfere, they produce a resultant wave whose amplitude is larger than either wave. This is called _____.

3. When two waves of equal frequency are out of phase and interfere, they produce a resultant wave whose amplitude is smaller than either wave. This is called _____.

4. The two voltage signals at the right are sent through a wire simultaneously. Sketch the resulting wave.

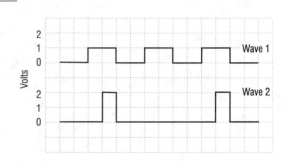

5. The two voltage signals at the right are sent through a wire simultaneously. Sketch the resulting wave.

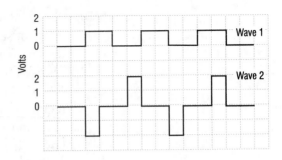

6. Trace or redraw waves 1 and 2 onto your paper. Sketch the wave resulting from the interference of 1 and 2.

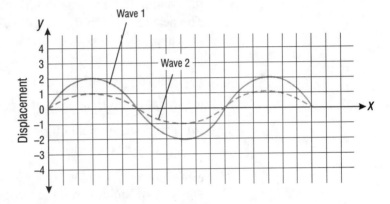

7. Trace or redraw waves 1 and 2 onto your paper. Sketch the wave resulting from the interference of 1 and 2.

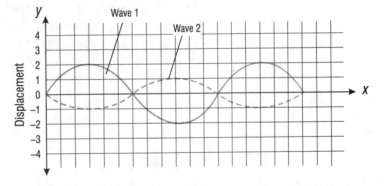

8. What is the value of displacement at the nodes of a standing wave in a stretched string?

9. When two interfering sound waves are very close in frequency, the resulting combined wave has regular, periodic variations in loudness. What are these variations called?

10. A pendulum consists of a mass, called the bob, suspended by a string. When the bob is pulled to one side and released, it swings back and forth. The period of a pendulum is the time required for the bob to complete one back-and-forth oscillation. Describe how you could measure the natural frequency of oscillation of a pendulum.

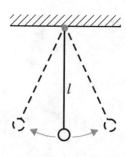

11. As long as the maximum angle of displacement of a pendulum is less than about 15°, the pendulum's period T depends on only its length l. The period is given by the following formula, where g is the acceleration of gravity.

$$T = 2\pi\sqrt{\frac{l}{g}}$$

(a) What is the frequency of a pendulum that is 1.2 m long?

(b) The Foucault pendulum in the National Museum of American History has a period of 8.0 s. How long is this pendulum?

12. The strings on a guitar vibrate to cause sound. Each string is anchored to the body of the guitar at the bridge. What role does the bridge of the guitar play in producing a standing wave in a guitar string?

13. The pilot of a twin-engine airplane hears a loud and annoying beat caused by the engines. This means that the engines are turning at slightly different rates. To eliminate the beat, the pilot "throttles down," or slowly decreases, one engine's rpm. If the beat frequency increases, are the engines' frequencies getting closer together or farther apart?

CHAPTER EIGHT SUMMARY

Waves transfer energy from one place to another without a transfer of matter. A wave that requires a medium is called a mechanical wave. In a transverse mechanical wave, particles of the medium move perpendicular to the direction of wave propagation. In a longitudinal wave, particles move parallel to the direction of wave propagation. Sound is a longitudinal mechanical wave.

The amplitude of a wave is the distance from the average, or equilibrium, position to the crest of the wave. The wavelength is the distance between adjacent crests or adjacent troughs. Wave frequency is the number of crests, troughs, wavelengths, or cycles that pass a point per second. The period is the time it takes for one wavelength or complete cycle of a wave to pass a point. The period and frequency are reciprocals. Wave speed is the distance traveled by the wave per unit time. Wave speed is the product of wavelength and frequency.

When an object or a system is set into vibration or oscillation and left alone, it oscillates at its natural frequency. When the frequency of forced vibration matches the natural frequency of an object or system, the amplitude of oscillation increases rapidly. This is called resonance.

CHAPTER

9

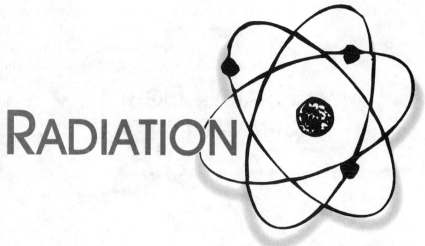

RADIATION

Radiation is a process of transferring energy. In this chapter, we discuss two types—electromagnetic radiation and nuclear radiation.

Electromagnetic radiation is a transfer of energy by means of electromagnetic waves. These waves travel at the maximum speed possible, 300 million meters per second (186,000 miles per second). They do not require a medium for propagation. They travel through empty space. The energy in an electromagnetic wave is carried in electric and magnetic fields.

Visible light is electromagnetic radiation. Different colors have different wavelengths. The wavelengths of visible light range from about 400 nm for red light to about 700 nm for violet light. (nm = 10^{-9} m) The eye responds only to electromagnetic waves with wavelengths between these limits. All objects radiate electromagnetic waves of all wavelengths, but the intensities of the different wavelengths vary.

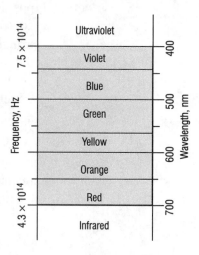

For example, a green lamp radiates visible light of highest intensity between 500 nm and 560 nm. The lamp also radiates electromagnetic waves of longer wavelength, called infrared, and shorter wavelength, called ultraviolet. Special instruments can be used to detect these wavelengths. Microwaves and radio waves have wavelengths longer than infrared. X rays and gamma rays have wavelengths shorter than ultraviolet.

All electromagnetic waves are generated by accelerating charge, mostly electrons. Electrons accelerated back and forth along antennas generate microwaves and radio waves. The frequency of the electromagnetic wave generated depends on the frequency at which the electrons move back and forth. Electrons changing position in atoms or molecules generate infrared, visible, ultraviolet, and X rays. This change happens very quickly, thus the frequencies of these radiations are high. Gamma rays are generated by moving charge in the nuclei of certain unstable atoms. These changes are the quickest of all, thus gamma rays have the highest frequencies.

Electromagnetic radiation is used to send and receive radio and television signals.

Gamma rays were discovered at about the same time that two other types of **nuclear radiation** were discovered. These are called alpha and beta radiation. They are made of particles of matter, not electromagnetic waves. All three types of radiation transfer energy away from unstable, or radioactive nuclei. An alpha particle is the same as a helium nucleus, two protons and two neutrons. A beta particle is an electron or its *antiparticle*, a *positron*.

Nuclear radiation is used in medicine to trace blood flow, to kill cancer cells, and to make images of internal organs and tissue.

Nuclear medicine imaging uses small amounts of radioactive substances to diagnose and treat diseases.

Energy from the nucleus can also be used to produce electricity. Nuclear fission and fusion release energy that can make steam to drive turbines. Turbines drive generators that produce electricity. Fission reactors exist, and provide approximately 20% of the electricity in the United States. The practicality of a fusion reactor has not yet been demonstrated.

9.1 ELECTROMAGNETIC RADIATION

Objectives

- Explain the nature and source of electromagnetic radiation.

- Explain how a changing electric field can produce an electromagnetic wave.

- Explain how the wavelength, frequency, and speed of an electromagnetic wave are related.

- Calculate the energy and momentum of a photon from the wavelength or frequency.

Electromagnetic Waves

INTERNET
connection

To find out more about electromagnetic radiation, follow the links at **www.learningincontext.com**.

In Section 5.3. you learned that an electric current in a wire produces a magnetic field that circles the wire. Figure 9-1 shows a wire with a constant potential difference and electric field through the wire. The potential difference causes electrons to move through the wire in the direction opposite the electric field. The current also produces a magnetic field that circles the wire in the clockwise direction as shown.

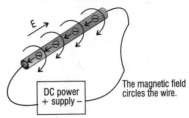

Electrons move opposite
the direction of the electric field.

E

DC power
+ supply −

The magnetic field
circles the wire.

Figure 9.1
An electric field causes current to flow through a wire.
The current creates a magnetic field.

Figure 9-2 shows the same arrangement with the electric field reversed. Both the direction of motion of the electrons and the direction of the magnetic field reverse direction.

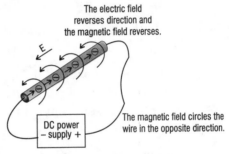

The electric field
reverses direction and
the magnetic field reverses.

E

DC power
− supply +

The magnetic field circles the
wire in the opposite direction.

Figure 9.2
When the electric field is reversed, the current
changes direction and so does the magnetic field.

Now consider what happens if the DC power supply is replaced by an AC power supply. The alternating potential difference has a sinusoidal waveform. Now the electric field continuously changes in amplitude and direction. The electrons in the wire oscillate back and forth following the changes in the electric field.

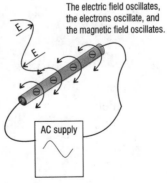

The electric field oscillates,
the electrons oscillate, and
the magnetic field oscillates.

E

E

AC supply

Figure 9.3
An AC power supply applies an alternating potential
difference and electric field across the wire.
The current and magnetic field continuously change direction.

The oscillating current in the wire produces a magnetic field that circles the wire, as before. But the magnitude of the field and its direction continuously change in step with the electric field. Therefore, a changing electric field produces a changing magnetic field.

In Section 5.3 you learned that an electromotive force (EMF) is produced in a wire when the wire is in a magnetic field that changes magnitude or direction. This process is called electromagnetic induction. The EMF is actually a potential difference, and therefore the induced EMF creates an electric field. The induced EMF and the magnitude and direction of the electric field change in step with the changing magnetic field.

These processes can be summarized as follows. When something like an AC power supply or a moving magnet causes an electric field or a magnetic field to change, the other field is produced and changes in step.

> *A changing electric field produces a changing magnetic field.*

> *A changing magnetic field produces a changing electric field.*

In the 1860s, the English physicist James Clark Maxwell predicted that changing electric and magnetic fields can transmit energy across empty space, without wires. The combination of the changing fields is called an **electromagnetic wave**. In 1887, the German physicist Heinrich Hertz demonstrated experimentally that Maxwell's theory was correct.

The wire connected to the AC power supply in Figure 9.3 is an **antenna**. The current in the wire changes at the same frequency as the power supply. The changing current produces changing electric and magnetic fields that move away from the antenna as an electromagnetic wave. The wave travels away from the antenna at the speed of light. The wave carries energy away from the current in the antenna. The energy is contained in the electric and magnetic fields of the wave. This energy is sometimes called **electromagnetic radiation**.

Speed, Wavelength, and Frequency of EM Radiation

Electromagnetic waves travel through a vacuum at the speed of light, 2.99792×10^8 m/s. In equations, we use c to represent this speed. For most calculations c can be rounded to three significant figures, 3.00×10^8 m/s. The speed in air is approximately the same as in vacuum, but in other media the speed is lower.

All electromagnetic waves travel at the same speed, but they can have vastly different wavelengths and frequencies. For example, you can change the wavelength and frequency of the wave radiated by the antenna in Figure 9.3

by changing the frequency of the AC power supply. Recall from Chapter 8 that the wavelength λ, frequency f, and speed of a wave are related. This relationship is expressed in the following equation for electromagnetic waves.

$$\text{speed} = \text{wavelength} \cdot \text{frequency}$$
$$c = \lambda f$$

The wavelength of an electromagnetic wave is the distance between peaks of the electric field or magnetic field in the wave. The frequency is the rate at which peaks pass a stationary point. Since the product λf is constant, as the wavelength increases, the frequency decreases (and vice versa).

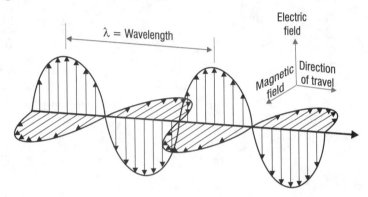

Figure 9.4

In an electromagnetic wave, the electric field is perpendicular to the magnetic field. Both fields are perpendicular to the direction of travel.

Note: Many important physical constants such as the speed of light, π, and the charge of an electron are known to a large number of significant figures. You should always use at least as many significant figures for these constants as are given in other numerical values in a problem. Notice the use of significant figures in the following examples.

Example 9.1 Wavelength of a Radio Wave

Find the wavelength of a 1200-kilohertz radio wave.

Solution: $c = \lambda f$

$$\lambda = \frac{c}{f} \qquad\qquad \left[\text{kHz} = 10^3 \text{ Hz}\right]$$

$$\lambda = \frac{3.0 \times 10^8 \text{ m/s}}{1200 \times 10^3 \text{ Hz}} = 250 \text{ m} \qquad \left[\text{Hz} = 1/\text{s}\right]$$

A 1200-kHz radio wave has a wavelength of 250 meters.

Example 9.2 Speed of Light in Glass

The light from a helium-neon laser has a wavelength of 632.8 nm in air. The same light has a wavelength of 472.2 nm in glass. The frequency of the light is the same in air and glass. Find the speed of the laser light in glass.

Solution: The speed is always the product of wavelength and frequency. The speed in air is approximately c, so $c = \lambda_{air} f$.

Find the frequency:

$$f = \frac{c}{\lambda_{air}}$$

$$= \frac{2.998 \times 10^8 \text{ m/s}}{632.8 \times 10^{-9} \text{ m}} \qquad [\text{nm} = 10^{-9} \text{ m}]$$

$$= 4.738 \times 10^{14} \text{ Hz}$$

Find the speed in glass:

$$c_{glass} = \lambda_{glass} f$$

$$= (472.2 \times 10^{-9} \text{ m})(4.738 \times 10^{14} \text{ Hz})$$

$$= 2.237 \times 10^8 \text{ m/s} \qquad [\text{Hz} = 1/\text{s}]$$

The glass is called a medium. The speed of light or any electromagnetic wave is less in a medium than in a vacuum.

The Electromagnetic Spectrum

The wavelengths of electromagnetic waves range from millions of meters to as short as 10^{-16} m. Figure 9.5 is a chart depicting this range of wavelengths (and frequencies) for the **electromagnetic spectrum**. Since the chart spans such a large range of values, it is scaled by the powers of ten. This type of scale is called a **logarithmic scale**.

For convenience, the spectrum is divided into sections, called **bands**, based on ranges of wavelengths. The bands have names. For example, *radio* waves are the longest electromagnetic waves, some as long as several thousand kilometers or as short as a few millimeters. *Microwaves* have very short wavelengths, some as short as 10^{-4} m. *Light* includes infrared, visible, and ultraviolet electromagnetic waves. Notice that the *visible* portion that we can detect with our eyes is very tiny. *X rays*, *gamma rays*, and *cosmic rays* have the shortest wavelengths.

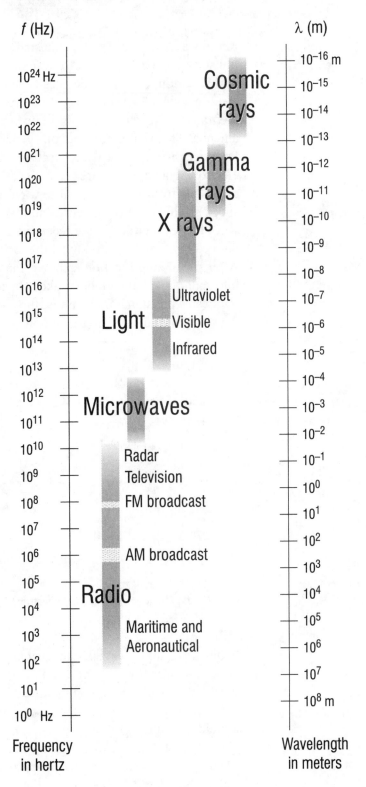

f (Hz) λ (m)

10^24 Hz   Cosmic   10^-16 m
                   rays   10^-15
10^23   10^-14
10^22   10^-13
10^21   Gamma   10^-12
10^20   rays   10^-11
10^19   10^-10
10^18   X rays   10^-9
10^17   10^-8
10^16   Ultraviolet   10^-7
10^15   Light Visible   10^-6
10^14   Infrared   10^-5
10^13   10^-4
10^12   Microwaves   10^-3
10^11   10^-2
10^10   Radar   10^-1
10^9   Television   10^0
10^8   FM broadcast   10^1
10^7   10^2
10^6   AM broadcast   10^3
10^5   10^4
10^4   Radio   10^5
10^3   Maritime and   10^6
10^2   Aeronautical   10^7
10^1   10^8 m
10^0 Hz

Frequency   Wavelength
in hertz   in meters

Figure 9.5
The electromagnetic spectrum

Radio Waves

Radio waves are used to transmit radio and television signals. The process of transmission and reception for a sound signal works as follows. At the radio or TV station, electronic devices called *transducers* convert sound into electrical signals (a time-varying current). These signals cause electrons in the transmitting antenna to oscillate back and forth along the length of the antenna. The oscillating electrons generate electromagnetic radiation whose frequency is the same as the electrons' frequency of oscillation. These electromagnetic waves are radio waves, and they are broadcast in all directions from the antenna. The waves travel to a receiving antenna at the speed c. The changing electric and magnetic fields in the electromagnetic wave cause electrons in the receiving antenna to oscillate back and forth, duplicating the electrical signal that originated at the radio or TV station. After signal amplification, another transducer changes the electrical signal into sound made by a loudspeaker. Since the electrical signal received duplicates the signal transmitted, the sound from the loudspeaker duplicates the sound at the radio or TV station.

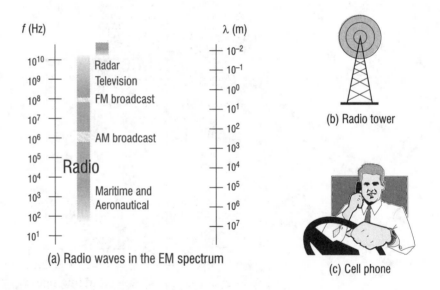

(a) Radio waves in the EM spectrum

(b) Radio tower

(c) Cell phone

Radio waves have wavelengths that range from less than a centimeter to tens or even hundreds of kilometers. FM (frequency modulated) radio waves are shorter than AM (amplitude modulated) radio waves. For example, an FM radio station at 100 on the radio dial (100 megahertz) would have a wavelength of about three meters. An AM station at 750 on the dial (750 kilohertz) uses a wavelength of about 400 meters. Cell phones use radio waves with frequencies between approximately 800 megahertz (800 MHz) and 2 gigahertz (2 GHz).

Microwaves

Microwave radiation has shorter wavelengths and higher frequencies than radio waves. Microwave wavelengths range from approximately one millimeter (the thickness of a pencil lead) to thirty centimeters (about one foot).

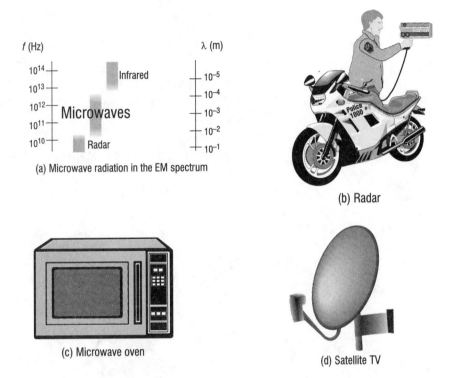

(a) Microwave radiation in the EM spectrum

(b) Radar

(c) Microwave oven

(d) Satellite TV

Figure 9.7
Microwave radiation

Microwaves are used in telecommunication. They carry information from point to point on the Earth, or from Earth to satellites and back down again using the satellite TV frequencies.

Microwaves can also be used in radar systems to detect and track moving objects. Radar waves are transmitted from an antenna, reflected by an object, and received by the transmitter. The direction of the reflected wave can be measured to locate the object. The reflected wave frequency is altered if the object is moving. The amount of change is determined by the object's speed.

In a microwave oven, the electromagnetic waves generated are tuned to frequencies that can be absorbed by water molecules. As water molecules absorb energy, they vibrate faster and faster and the temperature of the water increases. So, when you place food that contains water molecules in a microwave oven, the food gets hot. The dish holding the food doesn't absorb a significant amount of microwave energy. The dish stays cool until the heated food conducts thermal energy into the dish.

Infrared Radiation

Infrared radiation has longer wavelengths (and lower frequencies) than visible light, and shorter wavelengths than about one millimeter. Infrared waves include thermal radiation. For example, heat is transferred from an electric heater, burning wood or charcoal, and the sun with infrared waves.

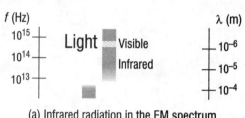

(a) Infrared radiation in the EM spectrum

(b) Electric heater

(c) Infrared thermometer

(d) Remote control

Figure 9.8
Infrared radiation

Infrared radiation is not visible—you cannot see it. But it can be measured using electronic detectors. For example, in medicine, a person's temperature can be measured with an electronic thermometer that detects infrared radiation. Infrared photographs are used to find heat leaking from houses. Infrared images obtained by sensors in satellites and airplanes can yield important information on the weather, the health of crops, and the location of forest fires obscured by smoke. Remote-control devices also use infrared radiation.

Visible Light

Visible light is a very small part of the electromagnetic spectrum, but it is probably the most important part. Sight is a result of our eyes detecting visible electromagnetic waves. The wavelengths of visible light are between 400 nanometers and 700 nanometers (400×10^{-9} m and 700×10^{-9} m).

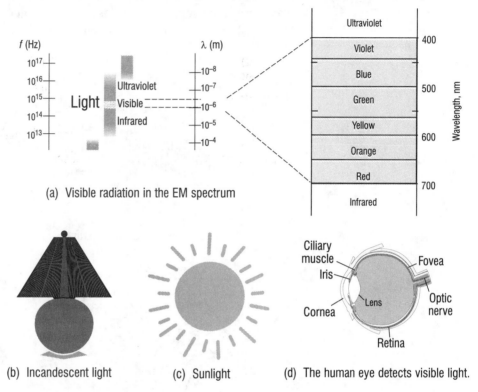

(a) Visible radiation in the EM spectrum

(b) Incandescent light

(c) Sunlight

(d) The human eye detects visible light.

Figure 9.9
Visible light

The human eye can detect the difference in colors in this wavelength range—from violet to blue to green to yellow to orange to red. Violet has the shortest wavelength (and highest frequency); red has the longest wavelength (and lowest frequency).

The sun radiates *white light*. This is light that mixes nearly equal amounts of light of all colors. When white light falls on an object, molecules on the object's surface absorb part of the light and reflect the rest. When a molecule absorbs electromagnetic energy, its energy level increases. The molecules *reradiate* some of the absorbed light. (If some of the absorbed energy is retained, the thermal energy of the molecule increases.)

This reradiation of light explains an object's color. A white sheet of notebook paper reradiates nearly equal amounts of light of all colors. But a ripe apple reradiates light primarily in the red part of the spectrum, between 650- and 700-nm wavelength. What part of the spectrum is reradiated by molecules in the surface of an apple that is not ripe?

Ultraviolet Radiation

Ultraviolet radiation has shorter wavelengths (and higher frequencies) than visible light. Like infrared, the human eye cannot see ultraviolet radiation. Sunlight contains ultraviolet waves, which can tan or burn your skin. Ozone molecules in the Earth's upper atmosphere absorb most of the ultraviolet waves from the sun. A small dose of ultraviolet radiation is beneficial to humans, but larger doses cause skin cancer and eye cataracts.

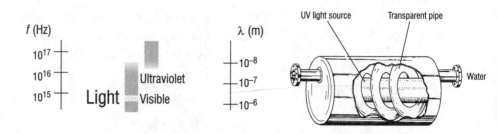

(a) Ultraviolet radiation in the EM spectrum

(b) Water purifier

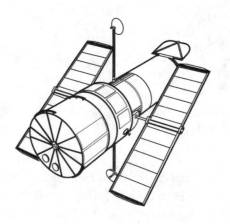

(c) Space-based telescope

(d) Sun-blocking lotion contains molecules that absorb ultraviolet waves.

Figure 9.10
Ultraviolet radiation

Ultraviolet wavelengths are used in water purifiers. In astronomy, telescopes and electronic detectors measure ultraviolet radiation from the atmospheres of other planets, stars, quasars, supernovae, and interstellar gas clouds. These measurements are best made from space, above the Earth's atmosphere.

Refer to Appendix F for a career link to this concept.

X Rays

X rays have short wavelengths and high frequencies. These are high-energy waves that have great penetrating power. They are used in medicine, in airport security systems, to detect fake gems and works of art, and in checking for flaws in welds—a process called nondestructive testing.

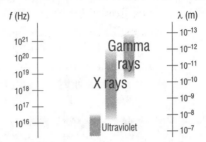

(a) X-ray radiation in the EM spectrum

(b) Airport security

(c) Dental X ray

Figure 9.11
X rays

X rays have enough energy to pass through human cell tissue, but not through bones or teeth. In an X-ray photograph of a broken arm, a doctor can see a shadow of the bone. This is like sunlight shining on a tree—the light can't penetrate the tree, so it leaves a shadow of the tree on the ground. Thin beams of lower-energy X rays are used in computerized axial tomography (CAT) scanners to create very clear pictures of any part of a patient's anatomy.

X rays are produced by an X-ray "gun." In this device, electrons are accelerated to high speeds with large voltages. The high-speed electrons are directed into a "target" that contains an element such as copper or molybdenum. The electrons stop abruptly when they hit a target atom. The rapidly decelerating electrons lose energy, which is emitted as electromagnetic radiation in the X-ray region of the spectrum.

X rays can be dangerous if not used with caution. Overexposure to X rays damages healthy cells, and can cause cancer. This is why X-ray technicians wear protective lead aprons or move to a shielded room when X-ray pictures are made.

Gamma Rays

Gamma rays have wavelengths of less than about ten trillionths of a meter. They have higher frequency and energy than X rays, and they are more penetrating than X rays. Gamma rays are produced by nuclear reactions and by radioactive nuclei (the plural of nucleus). They are used in many medical applications and to destroy bacteria on food. Detectors on satellites above the Earth's atmosphere have recorded images of the universe in the gamma-ray part of the electromagnetic spectrum. These images have yielded important information on the life and death of stars. You will learn more about gamma rays in the next section.

The Photoelectric Effect

All electromagnetic radiation has wavelength and frequency—two properties of waves. In the next chapter, you will learn how electromagnetic radiation reflects off a surface and refracts, or changes direction, when it travels from one medium into another. These are also wavelike properties. But sometimes electromagnetic radiation acts like a particle, not a wave. We say that electromagnetic radiation has both wavelike and particle-like properties.

The **photoelectric effect** is shown in a famous experiment that demonstrates the particle-like behavior of electromagnetic radiation. Figure 9.12 shows the equipment used in the experiment. A metal target, T, and a metal electrode cup are placed inside a glass container with a quartz window at the end. The air is pumped from the container. A light beam can pass through the window and through a hole in the cup to hit the target.

A potential difference, adjustable through a range of positive and negative voltage, is applied between the target and the cup. A sensitive ammeter can measure small currents through the circuit, and a voltmeter measures the potential difference between target and cup.

Experimenters first observed that, when the cup was positive with respect to the target, a current would flow any time sunlight hit the target. The current would stop when the sunlight was removed. Apparently the sunlight caused electrons to be released from the target. The electric field between the cup and the target caused the electrons to flow in the circuit. With no light, no electrons were emitted to conduct current across the gap.

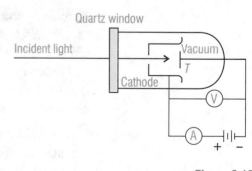

Figure 9.12
A photoelectric-effect experiment

More experimentation produced unexplainable results. When the sunlight was filtered so that only red light (long wavelength—low frequency) hit the target, *no current would flow*. Even very bright red light produced no current. However, very small amounts of blue (short wavelength—high frequency) light *would cause current to flow*. Careful measurements revealed that, for any given target metal, there was a lower limit to the frequency of light that would produce current. If the frequency was too low (wavelength too long), no intensity of light would produce current.

Albert Einstein provided an explanation, and he was awarded the Nobel prize in physics in 1921 for his insight. Einstein proposed that the incident light consisted of very small particle-like bundles of energy. These bundles of energy were later named **photons**. The energy of a photon is proportional to the frequency of the electromagnetic radiation. The constant of proportionality is called **Planck's constant**. We use the symbol h to represent Planck's constant. The numerical value is given below.

$$E_{photon} = hf = h\frac{c}{\lambda}$$

$$h = 6.626176 \times 10^{-34} \ \text{J} \cdot \text{s}$$

Example 9.3 Energy in an X-Ray Photon

Find the energy of an X-ray photon with a wavelength of 1.34×10^{-11} m.

Solution: $E_{photon} = h\frac{c}{\lambda}$

$$E_{photon} = (6.63 \times 10^{-34} \ \text{J} \cdot \text{s}) \left[\frac{3.00 \times 10^8 \ \text{m/s}}{1.34 \times 10^{-11} \ \text{m}} \right]$$

$$E_{photon} = 1.48 \times 10^{-14} \ \text{J}$$

Einstein explained that the electrons on the surface of the target were bound to the metal by the overall electrical force between the electrons and the nuclei of the metal atoms. A specific minimum amount of energy must be provided to "break" an electron out of the metallic surface. The minimum energy required is called the **work function**, ϕ, of the metal. A single photon had to have enough energy to break the electron loose and make it a free electron.

A photon with less energy than the work function would do nothing. Even many low-energy photons (as in a bright beam of red light) would do nothing, because only a single photon could be absorbed by an electron. A high-energy photon could transfer enough energy to break the electron loose, and any excess energy would provide kinetic energy to the free electron. In other words, energy is conserved.

Conservation of energy in the photoelectric effect requires the following relation to be true for a photon with frequency, f, interacting with an electron in a metal whose work function is ϕ.

$$\textit{photon energy} = \textit{work function} + \textit{kinetic energy}$$

$$hf = \phi + KE_e$$

Example 9.4 Kinetic Energy of a Photoelectron

A photon with a wavelength of 535 nm is absorbed by an electron on the surface of aluminum. The electron breaks free of the metal. The work function ϕ for aluminum is 1.88×10^{-19} J. What is the kinetic energy of the free electron?

Solution: $hf = \phi + KE_e$

$$h\frac{c}{\lambda} = \phi + KE_e \qquad \left[f = \frac{c}{\lambda}\right]$$

$$\left(\frac{(6.63 \times 10^{-34} \text{ J} \cdot \text{s})(3.00 \times 10^8 \text{ m/s})}{535 \times 0^{-9} \text{ m}}\right) = (1.88 \times 10^{-19} \text{ J}) + KE_e$$

$$KE_e = 1.84 \times 10^{-19} \text{ J}$$

Einstein also concluded that photons must carry momentum. The momentum of a photon p_{photon} depends on the wavelength of the photon as shown below.

$$p_{photon} = \frac{h}{\lambda}$$

Example 9.5 Momentum of a Microwave Photon

Find the momentum of a microwave photon with a wavelength of 2.54 cm.

Solution: $p_{photon} = \dfrac{h}{\lambda}$

$$p_{photon} = \frac{6.63 \times 10^{-34} \text{ J} \cdot \text{s}}{0.0254 \text{ m}}$$

$$p_{photon} = 2.61 \times 10^{-32} \frac{\text{kg} \cdot \text{m}}{\text{s}} \qquad \left[\text{J} = \text{kg} \cdot \text{m/s}^2\right]$$

Summary

- Electromagnetic radiation is a form of energy transfer produced by accelerating charge. The energy is transferred in the electromagnetic wave's electric and magnetic fields.

- The speed of an electromagnetic wave is the product of the wavelength and frequency.

$$c = \lambda f$$

In vacuum and air, $c = 2.99792 \times 10^8 \frac{m}{s}$.

- Visible light is a small part of the electromagnetic spectrum. Radio waves, microwaves, and infrared radiation have wavelengths longer than visible light. Ultraviolet radiation, X rays, and gamma rays have wavelengths shorter than visible light.

- Albert Einstein explained the photoelectric effect using a particle-like, or photon, model of electromagnetic radiation. A photon is a discrete "bundle" of energy that has no mass, travels at the speed of light, and has wavelength and frequency.

- The energy of a photon is the product of the frequency and Planck's constant.

$$E_{photon} = hf = h\frac{c}{\lambda}$$

$$h = 6.626172 \times 10^{-34} \text{ J} \cdot \text{s}$$

- Photons have momentum. The momentum of a photon is the ratio of Planck's constant to the wavelength of the photon.

$$p_{photon} = \frac{h}{\lambda}$$

Exercises

1. An AC power supply transfers energy to electrons that make up the current in a wire. Name two ways the electrons lose energy.

2. Explain why a radio station would not use a DC power supply to generate radio waves. When would a DC power supply create electromagnetic waves?

3. Do radio waves, visible light, or X rays have the greatest
   (a) frequency?   (b) wavelength?   (c) speed?

4. Find the frequency of an electromagnetic wave if the wavelength is 320.0 nm.

5. Find the wavelength of a cell-phone signal if the frequency is 985 MHz.

6. One of the wavelengths of light emitted by a mercury arc lamp is 496.0 nm.

   (a) Find the frequency of the light.

   (b) Find the energy of a photon of this light.

7. When a spark plug fires, the potential difference between the cathode and the anode is 15 kV (1.5×10^4 V).

   (a) An electron in the gap between the anode and the cathode is accelerated by this potential difference. What is the energy of the electron? (Remember from Section 1.3, the work done on the electron is $q\Delta V$.)

   (b) When the electron is stopped, it converts 25% of this energy to electromagnetic radiation. What is the wavelength of the radiation?

8. Extremely low-frequency (ELF) radio waves have been used to communicate with submarines while they are submerged. These long waves penetrate into water. Frequencies between 30 and 300 Hz have been used.

   (a) Find the wavelength of a 150-Hz radio wave in air.

   (b) The speed of an EM wave in water is about 2.24×10^8 m/s. Find the wavelength of a 150-Hz wave in water.

9. A tungsten electrode is exposed to a light source with a wavelength of 261.5 nm. The work function of tungsten is 7.28×10^{-19} J.

   (a) Find the kinetic energy of an electron on the surface of the tungsten that absorbs one of the photons and is ejected from the surface.

   (b) Find the speed of the electron. (The mass of an electron is 9.110×10^{-31} kg.)

10. A radar transmitter is operated at a wavelength of 1.8 cm. The transmitter emits pulses that last 120 ns. The maximum power output during the pulse is 75 MW.

    (a) Find the energy of a photon in the radar beam.

    (b) Find the momentum of one of the radar photons.

    (c) Find the maximum rate of photon emission (photons/second) of the transmitter.

    (d) Find the maximum force the beam would apply to a target that completely absorbed the radar beam.

    (e) Find the maximum force that would act on a target that completely reflected the beam back at the transmitter.

    (f) Find the impulse applied to the reflecting target by one pulse from the radar beam. Assume that the beam power is constant for the length of the pulse.

11. A helium-neon laser produces light with a wavelength of 632.8 nm.

   (a) What is the energy of a photon in the laser beam?

   (b) How many photons per second are emitted by the laser if the output beam power is 150 mW?

12. Find the momentum of one of the photons in exercise 11.

13. The laser beam in exercise 11 hits a target. Half of the photons are absorbed by the target. Half of the photons are reflected back toward the laser.

   (a) Find the power absorbed by the target.

   (b) Find the rate of change in momentum of the absorbed photons.

   (c) Find the rate of change in momentum of the reflected photons. (A reflected photon's momentum has the same magnitude as its initial momentum, but opposite direction.)

   (d) Find the force exerted on the target by the laser beam.

14. The laser in exercise 11 is part of an environmental monitoring system. The laser light is used to count particles of dust in the air. The beam is focused to a very small spot and hits a dust particle with a diameter of 12.64 mm and a mass of 1.28×10^{-12} kg. Half of the light is absorbed and half reflected as in exercise 13. Find the acceleration of the dust particle.

9.2 NUCLEAR RADIATION

Objectives

- Explain the difference between isotopes of the same element.

- Describe the force that holds nucleons together.

- Explain the relationship between mass and energy according to Einstein's theory of relativity.

- Given the atomic masses of the constituent particles, calculate nuclear binding energy and energy released in nuclear reactions.

- Describe alpha, beta, and gamma radiation. Predict the resulting isotope of a given alpha, beta, or gamma decay.

- Explain why it is possible to have a self-sustaining nuclear fission chain reaction.

- Explain why it is necessary to heat deuterium and tritium to millions of degrees to achieve nuclear fusion.

INTERNET *connection*

To find out more about nuclear radiation, follow the links at **www.learningincontext.com**.

An atom consists of a nucleus surrounded by electrons. The electrons are negatively charged, and they are held to the atom by the electric force of attraction to a positive charge in the nucleus. All the mechanical, fluid, electrical (and electromagnetic), and thermal properties discussed so far are results of interactions among atomic electrons. We have not yet discussed nuclear interactions.

However, the nucleus is extremely important. The nucleus can hold multiple positive charges, and this creates the difference between elements. In addition, nearly all the energy in the universe was created by nuclear reactions.

The Nucleus

The nucleus contains two types of particles: protons and neutrons. A proton has a charge equal and opposite to the charge of an electron. Remember, the elementary charge is 1.6022×10^{-19} C. We use the symbol e to represent this charge. A single electron has a charge of $-e$ and a proton has a charge of $+e$. Neutrons have no charge—they are neutral.

The vast majority of an atom's mass is in the nucleus. The mass of a proton is 1836 times that of an electron. Neutrons have a mass slightly larger than that of a proton. Atomic and nuclear masses are extremely small, and are conveniently expressed in terms of the **atomic mass unit**, abbreviated u. The value of the atomic mass unit is

$$1 \text{ u} = 1.660438 \times 10^{-27} \text{ kg}$$

The charges and masses of the three fundamental atomic particles are summarized in Table 9.1. Notice the number of significant figures listed for mass. You need to use approximately this many figures in nuclear calculations.

Table 9.1
Charge and Mass of the Fundamental Atomic Particles

Particle	Charge	Mass
Electron	$-e$	0.0005486 u
Proton	e	1.007277 u
Neutron	o	1.008665 u

Isotopes

The **atomic number** of an atom is the number of protons in the nucleus of the atom. We use Z to represent atomic number. The **mass number** is the number of protons plus the number of neutrons in the nucleus. We use A to represent mass number. Sometimes we refer to protons and neutrons jointly as *nucleons*. Thus, A is the number of nucleons in the nucleus of an atom. Notice that Z and A are always integers.

Elements are specified by atomic number. For example, oxygen is atomic number 8—there are eight protons in the nucleus of an atom of oxygen.

An oxygen atom is neutral (uncharged) if it also has eight electrons. Figure 9.13 illustrates the atomic composition of the four lightest elements.

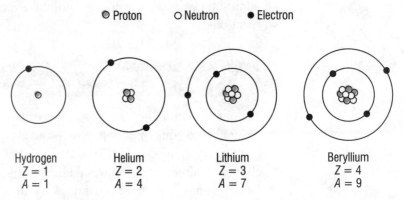

Figure 9.13
Electrons and nucleons of the four lightest elements
(The relative size of each nucleus is greatly enlarged to show the composition.)

An element has a given number of protons, Z. But it is possible for an element to have various values of mass number, A. The differing atoms of the same element are called **isotopes**. Oxygen has three isotopes, with mass numbers 16, 17, and 18. The number of protons and neutrons in the nucleus of each isotope is shown in Table 9.2.

Table 9.2

Atomic Number	Element	Mass Number (A)	Number of Protons (Z)	Number of Neutrons
8	Oxygen	16	8	8
		17	8	9
		18	8	10
9	Fluorine	19	9	10

We use the following symbolic notation to specify the nuclei of isotopes, or *nuclides*. Write the element symbol with the value of Z as a subscript to the left and the value of A as a superscript to the left. The atomic numbers of all the elements are listed in Appendix B.

$$^{A}_{Z}\text{element}$$

For example, the three nuclides of oxygen are written as follows:

$$^{16}_{8}\text{O} \qquad ^{17}_{8}\text{O} \qquad ^{18}_{8}\text{O}$$

It is redundant to write both Z and the element symbol. But we write the value of Z because, as you will see, it helps balance nuclear equations.

Example 9.6 Calculating the Number of Neutrons in a Nuclide

How many neutrons are in $^{64}_{29}\text{Cu}$?

Solution: From Appendix B, this is an isotope of copper. Since $Z = 29$, there are 29 protons in the nucleus. Since $A = 64$, there are 64 nucleons. The number of neutrons is the difference:

$$\begin{array}{ccc} \text{Number of} \\ \text{neutrons} \end{array} = \begin{array}{c} \text{number of} \\ \text{nucleons} \end{array} - \begin{array}{c} \text{number of} \\ \text{protons} \end{array}$$

$$= 64 - 29 = 35$$

There are 35 neutrons in $^{64}_{29}\text{Cu}$.

The Strong Nuclear Force

The diameter of the nucleus is approximately 10^{-14} m. This is less than 1/10,000 of the diameter of the atom. Thus, the distance d between adjacent nucleons is very small. Remember, the electrical force of repulsion between two like charges increases as the distance between the charges decreases. (The force varies as $1/d^2$.) This force is extremely large for values of d found in the nucleus. Without another, greater force of *attraction* the nucleus will fly apart. The force of attraction between nucleons is an entirely different kind of force, called the **strong force**. The strong force is important only when particles such as protons and neutrons are as close together as they are in the nucleus of an atom.

The strong force holds the nucleons together. To remove a nucleon from the nucleus, this force must be overcome. Therefore, work is required to remove a proton or neutron from a nucleus. The amount of work required is called the *binding energy* of the nucleon. The total amount of work required to separate all nucleons from a nucleus is called the **binding energy** of the nucleus. Stated another way, this is the total amount of energy that holds the nucleus together.

The binding energy of a nucleon is the energy required to remove the nucleon from the nucleus.

The binding energy of a nucleus is the energy required to separate all the nucleons.

Figure 9.14
Binding energy

Nuclear Binding Energy

Deuterium is an isotope of hydrogen, written as $_1^2\text{H}$. It contains one proton and one neutron. What would you predict for the mass of the deuterium nucleus? The mass should be the sum of the masses of a proton m_p and a neutron m_n. From Table 9.1:

$$m_p + m_n = 1.007277 \text{ u} + 1.008665 \text{ u} = 2.015942 \text{ u}$$

However, the mass of the deuterium nucleus has been measured very accurately, and it is actually 2.013554 u. The difference in nuclear masses for deuterium is an example of a general observation:

The mass of a stable nucleus is always less than the combined masses of the constituent nucleons.

The difference in the masses is called the **mass defect**. What happened to the missing mass?

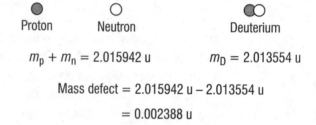

Proton   Neutron   Deuterium

$$m_p + m_n = 2.015942 \text{ u} \qquad m_D = 2.013554 \text{ u}$$

$$\text{Mass defect} = 2.015942 \text{ u} - 2.013554 \text{ u}$$

$$= 0.002388 \text{ u}$$

Figure 9.15
The mass of a deuterium nucleus is less than the sum of the masses of the constituents. The difference is the mass defect.

In 1905, Albert Einstein published his theory of relativity. Relativity links electricity and magnetism, time and space, and *mass and energy*. Einstein concluded that mass and energy are the same. The mass defect is not really "missing." It has been converted into energy—the binding energy of the nucleus. The amount of energy E can be calculated by Einstein's equation

$$E = mc^2$$

where m is the mass converted into energy and c is the speed of light. To five significant figures, $c = 2.9979 \times 10^8$ m/s.

When making nuclear calculations, it is convenient to use a new unit for energy—the **electron volt**, abbreviated eV. This is defined as the amount of energy gained by an electron when accelerated through a potential difference of one volt. You learned in Section 1.3 that this amount of energy is the product of the charge and voltage:

$$1 \text{ eV} = (1.6022 \times 10^{-19} \text{ C})(1 \text{ V}) = 1.6022 \times 10^{-19} \text{ J} \quad [\text{J} = \text{C} \cdot \text{V}]$$

Example 9.7 Binding Energy of Deuterium

Calculate the binding energy of $_1^2\text{H}$ in joules and in electron volts.

Solution: Let m represent the mass defect. As shown in Figure 9.15, $m = 0.002388$ u. Convert to kilograms.

$$m = (0.002388 \text{ u})(1.6604 \times 10^{-27} \text{ kg/u}) = 3.9650 \times 10^{-30} \text{ kg}$$

$$E = mc^2 = (3.9650 \times 10^{-30} \text{ kg})(2.9979 \times 10^8 \text{ m/s})^2$$

$$E = 3.5635 \times 10^{-13} \text{ J} \qquad\qquad \left[\text{kg} \cdot \text{m}^2/\text{s}^2 = \text{J}\right]$$

Convert to eV:

$$E = (3.5635 \times 10^{-13} \text{ J})\left(\frac{1 \text{ eV}}{1.6022 \times 10^{-19} \text{ J}}\right) = 2.224 \times 10^6 \text{ eV}$$

To three significant figures, the binding energy of the deuterium nucleus is 3.56×10^{-13} J or 2.22×10^6 eV. You can also write the binding energy as 2.22 MeV, where MeV $= 10^6$ eV.

Converting mass to energy is a common calculation in nuclear physics. It is convenient to use a mass-energy conversion factor. You will work with mass in atomic mass units and energy in electron volts. What is the energy equivalent of 1 u? (1 u $= 1.6604 \times 10^{-27}$ kg)

$$E = mc^2 = (1.6604 \times 10^{-27} \text{ kg})(2.9979 \times 10^8 \text{ m/s})^2$$

$$= 1.4923 \times 10^{-10} \text{ J}$$

Convert to eV:

$$E = (1.4923 \times 10^{-10} \text{ J})\left(\frac{1 \text{ eV}}{1.6022 \times 10^{-19} \text{ J}}\right) \approx 9.315 \times 10^8 \text{ eV}$$

$$= 931.5 \text{ MeV} \qquad\qquad \left[\text{MeV} = 10^6 \text{ eV}\right]$$

Rounded to four significant figures,

   a mass of 1 u is equivalent to an energy of 931.5 MeV.

Most of the time in nuclear calculations, masses are given as *atomic*, not nuclear masses. The atomic mass of an element or isotope includes the mass of the electrons. This mass should be removed from the calculation of nuclear binding energy. But, instead of subtracting the electron masses, you can use the *atomic* mass of $_1^1\text{H}$ instead of the mass of a proton. Then the electron masses cancel.

In the example below, helium (atomic number 2) has two neutrons, two protons, and two electrons. In the mass-defect calculation, the mass of two $_1^1H$ atoms is used instead of two protons. Thus, the two electron masses cancel in the subtraction.

Example 9.8 Binding Energy of Helium

The atomic mass of $_2^4He$ is 4.002603 u. The atomic mass of $_1^1H$ is 1.007825 u. What is the binding energy of the nucleus?

Solution: Calculate the mass of the constituents. There are two protons and two neutrons. Use the atomic mass of $_1^1H$ instead of a proton to include the electron mass.

$$2m_H + 2m_n = 2(1.007825 \text{ u}) + 2(1.008665 \text{ u}) = 4.032980 \text{ u}$$

Calculate the mass defect m. The electron masses cancel.

$$m = 4.032980 \text{ u} - 4.002603 \text{ u} = 0.030377 \text{ u}$$

The binding energy E is the energy equivalent of the mass defect.

$$E = (0.030377 \text{ u})(931.5 \text{ MeV/u})$$

$$= 28.30 \text{ MeV}$$

The binding energy of $_2^4He$ is 28.30 million electron volts.

Radioactivity

Refer to Appendix F for a career link to this concept.

In 1896, the French physicist Henri Becquerel accidentally discovered that a uranium compound would expose a covered photographic plate. The exposure resulted in an effect on the plate similar to that produced by light. But the plate was covered, and no light was emitted by the compound. Becquerel concluded that the uranium compound must be emitting a different kind of radiation. This radiation is not visible and it passes through a cover to expose the photographic plate underneath.

Several years later, the English scientist Ernest Rutherford described the properties of the radiation emitted by uranium. He discovered three different kinds of radiation, and he named them *alpha*, *beta*, and *gamma* radiation. In addition, Rutherford discovered the existence of the nucleus in 1911. This helped form our current understanding of the atom. It also explained the origin of alpha, beta, and gamma radiation. The nuclei of uranium and many other isotopes are unstable. This means they spontaneously transform themselves into other nuclides. When they do, they emit radiation. These unstable nuclides are said to be **radioactive**.

Alpha radiation consists of particles. Rutherford determined that alpha particles are the same as the nuclei of helium atoms, ^4_2He. When an unstable nucleus emits an alpha particle, it is said to undergo **alpha decay**. Since the mass number of an alpha particle is 4 and the atomic number is 2, the nucleus undergoing alpha decay loses 4 nucleons, including 2 protons. Therefore, its mass number decreases by 4 and its atomic number decreases by 2.

For example, $^{238}_{92}\text{U}$ is radioactive and emits an alpha particle. The following equation describes the alpha decay. This is called a **nuclear equation**.

$$^{238}_{92}\text{U} \rightarrow {}^{234}_{90}\text{Th} + {}^4_2\text{He}$$

In words, the equation says that uranium-238 yields thorium-234 plus an alpha particle.

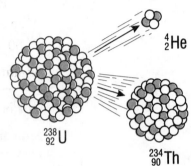

Figure 9.16
Alpha decay

Notice that *the total number of nucleons is conserved*. Uranium-238 has 238 nucleons, and thorium-234 plus the alpha has $234 + 4 = 238$ nucleons. In other words, the sum of the superscripts on the right must equal the sum of the superscripts on the left. Notice also that *the total charge is conserved*. Uranium-238 has 92 protons, and thorium-234 plus the alpha has $90 + 2 = 92$ protons. In other words, the sum of the subscripts on the right must equal the sum of the subscripts on the left. These two conditions must be satisfied for all nuclear equations.

Example 9.9 Alpha Decay

Plutonium-238 is radioactive, and it emits an alpha particle when it decays. What is the resultant nuclide?

Solution: From Appendix B, plutonium is atomic number 94. Write the nuclear equation with A, Z, and X representing the unknown atomic mass, atomic number, and element.

$$^{238}_{94}\text{Pu} \rightarrow {}^A_Z X + {}^4_2\text{He}$$

To conserve nucleons, $238 = A + 4$. So $A = 234$.

To conserve charge, $94 = Z + 2$. So $Z = 92$.

From Appendix B, the element with atomic number 92 is uranium.

The resultant nuclide is $^{234}_{92}\text{U}$.

Beta radiation also consists of particles. Beta particles are the same as electrons, but they can have charge of either sign. A positively charged electron is called a **positron**. Except for sign, it is identical to a negatively charged electron. A positron is an example of an *antiparticle*, a particle of *antimatter*.

Some unstable nuclei undergo beta decay by electron emission and some undergo positron emission. But how does a nucleus emit an electron when there are no electrons in the nucleus? In electron emission, a neutron in the nucleus is transformed into a proton. This transformation conserves charge. The neutron charge (0) equals the sum of the proton charge (+1) and the electron charge (–1). Since the mass number of an electron is 0 and the charge is –1, the nucleus undergoing electron emission loses no nucleons and its atomic number increases by 1.

Similarly, in positron emission a proton in the nucleus is transformed into a neutron. This transformation also conserves charge.

As examples, $^{234}_{90}$Th is radioactive and emits an electron, while $^{13}_{7}$N emits a positron. The following nuclear equations describe these beta-decay reactions.

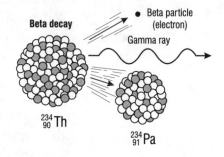

Figure 9.17
Beta decay

$$^{234}_{90}\text{Th} \rightarrow \, ^{234}_{91}\text{Pa} + \, ^{0}_{-1}e$$

$$^{13}_{7}\text{N} \rightarrow \, ^{13}_{6}\text{C} + \, ^{0}_{+1}e$$

Notice that nucleons and charge are conserved in each equation.

Example 9.10 Beta Decay

Strontium-90 is radioactive, and it emits an electron when it decays. What is the resultant nuclide?

Solution: From Appendix B, strontium is atomic number 38. Write the nuclear equation with A, Z, and X representing the unknown atomic mass, atomic number, and element.

$$^{90}_{38}\text{Sr} \rightarrow \, ^{A}_{Z}X + \, ^{0}_{-1}e$$

To conserve nucleons, $90 = A + 0$. So $A = 90$.

To conserve charge, $38 = Z - 1$. So $Z = 39$.

From Appendix B, the element with atomic number 39 is yttrium.

The resultant nuclide is $^{90}_{39}$Y.

Gamma radiation consists of high-energy photons. (See Figure 9.5, the electromagnetic spectrum, in the last section.) Photons have no mass or charge. If an unstable nucleus emits only a gamma ray, neither the atomic mass nor the atomic number of the nucleus changes. Gamma rays are often emitted with alpha and beta decay. (See Figure 9.17.)

Nuclear Fission

In the late 1930s, scientists discovered that neutrons can cause uranium to split into smaller nuclides. This process is called **fission**. The process begins when a nuclide such as uranium-235 absorbs a neutron. (The neutron must be supplied by some source.) The uranium-235 plus the neutron becomes uranium-236, which is so unstable that it breaks apart into two smaller nuclides, called *fission fragments*. Neutrons are also emitted during fission. These neutrons can be used to cause other uranium nuclei to fission. Thus the process can be continued in a *chain reaction*.

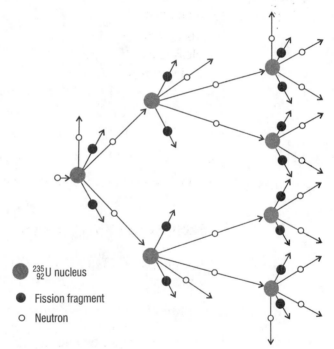

$^{235}_{92}$U nucleus

Fission fragment

Neutron

Figure 9.18
In a chain reaction, some of the neutrons produced by fission cause further fissions.

Once it begins, the chain reaction is self-sustaining. No additional neutrons from a source are needed to continue the reactions. The ability to create a self-sustained chain reaction enabled the development of nuclear reactors and nuclear bombs. In a reactor, energy released in nuclear fission provides power for electrical generating plants and submarines. Nuclear reactors can produce energy and power for years without refueling.

During a fission nuclear reaction, mass is converted into energy. This energy is carried away in gamma rays, kinetic energy of the fission fragments, and kinetic energy of the neutrons.

Example 9.11 Energy Release in a Fission Reaction

Calculate the energy released in the following fission reaction.

$$\_0^1n + \_{92}^{235}U \rightarrow \_{55}^{140}Cs + \_{37}^{93}Rb + 3\left(\_0^1n\right)$$

The atomic masses are listed in the table below.

Particle or Nuclide	Atomic Mass
Neutron	1.0087 u
U-235	235.0439 u
Cs-140	139.9173 u
Rb-93	92.9220 u

Solution: Calculate the mass defect m.

Mass before fission		**Mass after fission**	
1 neutron =	1.0087 u	3 neutrons =	3.0261 u
U-235 =	235.0439 u	Cs-140 =	139.9173 u
Total	236.0526 u	Rb-93 =	92.9220 u
		Total	235.8654 u

$$m = 236.0526 \text{ u} - 235.8654 \text{ u} = 0.1872 \text{ u}$$

This is the mass converted into energy during the fission reaction. Use the conversion factor 1 u = 931.5 MeV.

$$E = (0.1872 \text{ u})(931.5 \text{ MeV/u}) = 174 \text{ MeV}$$

The energy released is 174 million electron volts.

Example 9.11 shows two possible fission fragments, cesium-140 and rubidium-93. Hundreds of other combinations are possible, in fact any combination that conserves nucleons and charge. Almost all fission fragments are radioactive. The fission fragments are the source of highly radioactive waste from nuclear reactors and radioactive fallout from nuclear explosions.

(a) Nuclear reactor for electric power   (b) Nuclear reactor for submarine propulsion

Figure 9.19
In a nuclear reactor, energy released in fission provides
power for generating electricity and propelling submarines.

Nuclear Fusion

In nuclear fission, a single large nucleus splits into two smaller nuclei. In
nuclear fusion, two small nuclei combine to form a single larger nucleus. In
both fission and fusion, the mass of the particles after the reaction is less
than the mass before the reaction. Mass is converted into energy.

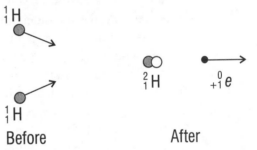

Before   After

Figure 9.20
The fusion of two protons produces
a deuterium nucleus plus an electron.

Nuclear fusion is the source of energy in the stars. For example, in the sun
most energy is produced by fusion reactions in a *proton-proton cycle*.

$$_1^1H + {}_1^1H \rightarrow {}_1^2H + {}_{+1}^0e$$

$$_1^1H + {}_1^2H \rightarrow {}_2^3He$$

$$_2^3He + {}_2^3He \rightarrow {}_2^4He + 2\left({}_1^1H\right)$$

The first two reactions must occur twice to produce the two nuclei for the last reaction. The net outcome of the cycle is that four protons produce one helium nucleus and two positrons.

Two nuclei must travel at very high speeds to overcome the electrical force of repulsion and get close enough together for the strong force to cause fusion. Thus, the nuclei must have very high thermal energies. This is why fusion is often called a *thermonuclear reaction*. On a star such as the sun, the thermal energy comes from a conversion of gravitational potential energy into kinetic energy of the reacting particles.

On Earth, scientists and engineers are trying to develop a reactor that uses fusion as a means of producing energy to generate electrical power. The most likely reaction will use two isotopes of hydrogen, deuterium $_1^2\text{H}$ and tritium $_1^3\text{H}$, as fuels. This is called a D-T fusion reaction.

$$_1^2\text{H} + _1^3\text{H} \rightarrow _2^4\text{H} + _0^1\text{n}$$

Deuterium can be extracted from seawater. Tritium can be produced in a fusion reactor using the neutrons produced by D-T fusion in a reaction with lithium.

$$_3^6\text{Li} + _0^1\text{n} \rightarrow _1^3\text{H} + _2^4\text{He}$$

To achieve D-T fusion, the deuterium and tritium must be heated to millions of degrees. At these temperatures, the materials will be in the plasma state. The plasma must be confined long enough to achieve fusion without being in contact with another material. (The plasma will be cooled if it touches another material.) There are two strategies for achieving these conditions. One uses a magnetic field to heat and confine the plasma. This method is called *magnetic confinement fusion*. The other uses laser beams to deposit energy on the surface of small spheres containing deuterium and tritium. The pressure created on the surface of the sphere forces the sphere to implode, compressing the D-T fuel and raising its temperature. This method is called *inertial confinement fusion*.

Using either method, a reactor for generating electricity is practical only if the power output from D-T fusion is greater than the power input to generate the magnetic field or the laser beams. The practicality has not yet been demonstrated.

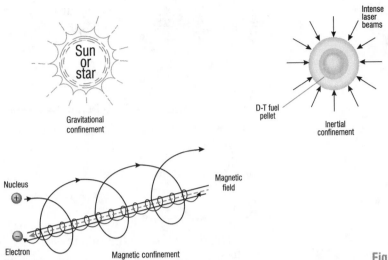

Gravitational
confinement

Intense
laser
beams

D-T fuel
pellet

Inertial
confinement

Nucleus

Electron

Magnetic
field

Magnetic confinement

Figure 9.21
Three ways to achieve nuclear fusion

Example 9.12 Energy Released in D-T Fusion

Calculate the energy released in the D-T fusion reaction. The atomic masses are listed in the table below.

Particle or Nuclide		Atomic Mass
neutron	$^{1}_{0}n$	1.008665 u
hydrogen	$^{1}_{1}H$	1.007825 u
deuterium	$^{2}_{1}H$	2.01410 u
tritium	$^{3}_{1}H$	3.01605 u
helium-3	$^{3}_{2}He$	3.01603 u
helium-4	$^{4}_{2}He$	4.00260 u

Solution: Calculate the mass defect m.

Mass before fusion		**Mass after fusion**	
$^{2}_{1}H$ = 2.01410 u		$^{4}_{2}He$ = 4.00260 u	
$^{3}_{1}H$ = 3.01605 u		$^{1}_{0}n$ = 1.00867 u	
Total 5.03015 u		**Total** 5.01127 u	

$$m = 5.03015 \text{ u} - 5.01127 \text{ u} = 0.01888 \text{ u}$$

Use the conversion factor 1 u = 931.5 MeV.

$$E = (0.01888 \text{ u})(931.5 \text{ MeV/u}) = 17.6 \text{ MeV}$$

The energy released is 17.6 million electron volts.

Summary

- Two isotopes of an element have the same atomic number (number of protons) but different mass numbers (number of nucleons).

- The strong force holds nucleons together. In a stable nucleus, the strong force is much greater than the electrical force of repulsion between protons.

- According to Einstein's theory of relativity, mass and energy are equivalent. The relationship is expressed mathematically as $E = mc^2$.

- The nucleus of an atom has less mass than the sum of its constituents. The difference in the two masses, called the mass defect, has been converted into nuclear binding energy.

- In a nuclear reaction, charge is conserved and nucleons are conserved. The total mass after the reaction is less than the total mass before the reaction. The difference in the two masses is converted into energy.

- Three forms of radioactive decay are alpha decay, beta decay, and gamma decay. Alpha particles are identical to helium nuclei. Beta particles are electrons or positrons. Gamma rays are electromagnetic radiation.

- Nuclear fission occurs when a nucleus such as $^{235}_{92}U$ absorbs a neutron, becomes highly unstable, and splits into two smaller nuclei. Other particles, such as neutrons, can also be emitted during fission.

- Nuclear fusion occurs when two high-speed nuclei collide, and come close enough together that the strong force of attraction overcomes the electrical force of repulsion.

Exercises

Note: You will need to use the atomic masses listed in the table in Example 9.12 for some exercises.

1. An atom contains 11 electrons, 11 protons, and 12 neutrons. What is the atomic number of the atom? What is the mass number?

2. How many protons are in the nucleus of each of the following isotopes? How many neutrons?

   (a) $^{50}_{26}Fe$ (b) $^{29}_{14}Si$ (c) $^{198}_{79}Au$ (d) $^{197}_{79}Au$

3. The mass of a $^{12}_{6}C$ nucleus is 0.0989 u less than the sum of the masses of six protons and six neutrons. What is the binding energy of the nucleus of $^{12}_{6}C$.

4. Calculate the binding energy of the tritium nucleus.

5. The atomic mass of $^{10}_{5}$B is 10.01294 u. What is the binding energy of the nucleus?

6. The binding energy of $^{7}_{3}$Li is 39.2 MeV. What is the atomic mass of $^{7}_{3}$Li?

7. Match the nuclear radiation with its common name on the right.

   (a) ___ alpha particle   1. proton
   (b) ___ beta particle   2. electron
   (c) ___ gamma radiation   3. neutron
                                    4. photon
                                    5. helium nucleus
                                    6. deuterium nucleus

8. What happens to the atomic number when a radioactive nucleus emits an alpha particle? What happens to the mass number?

9. What happens to the atomic number when a radioactive nucleus emits an electron? What happens to the mass number?

10. What happens to the atomic number when a radioactive nucleus emits a positron? What happens to the mass number?

11. The isotope $^{226}_{88}$Ra is radioactive, and it decays by emitting an alpha particle. Write the nuclear equation. What nuclide is produced by the alpha decay?

12. The isotope $^{131}_{53}$I is radioactive, and it decays by emitting an electron. Write the nuclear equation. What nuclide is produced by the beta decay?

13. The isotope $^{22}_{11}$Na is radioactive, and it decays by emitting a positron. Write the nuclear equation. What nuclide is produced by the beta decay?

14. Complete the following nuclear reactions.

    (a) $^{7}_{3}$Li + $^{1}_{0}$n → ? + $^{4}_{2}$He + $^{1}_{0}$n

    (b) $^{24}_{12}$Mg + ? → $^{28}_{14}$Si

    (c) $^{63}_{29}$Cu + ? → $^{61}_{28}$Ni + $^{4}_{2}$He

15. In a nuclear reactor, a $^{238}_{92}$U (mass 238.05078 u) nucleus absorbs a neutron, fissions, and produces two neutrons and two fission fragments. The fragments are $^{96}_{39}$Y (mass 95.91590 u) and $^{141}_{534}$I (mass 140.93483 u).

    (a) Write the nuclear equation for the fission reaction.

    (b) Calculate the mass defect.

    (c) How much energy is released by this reaction?

16. The radioactive isotope $^{238}_{94}$Pu is used to provide power for space probes. How much energy is released when $^{238}_{94}$Pu (mass 238.04955 u) alpha decays to $^{234}_{92}$U (mass 234.04095 u)?

17. When $^{239}_{94}$Pu (mass 239.05216 u) absorbs a neutron, it fissions. The fission results in three neutrons and two fission fragments: $^{96}_{42}$Mo (mass 95.90468 u) and $^{141}_{52}$Te (mass 140.94439 u).

    (a) Write the nuclear equation for the fission reaction.

    (b) Calculate the mass defect.

    (c) How much energy is released by this reaction?

18. A D-D fusion reaction has more than one possible result. Complete each of the following.

    (a) $^2_1$H + $^2_1$H → ?

    (b) $^2_1$H + $^2_1$H → ? + $^1_0$n

    (c) $^2_1$H + $^2_1$H → ? + $^1_1$H

19. Calculate the energy released by each of the reactions in exercise 18.

20. Since an electron and a positron have opposite charge, they are attracted to each other. When the force of attraction causes a collision, they can annihilate each other. An **annihilation reaction** converts all the mass of the two particles into energy in the form of gamma rays. The mass of an electron is 9.11×10^{-31} kg. The mass of a positron is the same. Calculate the energies of the gamma rays emitted in an electron-positron annihilation reaction.

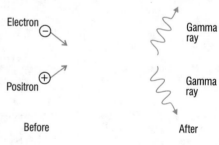

21. A nuclear reactor using $^{235}_{92}$U as fuel operates at a power level of 950 MW (9.5×10^8 watts).

    (a) $^{235}_{92}$U releases an average of 200 MeV per fission. How many fissions per second occur to yield 950 MW of power?

    (b) In one year of continuous operation, how much of the fuel's mass is lost?

CHAPTER NINE
SUMMARY

Radiation is an energy-transfer process. In this chapter you have learned about two types of radiation—electromagnetic and nuclear. Electromagnetic radiation transfers energy in self-propagating electric and magnetic fields of electromagnetic waves. Nuclear radiation is energy emitted by the decay of radioactive nuclei.

Visible light is electromagnetic radiation with wavelengths between 400 nm and 700 nm. The spectrum of visible light extends from red at long wavelengths to violet at short wavelengths. Infrared, microwave, and radio waves have wavelengths longer than visible light. Ultraviolet, X rays, and gamma rays have shorter wavelengths than visible light. For all electromagnetic waves, the speed equals the product of frequency and wavelength. $c = \lambda f$. The speed in a vacuum is the maximum possible speed of any entity, approximately 3×10^8 m/s. The energy transferred by electromagnetic waves is the product of Planck's constant and the frequency. $E = hf$.

Three types of nuclear radiation are alpha, beta, and gamma radiation. Alpha particles are the same as helium nuclei. Beta particles are electrons or positrons. Gamma rays are electromagnetic radiation.

Fission occurs when some heavy nuclei absorb neutrons, become unstable, and split into two lighter nuclei, or fission fragments. Fusion occurs when two highly energetic nuclei collide and join together. Both fission and fusion convert mass into energy. $E = mc^2$, where m is the difference between the total nuclear masses before the reaction and after.

LIGHT AND OPTICAL SYSTEMS

You learned in the last chapter that light is electromagnetic radiation. But the word "light" is a broad term that includes three regions of the electromagnetic spectrum. Light includes infrared radiation, visible radiation, and ultraviolet radiation. Radiation from the sun contains all of these wavelengths of light.

The wavelengths of infrared radiation are too long for our eyes to sense. We feel infrared radiation as heat on our skin.

Visible light stimulates sensing cells in our eyes. We sense the longer wavelengths of visible light as red light and the shorter as blue light.

The wavelengths of ultraviolet radiation are too short for our eyes to sense. This high-energy radiation produces both tanning and burning of our skin.

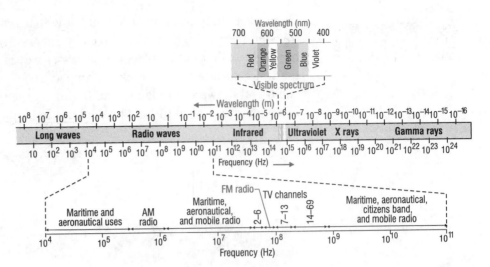

Wavelength (nm)

700   600   500   400

Red | Orange | Yellow | Green | Blue | Violet

Visible spectrum

← Wavelength (m)

10^8 10^7 10^6 10^5 10^4 10^3 10^2 10 1 10^{-1} 10^{-2} 10^{-3} 10^{-4} 10^{-5} 10^{-6} 10^{-7} 10^{-8} 10^{-9} 10^{-10} 10^{-11} 10^{-12} 10^{-13} 10^{-14} 10^{-15} 10^{-16}

Long waves | **Radio waves** | **Infrared** | **Ultraviolet** | **X rays** | **Gamma rays**

10 10^2 10^3 10^4 10^5 10^6 10^7 10^8 10^9 10^{10} 10^{11} 10^{12} 10^{13} 10^{14} 10^{15} 10^{16} 10^{17} 10^{18} 10^{19} 10^{20} 10^{21} 10^{22} 10^{23} 10^{24}

Frequency (Hz) →

FM radio | TV channels

Maritime and aeronautical uses | AM radio | Maritime, aeronautical, and mobile radio | 2–6 | 7–13 | 14–69 | Maritime, aeronautical, citizens band, and mobile radio

10^4 10^5 10^6 10^7 10^8 10^9 10^{10} 10^{11}

Frequency (Hz)

Figure 10.1
The electromagnetic spectrum

From Plato's time in ancient Greece to Max Planck in the 1920s, philosophers and scientists argued about whether light was a particle or a wave. Their confusion can be understood because electromagnetic radiation has both characteristics. Sometimes light acts like a wave as it passes through lenses in telescopes or our eyes. Sometimes light acts like tiny particles that are bundles of energy called photons. When a photon hits a grain of photographic emulsion on film, the photon energy supplies the energy to cause a chemical reaction. An electron in a neon atom in a laser can lose energy and produce a photon. Each of these ways of thinking about light can be helpful in different situations.

Figure 10.2
Light is represented by rays.

When we want to represent the path that light follows, we draw an *arrow* or **ray**. In Figure 10-2, light is shown moving from a lamp, down onto a tabletop, along straight lines. Then the light reflects off the tabletop and moves away along other straight lines. The direction along which the light travels is shown by the head of the arrow. Light rays drawn this way represent beams of light that are composed of millions of light photons traveling together.

From your study of Chapter 8, you know that water and sound waves transfer energy. Light waves also carry energy from a source, such as the sun or a light bulb, to other places. Like water waves that travel outward along the water surface when a rock is dropped into a pond, light waves from the sun travel outward through space. In this chapter you'll learn about the behavior and control of light by dealing first with light rays and then with light waves.

(a) Water waves move energy outward.

(b) Light waves move energy outward.

Figure 10.3
Water waves and light waves transfer energy.

Optical systems are made up of light sources, a variety of optical components, detectors, and computers that use light to perform useful functions. Our eyes are very complex optical systems that use light to form images. These images are interpreted by our brains.

Combinations of laser light sources, telescopes, light detectors, and microcomputers make up optical surveying systems that locate roads, bridges, and buildings with millimeter precision. Diode lasers and photodiode detectors are components in optical systems that record and read CDs. The Hubble telescope uses mirrors and lenses to form images. Each image is divided into pixels—a small subdivision of the image—which can be described by numbers and transmitted to Earth. Computers convert the numbers back into a visible image. All of the components needed to complete this process form an optical system.

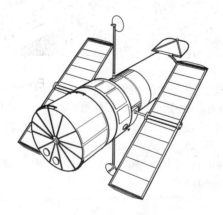

Figure 10.4
Hubble telescope

One of the most useful optical systems in science and technology is the laser. Energy can be "pumped" into the electrons of certain atoms or molecules and stored there for a short time. When that energy is released from the electrons in the form of photons, all the photons emitted have the same energy and wavelength. This stream of photons makes a beam of light that is very pure in color (they have very nearly the same wavelength). All the wave components of the beam are phase coherent, that is, they are in step as shown in Figure 10.5.

Figure 10.5
Coherent waves are in phase with each other.

In addition to the pure color and phase coherence, the physical construction of most lasers produces a light beam that spreads very little over long distances. This characteristic can be improved with some external lenses. For example, a lens enables a beam sent from the Earth to the moon to have a diameter of only few hundred meters when it hits the moon.

These three properties of laser light—color purity, coherence, and low divergence—allow laser light to be focused to very small spots and produce very high power densities. High power densities are used for laser surgery, metal cutting, and trimming electronic parts.

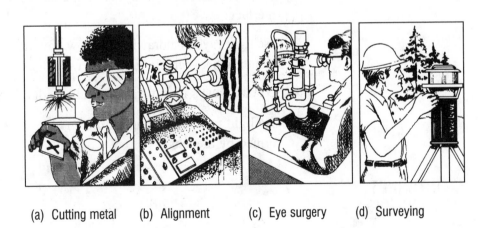

(a) Cutting metal   (b) Alignment   (c) Eye surgery   (d) Surveying

Figure 10.6
Uses of laser light

10.1 RAY OPTICS: REFLECTION AND REFRACTION

Objectives

- Explain what is meant by the curvature and focal length of mirrors and lenses. Explain how curvature and focal length are related.

- Use light rays to trace light from an object to a mirror to the image formed by the mirror.

- Define index of refraction.

- Show how Snell's law is used to model refraction at an optical interface.

- Use light rays in a drawing to show how light is refracted at an optical boundary between air and another medium.

- Explain what's meant by the focal length of a lens.

- Use light rays to trace light from an object through a lens to an image formed by the lens.

INTERNET *connection*

To find out more about reflection and refraction, follow the links at **www.learningincontext.com**.

Light, whether thought of as photons or as waves, travels in straight lines through space or a uniform medium. Objects like mirrors can change the path of a light ray to a new straight line. Light can change direction to a new straight line by reflecting off a polished surface.

Figure 10.7
Shadows seem to indicate that light
travels in straight lines or rays.

If light encounters an interface that changes the medium, such as from air to glass, it may change direction to a new straight line. These processes that make light change direction are called *reflection* and *refraction*. We represent the path of a photon through an optical system by a series of straight arrows called **rays**. The study of light motion in optical systems by using rays is called **ray optics**.

Reflection

When a light ray strikes the surface of a material, some of the light may bounce off the surface, much like a billiard ball bounces off the edge of a billiard table. This process is called **reflection**. Reflected light acts a lot like a billiard ball. Both the ball and the light ray hit and bounce off the surface at equal angles. In Figure 10.8, the light ray is shown to reflect from the surface of the table at the same angle at which it strikes the table.

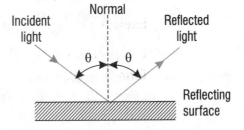

Figure 10.8
Light strikes and reflects from a surface at the same angle.

The angles of the incident and reflected light rays are measured from the **normal** line at the point of reflection. The normal line is a line perpendicular to the surface at the point of reflection. The **angle of incidence** is the angle between the incoming light ray and the normal line. The **angle of reflection** is the angle between the normal line and the reflected ray.

From observations and experiments, we know that *the angle of incidence is always equal to the angle of reflection*. That is, light reflects at the same angle at which it strikes the smooth surface of a material. This is called the **law of reflection**. Note that the incident ray, the normal, and the reflected ray all lie in the same plane. This plane is called the **plane of incidence**.

The amount of light that's reflected from a surface varies a lot. You've probably noticed that the polished surface of a new car reflects much more light—it appears brighter—than the surface of a rusted, dirty surface. Highly polished surfaces used to reflect light are called **mirrors**. Mirror surfaces of aluminum and silver reflect about 90% of the light that strikes them.

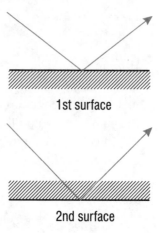

1st surface

2nd surface

Figure 10.9
First- and second-surface mirrors

Most common mirrors are made by putting a thin metal coating on glass. The glass provides the flat surface, but the metal makes the surface highly reflective. Smaller amounts of light can be reflected from an uncoated glass surface. If the metal coating is on the first surface the light hits, the mirror is a first-surface mirror. Most very-high-quality mirrors in optical systems are first-surface mirrors. Common household mirrors have the glass in front of the coating to provide protection for the thin metal coating. A common household mirror is a second-surface mirror.

Mirrors are further classified by the shape of the surface. Mirrors with flat surfaces are called **plane mirrors**. Mirrors with spherical reflecting surfaces are called **spherical mirrors**.

As shown in Figure 10.10, an **object** is a source of light rays. It may emit light, as in a lamp or a laser, or it may be illuminated by an unknown source, as in Figure 10.10. When you view the reflection of an object in a mirror, you see an **image**. A plane mirror produces an image that is reversed (right becomes left and vice versa). The image formed by a plane mirror appears to be located the same distance behind the mirror as the object is in front of the mirror ($s_o = s_i$).

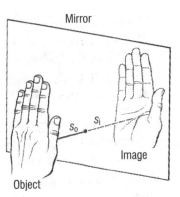

Mirror

S_o S_i

Image

Object

Figure 10.10
A plane mirror reverses left and right.
Light leaves the object, reflects off the mirror, and forms an image.

When parallel light rays strike the flat surface of a plane mirror, the reflected rays leave the mirror as a parallel beam. Notice in Figure 10.11 that each of the rays—a, b, c—obeys the law of reflection.

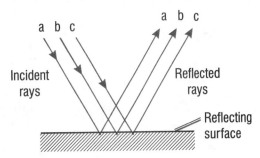

a b c   a b c

Incident   Reflected
rays   rays

Reflecting
surface

Figure 10.11
Parallel light rays striking and reflecting from the flat surface of a plane mirror

Some mirrors have spherical reflecting surfaces. Spherical mirrors can be **convex**, like the *outside* surface (or back) of a spoon, or **concave**, like the *inside* surface of a spoon. You've probably seen convex mirrors in stores, where they are used for security. Many cars and trucks have convex spherical rearview mirrors on the passenger sides. These mirrors provide wide-angle views for the drivers, at the price of making objects appear farther away than they are.

When parallel light rays strike the surface of a concave mirror, they're reflected to a point in front of the mirror. (See Figure 10.12 on the next page.) Why does this happen? The parallel rays are all reflected according to the law of reflection. But notice that the normal line—always a radius of the mirror—changes its direction at each point along the curved surface of the mirror. The changing normal line causes the reflected rays to bounce off as nonparallel lines. Thus, the incident rays are parallel but the reflected rays are not. The reflected rays come to a focus in front of the mirror and continue outward. The point in front of the mirror at which the reflected rays all meet is called the **focal point**. (Actually, a mirror or lens with a spherical shape does not have an exact focal point. All the reflected rays converge to a small volume around the focal point. For a mirror or lens that has a radius of curvature that is large compared to the size of the mirror or lens, the volume is small enough to be considered a point. When a very precise focal point is required, a parabola-shaped surface is used instead of a spherical surface.)

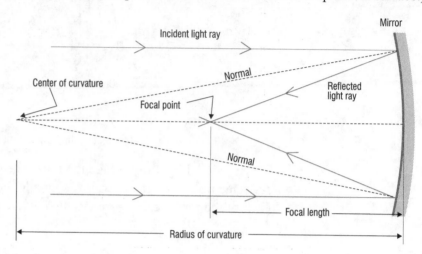

Figure 10.12
The focal point of a concave mirror is in front of the mirror.
The focal length is ½ the radius of curvature.

The focal length f of a spherical mirror is ½ the radius of curvature r.

$$f = \tfrac{1}{2}r$$

Example 10.1 Calculating the Focal Length of a Mirror

Find the focal length of a concave mirror with a radius of curvature of $r = 16$ cm.

Solution: $f = \frac{1}{2}r$

$f = \frac{1}{2}(16 \text{ cm})$

$f = 8$ cm

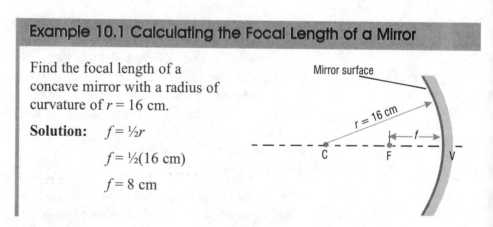

When parallel light rays strike the surface of a convex mirror, they're reflected back along spreading or divergent paths. They're all reflected according to the law of reflection. Again, the orientation of the normal line changes at each point along the curved surface of the mirror. Just as for concave mirrors, this changing normal line causes the reflected rays to be nonparallel. See Figure 10.13. After reflection, they diverge, as shown. To someone looking at the surface of the mirror, the light rays **seem** to come from a point F located *behind* the mirror. The point is the focal point F for the mirror and is behind the convex mirror.

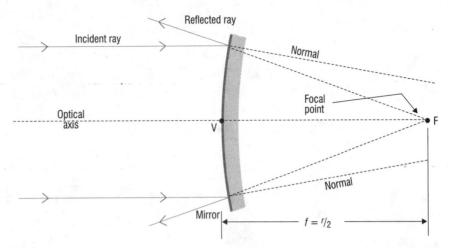

Figure 10.13
The focal point of a convex mirror is behind the mirror. The focal length is negative.

We see most objects by reflected light. For example, when light from the sun strikes a tree, the light is reflected off the surface of the tree. Some of the reflected light enters our eye. Our eye forms an image of the tree that is interpreted by our brain as sight.

Figure 10.14
Reflected light creates most of the images we see.

Figure 10.12 shows light from an object striking a mirror and reflecting through the focal point of the mirror. The reflected rays form an image of the object. This is called a **real image**, because light rays converge to pass through the image. You can see a real image if you place a small screen or piece of paper at the point at which the rays converge.

Figure 10.13 shows light from an object striking a mirror and reflecting away from the focal point. The reflected rays appear to diverge from the focal point, which is located behind the mirror. There are no light rays actually behind the mirror, so the image that appears to cause the reflection is called a **virtual image**. You cannot see a virtual image on a screen or piece of paper since no light rays actually converge at the image.

In Figure 10.15, two light rays are traced from an object to its image. An incident ray (ray 1), parallel to the optical axis, is reflected to pass through the focal point F. An incident ray (ray 2) passing through the focal point is reflected parallel to the optical axis.

The two rays start from a point at the top of an object—point P. The point P′ where the two rays meet is the location of the real image of point P. All other points on the tree have similar image points that make up a complete image of the tree. You can see the real image if you place a small screen or piece of paper at the location of the image.

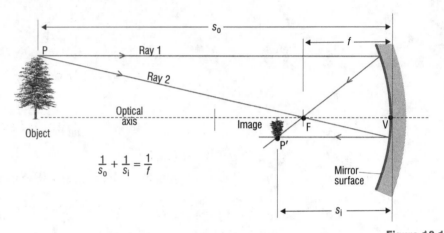

Figure 10.15
Ray tracing from an object to a concave mirror and on to an image point

Figure 10.15 also shows the distance from the object to the vertical plane passing through the vertex V of the mirror. This is called the **object distance** s_o. The **image distance**, s_i, is also shown. The object and image distances are related to the focal length f by the **mirror equation**:

$$\frac{1}{s_o} + \frac{1}{s_i} = \frac{1}{f}$$

When you use this equation, be sure to use the following signs (+ or –) for s_o, s_i, and f :

1. The object distance s_o and image distance s_i are positive for real objects and images. They are negative for virtual objects and images.

2. The focal length f and radius of curvature r are positive if the center of curvature lies on the side of the mirror from which the light comes. They are negative if the center of curvature lies on the side where there is no light.

For example, in Figure 10.15, s_o, s_i, and f are all positive. In Figure 10.13, s_o is positive but s_i and f are negative.

Example 10.2 Image Distance for a Concave Mirror

A concave mirror such as in Figure 10.15 has a focal length of 25 cm. An object is located 35 cm in front of the mirror on the optical axis. Where will the image of the object be found?

Solution: The light comes from the left, and the center of curvature is on the left. Therefore, f is positive. The object is real, so s_o is positive. Use the mirror equation.

$$\frac{1}{s_o} + \frac{1}{s_i} = \frac{1}{f}$$

$$\frac{1}{35 \text{ cm}} + \frac{1}{s_i} = \frac{1}{25 \text{ cm}}$$

$$\frac{1}{s_i} = \frac{1}{25 \text{ cm}} - \frac{1}{35 \text{ cm}} = \frac{35 \text{ cm} - 25 \text{ cm}}{25 \cdot 35 \text{ cm}^2} = \frac{10}{875 \text{ cm}}$$

Thus,

$$s_i = 87.5 \text{ cm or about 88 cm}$$

The image is on the left side of the mirror, 88 cm away from the mirror vertex.

Suppose the mirror in Example 10.2 is convex. Can you show that $s_i = -14.6$ cm? Is the image real or virtual?

Ray tracing for a convex mirror is similar, as shown in Figure 10.16. Ray 1 is parallel to the optical axis and reflects so that its extension passes through the focal point. Ray 2 is directed to the focal point, but reflects parallel to the optical axis. The two reflected rays diverge, as if they came from a point behind the mirror. The image is virtual.

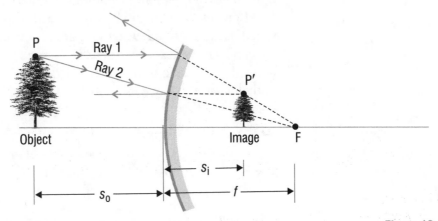

Figure 10.16
Ray tracing for a convex mirror

Refraction

When light strikes a mirrored surface, it is reflected. When light strikes a different kind of surface—like transparent glass, plastic, or water—some light is reflected and some light passes through the material. But when light passes from one material to another the direction of travel of the light changes. The amount of the change depends on the angle at which the light hits the interface and on the speed at which the light travels through each material. This change of direction at an interface between two materials is called **refraction**. Refraction is the process that enables us to make lenses for eyeglasses, telescopes, cameras, and microscopes.

Figure 10.17
Refraction of light makes
a straw appear to be bent.

You have seen refracted light many times. One common example is the way a drinking straw that's placed in a glass of water looks "bent" at the surface of the water. This appearance is the result of a change in the direction of light as it goes from water to glass to air.

Recall that the speed of light in *vacuum* never changes. But the speed of light in any transparent medium is less than the speed of light in a vacuum. Light moves through air slightly more slowly than through a vacuum. The speed of light through water or glass is considerably slower than through a vacuum. The **index of refraction** is a property of a transparent material defined as the ratio of the speed of light in a vacuum (c) to the speed of light in the material (v). We use n to represent the index of refraction of a material.

$$n = \frac{\text{speed of light in vacuum}}{\text{speed of light in material}}$$

$$n = \frac{c}{v}$$

Example 10.3 Index of Refraction for Diamond

The speed of light in a diamond is 1.24×10^8 m/s. Find the index of refraction of the diamond.

Solution: The index of refraction is the ratio of the speed of light in vacuum to the speed of light in the material. Since $c = 3.00 \times 10^8$ m/s,

$$n = \frac{3.00 \times 10^8 \text{ m/s}}{1.24 \times 10^8 \text{ m/s}} = 2.42$$

The index of refraction for diamond is 2.42.

Table 10.1 gives the indexes of refraction for several materials. Note that the index of refraction of air is very nearly that of vacuum. Unless you need to use five significant figures, use 1.000 for the index of refraction of air.

Table 10.1
Index of Refraction

Substance	n
Vacuum	1.0000
Air	1.0003
Ice	1.31
Water	1.34
Quartz	1.46
Crown glass	1.52
Flint glass	1.63
Diamond	2.42

Example 10.4 Speed of Light in Ice

Find the speed of light in a cube of ice.

Solution: From Table 10.1, the index of refraction of ice is 1.31.

$$n = \frac{c}{v}$$

$$v = \frac{c}{n} = \frac{3.00 \times 10^8 \text{ m/s}}{1.31}$$

$$v = 2.29 \times 10^8 \text{ m/s}$$

The speed of light in ice is 2.29×10^8 m/s.

Snell's Law of Refraction

When light goes from air into glass, it is bent toward the normal, as shown in Figure 10.18. The light ray in air is called the incident ray, and in glass it is called the refracted ray. The angle of incidence θ_1 is the angle between the incident ray and the normal. The **angle of refraction** θ_2 is the angle between the refracted ray and the normal. Notice that $\theta_2 < \theta_1$; the angle of refraction is less than the angle of incidence.

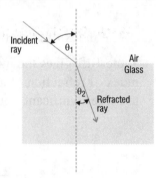

Figure 10.18
Light is refracted toward the normal when it travels from air to glass.

What happens when the light ray hits the bottom surface of the glass block? As shown in Figure 10.19, it is bent away from the normal. This time, the incident ray is traveling in the glass and the refracted ray is in air. Notice that the angle of refraction is greater than the angle of incidence.

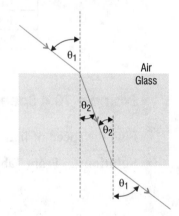

Figure 10.19
Light is refracted away from the normal when it travels from glass to air.

The general relationship between angles of incidence and refraction was found by the Dutch scientist Willebrod Snell in 1621. **Snell's law** can be written as a ratio as follows:

$$\frac{\sin\theta_1}{\sin\theta_2} = \frac{n_2}{n_1}.$$

If you cross multiply,

$$n_1 \sin \theta_1 = n_2 \sin \theta_2$$

In Snell's law, n_1 is the index of refraction of the medium for the incident ray and n_2 is the index of refraction of the medium for the refracted ray. Thus, from Snell's law, if light travels from air to glass ($n_2 > n_1$), it is refracted toward the normal ($\sin \theta_2 < \sin \theta_1$ or $\theta_2 < \theta_1$). If light travels from glass to air ($n_2 < n_1$), it is refracted away from the normal ($\theta_2 > \theta_1$).

Example 10.5 Using Snell's Law

Sunlight shines on the smooth surface of a lake with an angle of incidence of 40°. What is the angle of refraction?

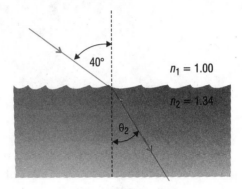

Solution: From Table 10.1, $n_1 = 1.00$ and $n_2 = 1.34$. Use Snell's law.

$$n_1 \sin \theta_1 = n_2 \sin \theta_2$$
$$(1.00) \sin (40°) = (1.34) \sin \theta_2$$
$$\sin \theta_2 = \frac{\sin 40°}{1.34} = 0.480$$
$$\theta_2 = 28.7°$$

In the result for Example 10.5, is the light ray bent toward or away from the normal? Is this the correct direction?

In reality, the index of refraction of a particular material is slightly different for different wavelengths of light. Blue light passing from air into glass, for example, is bent a little more than red light. Sunlight, or white light, contains all wavelengths of visible light. When white light passes through a prism (a piece of glass of triangular cross section) the blue part of the white light is bent the most. The red part is bent the least. The prism separates the white light into its different colors, giving the familiar rainbow effect.

Total Internal Reflection

When light passes from a medium of higher index of refraction into air, the light is refracted away from the normal. For example, when a light ray passes from water into air, the angle of refraction is greater than the angle of incidence. When you see a fish beneath the surface of a pond, its actual and apparent locations are not the same.

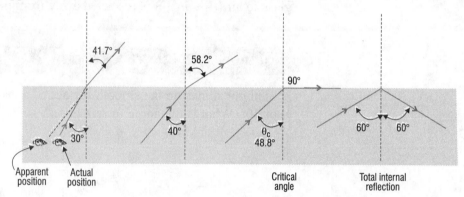

Figure 10.20 shows that, as the angle of incidence increases, the angle of refraction increases, until at some point the angle of refraction reaches 90°. The angle of incidence is called the **critical angle** at this point. We use θ_c to represent the critical angle. When the measure of the angle of incidence exceeds the measure of θ_c, the incident ray does not leave the water—it is reflected at the surface, not refracted. This is called **total internal reflection.** When light from the fish undergoes total internal reflection, you can no longer see the fish from the air.

What is the measure of θ_c for light traveling from water into air? From Snell's law

$$n_{water} \sin \theta_1 = n_{air} \sin \theta_2$$

when $\theta_1 = \theta_c$, $\theta_2 = 90°$.

$$\sin \theta_c = \frac{n_{air} \sin 90°}{n_{water}} = \frac{(1.00)(1.00)}{1.33} = 0.752$$

$$\theta_c = 48.8°$$

When light travels from water into air, total internal reflection occurs when the angle of incidence exceeds 48.8°.

Total internal reflection has an important application in optical fibers. These devices transmit optical signals for data, audio, and video for computer networks and the telecommunication industry. The core of an optical fiber is a long, thin strand of transparent glass or plastic. Light signals from lasers are transmitted by the fibers. As the light travels through the fiber's core, it strikes the surface of the fiber with an angle of incidence greater than the critical angle for the glass or plastic. The light stays in the fiber since each interaction is total internal reflection.

Figure 10.21
Optical fibers use total internal reflection to transmit light signals.

Refer to Appendix F
for a career link
to this concept.

Lenses

A **lens** is a carefully ground or molded piece of transparent material such as glass or plastic. Lenses are used in many familiar optical systems to change the directions of light rays. These systems include cameras, microscopes, telescopes, binoculars, contact lenses, eyeglasses, and magnifying glasses. Your eye contains a lens. Sharp vision in each eye depends on the ability of your lens to accurately focus light.

A lens has two surfaces. Each surface is part of a sphere. We will study two types of lenses—convex and concave. A **convex lens** is thicker at its center than at its edges. This shape causes a convex lens to be a converging lens. When parallel rays of light pass through a convex lens, they are refracted so they meet at a point (or converge) on the other side of the lens. A **concave lens** is thinner at its center than at its edges. Concave lenses are diverging lenses. Parallel rays spread apart (or diverge) when they pass through a concave lens.

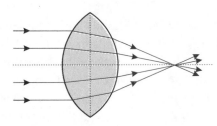

(a) Convex (converging) lens

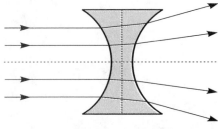

(b) Concave (diverging) lens

Figure 10.22
Convex and concave lenses bend light rays.

Focal Point and Focal Length for Thin Lenses

When light passes through a lens, it is refracted at each surface. You can use Snell's law to predict the change in the path of each light ray at each surface. Alternatively, you can use the *thin-lens approximation*. A thin lens is one in which the thickest part of the lens is small compared to the focal length of the lens. With this approximation, you model all refraction of light with a single change in direction occurring on the plane at the center of the lens. All lenses in this book are "thin." In addition, we will study symmetric lenses only. In a symmetric lens, the radius of curvature of one face equals the radius of curvature of the other face.

Figure 10.23 uses the thin-lens approximation to illustrate the focal points and focal length of a convex lens. In Figure 10.23a, incident parallel rays on the left are refracted and then converge at a point F on the right. This point is called the **focal point**. The distance from the center plane of the lens to the focal point is the **focal length** f.

The convex lens also has a focal point on the left. As shown in Figure 10.23b, when light rays leave this point, the lens refracts the diverging rays so that they emerge as parallel rays. Since the lens is symmetric, the focal length on the left equals the focal length on the right.

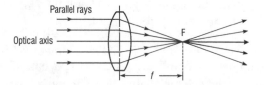
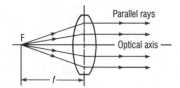

(a) Incident parallel rays are refracted to converge at the focal point on the opposite side.

(b) Incident diverging rays from the focal point are refracted as parallel rays on the opposite side.

Figure 10.23
Focal points F and focal length f for a convex lens

Figure 10.24 shows the focal points and focal length for a concave lens. When parallel rays are incident, as in Figure 10.24a, the lens spreads the rays apart. If the directions are traced backward to the left side of the lens, it appears that the rays diverge from a single point. This is the focal point on the left side of the concave lens. The lens also has a focal point on the right side. When incident rays converge at this point, the lens diverges the rays and makes them parallel. Since the lens is symmetric, the focal lengths on the left and right are equal.

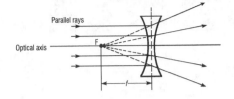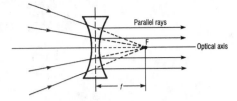

(a) Incident parallel rays are refracted to diverge on the opposite side. Each ray appears to come from the focal point.

(b) When incident rays appear to converge at the focal point, they are refracted as parallel rays.

Figure 10.24
Focal points F and focal length *f* for a concave lens

Effect of Lens Diameter

The greater the diameter of a lens, the greater the amount of light that passes through it. A larger lens will "catch" more light in the same way that a wider-mouthed jar is likely to catch more rainwater. A lens that's twice the diameter of another lens catches four times as much light. (Can you explain why?) Large astronomical telescopes, such as the 82-inch Otto Struve telescope at McDonald Observatory, are big so they can capture as many photons from distant stars as possible.

Figure 10.25 shows two lenses. They both collect the light that passes through them and focus it to a point. However, more light is being focused by the larger lens. In the same way, the larger the lens used to form an image of an object, the brighter that image is likely to be. That's because it receives and refracts more of the light coming from the object.

The size of the lens in our eye doesn't change. But the opening that allows light into the eye—the *pupil*—can change. In a darkened room, the pupil is relatively large (about 8 mm in diameter). Most of the eye lens is exposed to light. On a sunny day, the pupil is smaller (about 2 mm in diameter). Less of the eye lens is exposed to light.

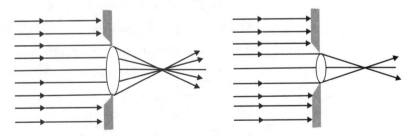

Figure 10.25
A lens twice the diameter of another lens refracts four times as much light.

The most important use for lenses is to form images. As shown in Figure 10.26, you can use ray tracings similar to those used for mirrors to predict the location and size of an image. An object is located on the optical axis to the left of a convex lens. Ray 1 travels from point P on the object parallel to the optical axis. The lens refracts ray 1 so that it passes through the focal point. Ray 2 passes through the focal point on its way to the lens. The lens refracts ray 2 so that it is parallel to the optical axis. The point of intersection of ray 1 and ray 2 is the point P' in the image.

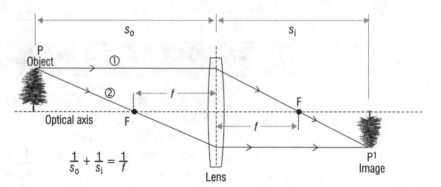

Figure 10.26
Ray tracing of image formed by a convex lens

Rays from all other points on the object would be refracted to the corresponding image points on the image. The image created is real—it can be seen if a screen is placed at its location since light actually travels to this location. The image is also inverted and smaller than the object.

The object distance s_o, image distance s_i, and focal length f of the lens are related by the **lens equation**.

$$\frac{1}{s_o} + \frac{1}{s_i} = \frac{1}{f}$$

Notice that the lens equation is the same as the mirror equation. Use the following signs (+ or −) for s_o, s_i, and f in the lens equation:

1. The object distance s_o is positive on the object side of the lens.

2. The image distance s_i is positive on the image side of the lens (where images are real). It is negative on the object side (where images are virtual).

3. The focal length f is positive for convex lenses and negative for concave lenses.

For example, in Figure 10.26, s_o, s_i, and f are all positive. In Figure 10.24a, s_o is positive but s_i and f are negative.

Example 10.6 Focal Length of a Convex Lens

An object is located 40.0 cm from a convex lens that has a **focal length of** 22.0 cm. Where should you place a screen to see the image?

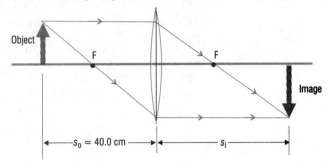

Solution: Since this is a convex lens and it produces a real image, s_o, s_i, and f are all positive.

$$\frac{1}{s_o} + \frac{1}{s_i} = \frac{1}{f}$$

$$\frac{1}{s_i} = \frac{1}{f} - \frac{1}{s_o} = \frac{1}{22.0 \text{ cm}} - \frac{1}{40.0 \text{ cm}}$$

$$\frac{1}{s_i} = \frac{40.0 - 22.0}{(22.0)(40.0)} = \frac{18.0}{880 \text{ cm}}$$

$$s_i = \frac{880}{18.0} \text{ cm} = 48.0 \text{ cm}$$

A real image is formed 48.0 cm from the center of the lens.

The image formed by a lens can be smaller than the object (as in Figure 10.26) or larger than the object (as in Example 10.6). **The ratio of the** image size to the object size is called the **magnification** of the image. Using similar triangles on a ray diagram, you can show that magnification M depends on only the image distance s_i and object distance s_o:

$$\text{Magnification} = \frac{\text{image size}}{\text{object size}}$$

$$M = -\frac{s_i}{s_o}$$

A negative magnification means the image is inverted. In **Example 10.6, the** magnification is

$$M = -\frac{s_i}{s_o} = -\frac{48}{40} = -1.2$$

The image in Example 10.6 is an enlargement since $|M| > 1$. **The image is** inverted since M is negative.

Example 10.7 Size of a Virtual Image

A convex lens in a magnifying glass has a focal length of 8.0 cm. Suppose you hold the lens 6.0 cm from a 0.5-cm ant.

(a) Make a ray-trace drawing showing the object and image.

(b) How large is the image of the ant?

Solution:

(a) As before, draw two incident rays from the object—one parallel to the optical axis and one through the focal point. Ray 1 is refracted to pass through the focal point on the right. The object is located between the focal point and the lens, so, to find the direction of ray 2, extend an imaginary line to F.

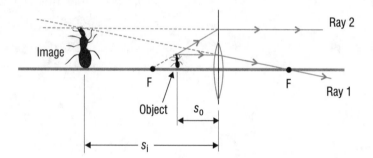

Notice that ray 1 and ray 2 diverge as they leave the lens. Extending the rays to the left, it appears as if they originate from a point on the virtual image.

(b) Find the image distance s_i, and then use the equation for magnification. Find s_i from the lens equation.

$$\frac{1}{s_o} + \frac{1}{s_i} = \frac{1}{f}$$

$$\frac{1}{s_i} = \frac{1}{f} - \frac{1}{s_o} = \frac{1}{8.0 \text{ cm}} - \frac{1}{6.0 \text{ cm}}$$

$$\frac{1}{s_i} = \frac{6.0 - 8.0}{(8.0)\,(6.0)} = \frac{-2.0}{48 \text{ cm}}$$

$$s_i = \frac{48}{-2.0} \text{ cm} = -24 \text{ cm}$$

The image is virtual since s_i is negative.

$$M = -\frac{s_i}{s_o} = -\frac{(-24 \text{ cm})}{6.0 \text{ cm}} = 4.0$$

$$\frac{\text{image size}}{\text{object size}} = M$$

Image size $= M(\text{object size}) = 4.0(0.5 \text{ cm}) = 2.0 \text{ cm}$

The virtual image of the ant is 2.0 cm long.

Summary

- An object is a source of light rays that diverge from the object.

- Ray optics is a method of predicting the locations of images by modeling the paths followed by light rays as straight lines.

- The law of reflection states that, when light reflects from a surface, the angle of reflection is equal to the angle of incidence.

- A spherical mirror has a focal point on the optical axis midway between the mirror and the center of curvature. (F = r/2)

- For a concave mirror, incident parallel rays are reflected to converge at the focal point. For a convex mirror, incident parallel rays are reflected to diverge as if they originated at the focal point on the opposite side of the mirror.

- For mirrors and lenses, the focal length, object distance, and image distance are related by the mirror equation and the lens equation:

$$\frac{1}{s_o} + \frac{1}{s_i} = \frac{1}{f} \ .$$

- The index of refraction of a material is the ratio of the speed of light in vacuum to the speed of light in the material.

- Light is refracted at the interface of two materials. Snell's law states the relationship between the angles of incidence and refraction and the indexes of refraction.

$$n_1 \sin \theta_1 = n_2 \sin \theta_2$$

- The magnification provided by a lens or mirror is given by $M = -\frac{s_i}{s_o}$.

Exercises

1. The law of reflection states that the angle of _____ equals the angle of _____.

2. Light strikes a vertical surface from the left with an angle of incidence of 30°. Sketch the surface, normal to the surface, an incident light ray, and the reflected light ray. Label the measures of the angles of incidence and reflection.

3. In an optics lab, how can you prove that an image is a real image?

4. Suppose you have extremely sensitive photographic film and you can expose it in an optical system for a very long time. Will you be able to record a virtual image on the film? Explain.

5. A concave mirror has a radius of curvature of 12 cm. What is the focal length?

6. A convex mirror has a focal length of 8.2 cm. What is the radius of curvature?

7. A 1.5-cm-high arrow is located 11.0 cm in front of a concave mirror that has a 6.0-cm center of curvature.

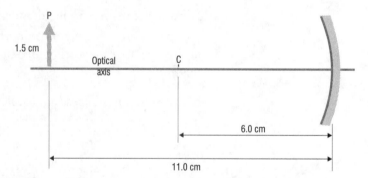

(a) Make an accurate drawing of the mirror, optical axis, and object. Locate the focal point on the optical axis.

(b) Use a ray diagram to find the image of the arrow. From your drawing, what is the image distance s_i? Is the image real or virtual?

(c) Calculate the image distance from the mirror equation, and compare to the measured distance.

(d) The magnification of the image is defined as the ratio of the size of the image to the size of the object:

$$\text{Magnification} = \frac{\text{image size}}{\text{object size}}$$

What is the magnification for your ray diagram?

8. A 2.0-cm-high arrow is located 5.0 cm in front of a convex mirror that has a 4.0-cm focal length.

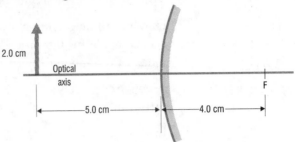

(a) Make an accurate drawing of the mirror, optical axis, and object. Locate the focal point on the optical axis.

(b) Use a ray diagram to find the image of the arrow. From your drawing, what is the image distance s_i? Is the image real or virtual?

(c) Calculate the image distance from the mirror equation, and compare to the measured distance.

(d) What is the magnification (from your ray diagram)?

9. Use Table 10.1 to find the speed of light in the following:

(a) a block of ice (b) a quartz window (c) a crown-glass window

10. What is the index of refraction of a plastic if the speed of light in the plastic is 2.20×10^8 m/s?

11. Sunlight strikes the surface of a lake at an angle of incidence of 55.0°. What is the angle of refraction?

12. The speed of light in a clear liquid is 1.41×10^8 m/s. When light is incident on the surface of the liquid, the angle of refraction is 36.2°. What is the angle of incidence?

13. Light traveling in air strikes a vertical surface of a block of glass from the left with an angle of incidence of 25.0°. The angle of refraction is 15.5°.

(a) Sketch the vertical surface, normal, incident ray, and refracted ray. Label the measures of the angles of incidence and refraction.

(b) What is the index of refraction of the glass?

14. The sides of an aquarium are made of glass, whose index of refraction is 1.50. As shown at the right, light traveling in the water inside the aquarium strikes the glass with an angle of incidence of 30.0°. At what angle θ_3 does the light enter the air?

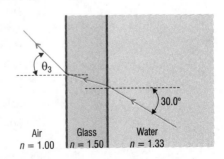

15. What is the critical angle for light traveling from crown glass into water?

16. What is the critical angle for light traveling from water into crown glass?

17. One way of determining a material's index or refraction is to measure the critical angle for light traveling from the material into air. Calculate the index of refraction of plastic that has a critical angle of 43.8°.

18. A convex lens has a focal length of 3.0 cm. An object is placed 7.0 cm to the left of the lens. Make a ray-trace diagram to find the location of the image.

19. Two lenses have exactly the same sizes and shapes, but they have different focal lengths. What is different about the two lenses?

20. A copy machine uses a convex lens with a focal length of 20.0 cm.

    (a) The machine is set to makes copies (images) of printed pages that are the same size as the originals (objects). What is the relationship between the object distance s_o and image distance s_i in the machine?

    (b) Calculate the values of s_o and s_i.

21. The setting for the copy machine of exercise 20 is adjusted so the original is 32.0 cm from the lens.

    (a) To make a copy, the machine prints the image on a blank sheet of paper. How far from the lens should the blank paper be located?

    (b) What is the magnification? Is the copy an enlargement or a reduction of the original?

22. A magnifying glass has a convex lens with a focal length of 16.0 cm. A stamp collector uses the glass to view a stamp placed 8.6 cm from the lens.

    (a) How far does the image of the stamp appear to be from the lens?

    (b) Is the image real or virtual?

    (c) If the stamp has a width of 1.20 cm, how wide is its image?

23. A prism made of crown glass is in the shape of an equilateral triangle. Each side of the triangle measures 5 cm. A laser beam is directed into the midpoint of one side, parallel to the adjacent side. Make an accurate ray-trace drawing of the laser beam through the prism. Find each angle of incidence and angle of refraction. Label the angles on your drawing.

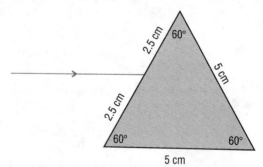

24. Ray tracing through a concave lens is similar to that for a convex lens. But remember, a concave lens diverges incident rays. An incident ray parallel to the optical axis is refracted in a direction it would have if it originated at the focal point. An incident ray traveling toward the opposite focal point is refracted parallel to the optical axis. The intersection of the lines containing these rays shows the apparent origin of the refracted rays.

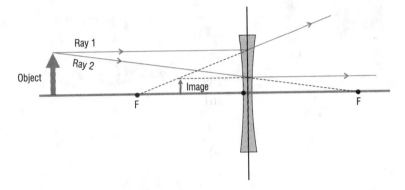

A nearsighted person uses concave lenses in eyeglasses to see clearly. An object 20 m away forms a virtual image at an image distance of –15 m. What is the focal length of the lens?

25. A "50-mm camera lens" means the focal length of the lens used by the camera is 50 mm. The lens refracts light from an object onto film in the back of the camera. The lens moves forward or backward along the optical axis to adjust the image distance, so the image is focused on the film.

(a) A 50-mm camera lens focuses on an object 3 meters in front of the lens. What is the image distance? The lens is refocused on an object 30 meters away. What is the new image distance? How far (in millimeters) is the lens moved to refocus on the second object?

(b) The camera lens is replaced with a 200-mm lens. This lens focuses on an object 3 meters away. Then the lens is refocused on an object 30 meters away. How far (in millimeters) is this lens moved to refocus on the second object?

10.2 WAVE OPTICS: INTERFERENCE AND DIFFRACTION

Objectives

- Use wave properties to explain interference and diffraction of light.

- Explain how double slits, a diffraction grating, a single slit, and an aperture produce interference patterns.

- Use measurements from double slits, a diffraction grating, a single slit, or an aperture to calculate the wavelength of light or the angles of deviation.

- Explain how diffraction limits the resolving power of optical instruments.

INTERNET *connection*

To find out more about interference and diffraction, follow the links at **www.learningincontext.com**.

In the last section, you used *ray optics* to model how mirrors and lenses form images. In the ray optics model (sometimes called *geometric optics*), light travels in straight lines unless it is reflected or refracted at a surface. However, the ray optics model fails to explain two other behaviors of light in optical systems. These behaviors are *interference* and *diffraction*.

You learned about interference in mechanical waves in Section 8.2. In optics, interference occurs when light from one source mixes with light from another source. **Diffraction** occurs when light bends around the edge of an obstacle. Light must be modeled as a wave to explain these behaviors. The study of the wave nature of light in optical systems, including interference and diffraction, is sometimes called *physical optics*.

Refer to Appendix F
for a career link
to this concept.

Interference of Light Waves

About 100 years before James Clerk Maxwell published the electromagnetic wave theory of light, a Dutch scientist named Christian Huygens developed a simpler model. Huygens developed a wave model for light in an attempt to explain the observation that objects with sharp boundaries have shadows that are not sharp. There is a slight spreading of light around these barriers.

Huygens' model uses wave fronts—imaginary surfaces that join points on waves at which all the waves are in the same phase. For example, Figure 10.27 shows a point source of waves. These can be circular water waves from a rock thrown in a lake, spherical sound waves from a speaker, or spherical light waves from a lamp. At a long distance from the source, the curvature of the wave fronts is not noticeable. They appear to be straight lines or planes.

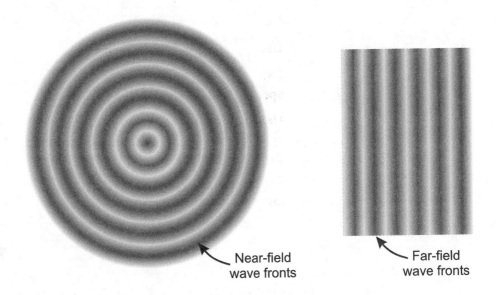

Near-field
wave fronts

Far-field
wave fronts

Figure 10.27
Wave fronts from a point source are circular or spherical near the source.
They become plane wave fronts at a long distance from the source.

In Huygens' model, all the points on a wave front can be thought of as new sources of waves, called wavelets. The wavelets spread out from each point source and are in step (or in phase) with each other. At any time after the wavelets are emitted, the wave front is the sum of all the wavelets. Figure 10.28 shows how Huygens' model applies to the propagation of a plane wave.

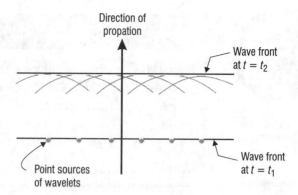

Direction of
propation

Wave front
at $t = t_2$

Point sources
of wavelets

Wave front
at $t = t_1$

Figure 10.28
Huygens' model predicts the location
of the wave front at a later time.

Example 10.8 Distance Traveled in Glass

Light traveling as plane waves in air strikes the surface of glass. If the index of refraction of the glass is 1.52, how far does the wave front travel in the glass in 3.0 ps? (1 ps = 1 picosecond; pico = 10^{-12}) Draw the refracted wave front, and show the distance traveled.

Solution: The wave front travels as a plane in the glass (except near the edges). The wave front begins at the surface of the glass and propagates at a refracted angle. The plane at 3.0 ps later can be drawn using Huygens' model. Let d represent the path length.

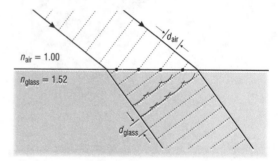

$n_{air} = 1.00$

$n_{glass} = 1.52$

d_{air}

d_{glass}

The distance traveled can be calculated from the speed of light in the glass. Use the definition of index of refraction.

$$n = \frac{c}{v}$$

$$v = \frac{c}{n} = \frac{3.00 \times 10^8 \text{ m/s}}{1.52} = 1.97 \times 10^8 \text{ m/s}$$

$$d = v\Delta t = (1.97 \times 10^8 \text{ m/s})(3.0 \times 10^{-12} \text{ s})$$

$$d = 5.9 \times 10^8 \text{ m} \quad \text{or} \quad 0.59 \text{ mm}$$

The light travels a path of length 0.59 millimeter.

As you learned in Section 8.2, when two waves travel past a point at the same time, they *interfere*. The new wave at this point and time can be determined from the *superposition principle*: The amplitude is the sum of the amplitudes of the two waves. If the waves are in phase (see Figure 10.29a), there is a reinforcement of amplitudes. This is called constructive interference. If the waves are out of phase (see Figure 10.29b), there is a partial or complete cancellation of amplitudes. This is called destructive interference.

You can easily observe interference in overlapping water waves and sound waves (in beats), but interference is difficult to observe for light. There are two reasons. First, light waves have very short wavelengths. Remember, the wavelengths of light range from 400 nm (violet) to 700 nm (red). Second, natural sources of light are **incoherent**—they emit light waves randomly, with no fixed phase relationship between waves. This causes interference to be averaged out, so no patterns can be observed without special equipment and procedures.

You can more readily observe constructive and destructive interference patterns if the interfering waves are **coherent**. This means the phases of the waves have a fixed relationship. In other words, any difference in phase between the waves does not change. Obviously, two waves that are in phase are coherent. Figure 10.29 shows examples of constructive and destructive interference of two in-phase waves. Notice that the waves' crests and troughs occur at the same time—this means they are in phase.

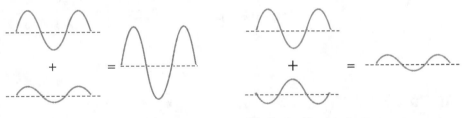

(a) Constructive interference   (b) Destructive interference

Figure 10.29
Constructive and destructive interference
of two in-phase waves

Today we can use lasers as sources of coherent light. You will learn more about lasers in the next section. In 1801, long before lasers were invented, an English physician and scientist named Thomas Young designed an experiment to produce coherent light. Young was actually studying vision and the human eye, but his experiment demonstrated the wave nature of light and interference of light. He also created a way to measure the wavelength of light.

Young's Double-Slit Experiment

Young's experimental setup is illustrated in Figure 10.30. He placed a source of *monochromatic* light behind a barrier containing a narrow slit. **Monochromatic** light has a single wavelength. He placed another barrier, with two narrow slits, A and B, in front of the first barrier. Each of these slits is the same distance from the single slit. He placed a viewing screen on the other side of the double-slit barrier.

Notice that, if light traveled only in a straight line as in the ray model, the screen would be blank. No light could reach the screen from the slits. However, light is diffracted at each slit, and in fact the entire screen is illuminated. But the screen is not evenly illuminated. There is a pattern of alternate light and dark bands on the screen. These are the result of constructive and destructive interference of the light waves from the double slits.

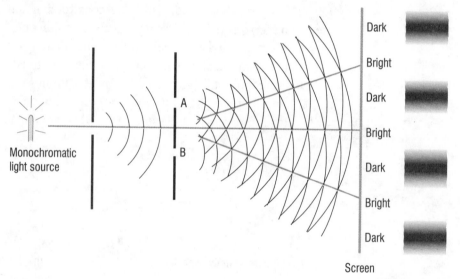

Figure 10.30
Young's double-slit experiment. Using Huygens' model, each slit acts as a source of wavelets.

You can use Huygens' wavelet model for light emerging from each slit. Since A and B are the same distance from the single slit, light waves from A and B are in phase. The semicircles in Figure 10.30 represent the crests of spherical waves emerging from the slits. The troughs are midway between the crests. Where crests overlap crests or troughs overlap troughs, waves interfere constructively. This creates a bright band on the screen. Where crests and troughs overlap, waves interfere destructively. This creates a dark band on the screen.

Calculating the Wavelength of Light

Figure 10.31 shows the geometry Young used to calculate the wavelength of the light in his experiment. To allow you to see the details, the diagram is not drawn to scale. (The distance L between the double slits and the screen is actually about 100,000 times the distance d between the slits.) Whatever wavelength of light is used in the experiment, it travels the same distance from each slit to the point P on the screen. Therefore, light arriving at P from each slit has the same phase, with crests arriving with crests, troughs arriving with troughs. These waves interfere constructively. Point P is the *central* bright band observed on the screen as shown in Figure 10.31.

Point Q is the center of the *first* bright band above P. Waves arriving at this point also interfere constructively, but these waves have traveled different distances. Let s represent the difference in their path lengths. For constructive interference, s must equal an integer multiple of λ, the wavelength of the light. For the first bright band, the integer is 1 and $s = \lambda$. The next bright band appears when $s = 2\lambda$, and so on.

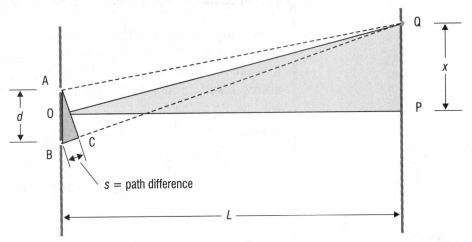

Figure 10.31
In the double-slit experiment, waves from A and B interfere constructively at points P and Q. The waves travel the same distance at P, but different distances at Q.

The center of the first dark band above P occurs halfway between P and Q. Waves arriving at this point interfere destructively—the crest of the wave from A arrives at the same time as the trough of the wave from B. Therefore, the wave from B travels a distance $\frac{1}{2}\lambda$ farther than the wave from A. How much farther does the wave from B travel to create the second dark band above P?

In Figure 10.31, the difference in the two path lengths s is a leg of a right triangle CBA. The measure of angle CAB approximately equals the measure of angle POQ. (They are approximately equal because L is very much greater than d and line segment AQ is approximately parallel to OQ. The error involved in equating the angles is about one in 10,000.) Therefore, triangle CBA is similar to triangle PQO. The ratios of corresponding sides of similar triangles are equal:

$$\frac{x}{OQ} = \frac{s}{d}$$

Since Q corresponds to the first bright band, $s = \lambda$. Since L is very much greater than x, $OQ \approx L$. The proportion can therefore be written as follows.

$$\frac{x}{L} = \frac{\lambda}{d}$$

Solve for the wavelength λ by cross multiplying.

$$\lambda = \frac{xd}{L}$$

Example 10.9 Calculating the Wavelength of Light

Yellow light illuminates two narrow slits 0.520 mm apart. A viewing screen is placed 1.20 m away. On the diffraction pattern on the screen, you measure the distance between the central bright line and the bright line nearest it as 1.35 mm. (See Figures 10.30 and 10.31.) Calculate the wavelength of the light.

Solution: Convert the distances to meters.

$$d = (0.520 \text{ mm})(10^{-3} \text{ m/mm}) = 5.20 \times 10^{-4} \text{ m}$$
$$x = (1.35 \text{ mm})(10^{-3} \text{ m/mm}) = 1.35 \times 10^{-3} \text{ m}$$

For the first bright line from the center,

$$\lambda = \frac{xd}{L} = \frac{(1.35 \times 10^{-3} \text{ m})(5.2 \times 10^{-4} \text{ m})}{1.20 \text{ m}} = 5.85 \times 10^{-7} \text{ m}$$
$$\lambda = 585 \text{ nm}$$

The wavelength of the light is 585 nanometers.

Diffraction Gratings and Spectrometers

There are two obstacles to accurate measurement of wavelengths of light using a double slit. First, the "bright" lines on the screen are actually very faint unless an intense source of light is used. Second, the "lines" on the screen are actually quite broad and it is not easy to locate their centers to measure the spacing. These obstacles to accurate measurements can be overcome with a *diffraction grating*. A **diffraction grating** is an optical device that uses a large number of parallel slits to transmit or reflect light to form an interference pattern.

Gratings are made by scratching very fine lines in a glass or metal plate with a diamond. The slits are the spaces between the lines. Gratings have between 2000 and 10,000 lines per centimeter. Each slit diffracts light by transmission (if the grating is made of glass) or by reflection (if the grating is made of metal). The spaces between the grooves of a compact disc act like a diffraction grating. You can see the colors separated from white light reflected from a CD. You can also see color separation when white light reflects from a grating.

The interference pattern created by a diffraction grating has alternating bright and dark bands in the same locations as those created by a double slit. But with a diffraction grating the bright bands are brighter and narrower. Figure 10.32 shows the first bright band formed on a screen by a grating. Instead of measuring the distance x from the center band to the first band, most laboratory instruments measure the angle θ between the centerline and the first band. The condition for constructive interference—and a bright band on the screen—is the following.

$$\sin\theta = n\frac{\lambda}{d} \qquad \text{where } n = 1, 2, 3, \dots \qquad \text{(maxima)}$$

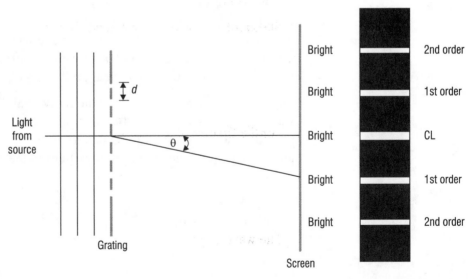

Figure 10.32
The angle of deviation for constructive interference of light producing the first bright band with a diffraction grating. The slit spacing d is about 10^{-6} m.

As shown in Figure 10.32, the central bright band created by a diffraction grating is labeled CL. The bands that appear as the first pair on either side of CL are the first order ($n = 1$). The second pair is the second order ($n = 2$), and so on.

Example 10.10 Angular Deviation for a Diffraction Grating

A laser produces monochromatic red light at a wavelength of 632.8 nm. If the laser beam passes through a diffraction grating ruled with 8000 lines/cm, what is the angular deviation to the first-order line?

Solution: First calculate the slit spacing d for the grating.

$$d = \frac{10^{-2} \text{ m/cm}}{8 \times 10^3 \text{ lines/cm}} = 1.25 \times 10^{-6} \text{ m}$$

For the first-order line, $n = 1$, so

$$\sin \theta = n\frac{\lambda}{d} = \frac{632.8 \times 10^{-9} \text{ m}}{1.25 \times 10^{-6} \text{ m}} = 0.506$$

$$\theta = 30.4°$$

The angular deviation to the first-order line is 30.4 degrees.

In Example 10.10, what is the angular deviation to the second-order line?

The diffraction pattern in Figure 10.32 is created by a single wavelength (or color) of light. If the light passing through a diffraction grating has two wavelengths (or colors), two separate patterns are created. This is because the angle of deviation θ depends on wavelength λ. Each pattern can be identified, even when they appear on the same screen.

Figures 10.33a and 10.33b show the individual diffraction patterns of light of wavelengths 400 nm and 500 nm. If light consisting of both wavelengths is passed through the grating, the pattern in Figure 10.33c is produced. You can identify each separate wavelength pattern in the combined pattern.

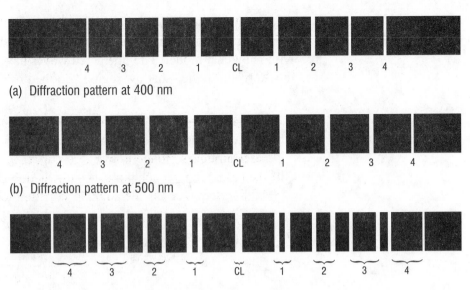

(a) Diffraction pattern at 400 nm

(b) Diffraction pattern at 500 nm

(c) Combined diffraction pattern at 400 nm and 500 nm

Figure 10.33
A grating diffraction pattern
for two wavelengths of light

The optical instrument that uses a diffraction grating to measure wavelengths is called a **grating spectrometer**. Spectrometers can be used to separate light into different wavelengths that may be needed in optical systems. They can also be used to identify unknown elements. For example, burning carbon and burning hydrogen both emit light of specific wavelengths, but the wavelengths for carbon are different from those for hydrogen.

Astrophysicists use grating spectrometers to identify the gases in stars. A telescope collects light from a star. The light is collimated and passed through a spectrometer. Each gas in the star produces a distinct set of bands. The diffraction pattern from the star is compared to patterns of known gases, and the gases from the star can be identified.

Single-Slit and Aperture Diffraction

You have seen how diffraction patterns are produced when light passes through double slits and multiple slits. Light is also diffracted when it passes through a single slit or an aperture—a "circular slit" like a pinhole in a piece of paper.

All waves diffract when they bend around the edges of obstacles in their paths. For example, you can hear a sound even if you are standing around the corner of a building from the source. The sound waves diffract around the edge of the building. Figure 10.34 shows diffraction of waves through a single slit in a barrier. The waves can be water waves on the surface of a lake, sound waves traveling through air, or light waves. Diffracted waves spread out from the slit as though they originated at the slit, in accordance with Huygens' model. The diffracted waves have reduced amplitudes, but they travel into the "shadow region" defined by the edges of the slit.

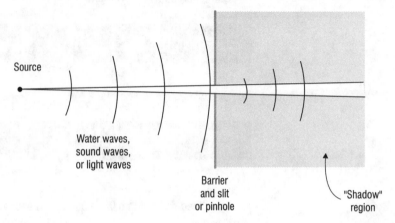

Figure 10.34
Diffraction of water, sound, or light waves
by a single slit or aperture

The analysis of diffraction patterns produced by light through a single slit is similar to that for a double slit or grating. But, this time, each point in the slit is source of Huygens' wavelets. On the screen, there is a broad central region of bright light caused by waves that undergo little or no change of direction through the slit. There are also alternating bands of darkness (minima) and brightness (maxima). Since the dark bands are smaller and easier to locate, we use them for analysis. The dark bands, or minima, represent cancellation of light, or destructive interference.

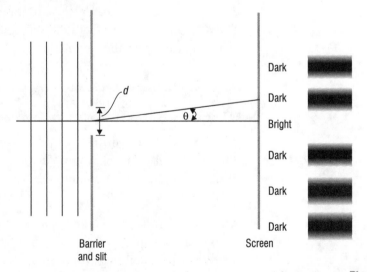

Figure 10.35
The angle of deviation for destructive interference of light
producing the first dark band with a single slit

A minimum occurs when the crest of a wave from each point in the upper half of the slit arrives at the same time as the trough of a wave from the corresponding point (equidistant from the center of the slit) in the lower half. In other words, a wave from each point in the top half of the slit destructively interferes with a wave from a point in the lower half. Mathematically, the following satisfies this condition.

$$\sin \theta = n\frac{\lambda}{d} \quad \text{where } n = 1,\ 2,\ 3,\dots \quad \text{(minima)}$$

In this equation, λ is the wavelength of the light, d is the width of the slit, and θ is the angle defined by the line through the center of the slit and the line through the center of the minimum, or dark band. (See Figure 10.35.)

Light also diffracts when it passes through a circular aperture. A circular aperture can be a pinhole in a sheet of paper or the boundary of a circular convex lens in a telescope or microscope. In this case, the edge that causes diffraction is a circle, rather than the edges of a narrow slit. The diffraction pattern is a bright central disk (analogous to the central band for the slit) surrounded by secondary rings created by constructive and destructive interference.

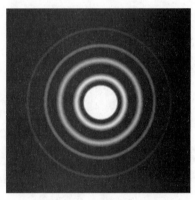

Figure 10.36
The diffraction pattern of a circular aperture consists of a central maximum surrounded by circular minima and maxima.

The first minimum of the diffraction pattern is the first dark band in Figure 10.36. For a circular aperture of diameter d, the first minimum occurs at an angle θ given by the following. (This angle has the same meaning as for the single slit in Figure 10.35.)

$$\sin \theta = 1.22\,\frac{\lambda}{d}$$

The factor 1.22 is a result of sources of Huygens' wavelets being spread over the area of a disk, rather than along a line.

Light is always diffracted when it passes through circular apertures. This means that images produced by lenses and mirrors are actually diffraction patterns.

Example 10.11 Angular Deviation for a Telescope Image

The converging lens of a telescope has a diameter of 0.600 m. The telescope focuses the image of a star on photographic film placed at the focal plane. The film is exposed by infrared radiation of wavelength 11.8 μm. (μm = 10^{-6} m) What is the angular deviation to the first minimum in the recorded image? If the focal length of the telescope is 5.8 m, what is the diameter of the image to the first minimum?

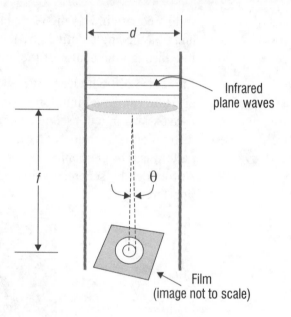

Infrared plane waves

θ

Film
(image not to scale)

Solution:

$$\sin \theta = 1.22 \frac{\lambda}{d} = 1.22 \left(\frac{11.8 \times 10^{-6} \text{ m}}{0.600 \text{ m}} \right) = 2.40 \times 10^{-5}$$

$$\theta = 2.40 \times 10^{-5} \text{ radians}$$

Let r represent the radius of the first minimum. Since the angle is very small, you can approximate $\sin \theta \approx r/f$. Solve for r.

$$r = f \sin \theta = (5.8 \text{ m})[\sin (2.40 \times 10^{-5} \text{ radians})] = 1.4 \times 10^{-5} \text{ m}$$

Let x represent the diameter.

$$x = 2r = 2.8 \times 10^{-4} \text{ m} \quad \text{or} \quad 0.28 \text{ mm}$$

The diameter of the image to the first minimum is 0.28 millimeter.

In Example 10.11, use your calculator to find the value of $\sin \theta$ to six significant figures. Find the measure of θ, in radians, to six significant figures. For small angles, you can approximate $\sin \theta \approx \theta$, where the angle is measured in radians.

Diffraction Limits for Optical Systems

The primary purpose of optical systems such as telescopes and microscopes is to create images of objects that are either very small or very far away. The ability to see fine details of an object is called *resolution*. The **resolving power** of a telescope or microscope is measured by the minimum separation of two objects for which their images appear separate and distinct when viewed through the instrument. This minimum separation can be the distance the two are apart or, more commonly, the angle of separation, as viewed from the telescope or microscope lens. Because of diffraction, all optical systems have unavoidable limits to their resolving power.

Figure 10.37 illustrates resolving power by showing the overlapping diffraction patterns of two objects that are separated by a small angle. The objects could be two stars viewed by a telescope or two bacteria viewed by a microscope. We say the two objects are just resolved if the central bright disk of one object falls on the first dark ring of the other. This is known as the **Rayleigh criterion**, after Lord Rayleigh who recommended it around 1900. Let θ_R represent the separation angle that just satisfies the Rayleigh criterion.

$$\sin \theta_R = 1.22 \frac{\lambda}{d}$$

In Figure 10.37a the objects cannot be distinguished from a single object—they are not resolved. The angular separation between the objects θ is less than θ_R. In (b) the objects are barely resolved, and $\theta = \theta_R$. In (c) the objects are fully resolved. The angular separation θ is greater than θ_R.

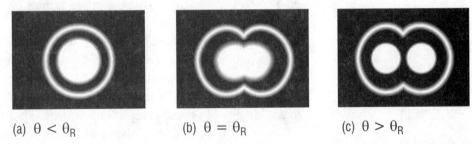

(a) $\theta < \theta_R$ (b) $\theta = \theta_R$ (c) $\theta > \theta_R$

Figure 10.37
The images of two objects can be resolved
if the separation angle satisfies the Rayleigh criterion.

When the equation for the Rayleigh criterion is used, the diameter d of the aperture is usually the diameter of the lens or mirror used to gather light. This assumes all the light falling on the lens of the optical instrument is used to form the image. If this is not the case, an aperture size will be given.

Example 10.12 Resolution for a Telescope

The telescope in Example 10.11 is used to record the image of two closely spaced stars. What is the angular separation of the stars if they are just resolvable using visible light of wavelength 560 nm? How far apart are the centers of the diffraction patterns in the focal plane of the lens?

Solution: When they are just resolvable, the stars satisfy the Rayleigh criterion.

$$\sin \theta_R = 1.22 \frac{\lambda}{d} = (1.22) \left(\frac{560 \times 10^{-9} \text{ m}}{0.600 \text{ m}} \right) = 1.14 \times 10^{-4}$$

Since the angle is very small, $\sin \theta \approx \theta$, so

$$\theta_R = 1.14 \times 10^{-4} \text{ radian}.$$

Let x represent the separation distance between the centers of the diffraction patterns.

$$x = f \sin \theta_R \approx f \theta_R = (5.8 \text{ m})(1.14 \times 10^{-4} \text{ radian})$$

$$x = 6.6 \times 10^{-4} \text{ m} = 0.66 \text{ mm}$$

How would you change an optical experiment to resolve smaller objects? You would reduce the size of the bright central disk and the angle θ, and therefore $\sin \theta$.

From the equation $\sin \theta = 1.22 \frac{\lambda}{d}$, there are two ways to reduce the value of $\sin \theta$. First you can increase the diameter d of the lens or, in other words, use a larger telescope or microscope. This not only produces a sharper image, it also collects more light so you can see fainter objects. Second, you can use light with a shorter wavelength λ. For example, if you can use ultraviolet light instead of visible light, you can record finer details of the object. Some microscopes even use electron beams, which behave like waves under certain conditions. The wavelength of an electron beam is about 100,000 times shorter than visible light. Scanning electron microscopes can make images of objects as small as viruses. These objects cannot be seen with optical microscopes because of the limitations of diffraction.

Summary

- Interference and diffraction are wave properties of light.

- When light passes through two narrow slits spaced close together, it produces an interference pattern consisting of alternating bright and dark bands on a screen. You can measure the wavelength of light from the interference pattern.

- Diffraction is the bending of light around the edges of an obstacle.

- A diffraction grating consists of a large number of slits. When light passes through or reflects from a diffraction grating, it produces narrow interference patterns. Diffraction gratings are used to measure the wavelength of light or to separate wavelengths from light.

- When light passes through a single narrow slit or small hole, it diffracts and produces an interference pattern on a screen.

- Interference patterns depend on the wavelength of light, the width or separation of the slits, and the distance to the viewing screen.

- Diffraction limits the resolving power of optical systems. The Rayleigh criterion sets the minimum angular separation between two closely spaced objects for them to be resolved.

Exercises

1. Why is it difficult to observe the interference and diffraction of light waves, while interference and diffraction of sound waves are part of our familiar experiences? Give at least two reasons.

2. For two beams of light to produce an interference pattern, their sources must be _____ (coherent or incoherent).

3. (a) In the double-slit experiment, waves from slit A interfere constructively with waves from slit B to create the central bright band. (See Figures 10.30 and 10.31.) Which waves travel farther to this band, those from slit A or those from slit B?

   (b) Constructive interference also creates the first bright band above the central band. Which waves travel farther to this band, those from slit A or those from slit B? How much farther?

   (c) Destructive interference creates the first dark band below the central band. Which waves travel farther to this band, those from slit A or those from slit B? How much farther?

4. Blue light is incident on two slits separated by 0.091 mm. A screen is located 1.2 m from the slits. If the first-order bright line appears 5.6 mm from the central line, what is the wavelength of the light?

5. Light from a helium-neon laser has a wavelength of 632.8 nm. The laser beam is aimed at two slits placed 0.80 m from a screen. If you measure the first-order bright line 58.5 mm from the central line, what is the slit spacing?

6. A sodium lamp emits light of wavelength 596 nm. This light is incident on two slits separated by 16 μm. The slits are located 0.75 m from a screen. What is the spacing between the central line and the first-order bright line?

7. When white light passes through a diffraction grating, which color produces a bright line closest to the central bright line? Farthest away?

8. A beam of monochromatic laser light passes through diffraction grating A, with 2500 lines per cm. A beam from the same laser passes through grating B, with 5000 lines per cm. How does the interference pattern produced by A compare to that produced by B?

9. A diffraction grating is etched with 4500 lines per cm.

    (a) How far apart are two lines in the grating?

    (b) If light of wavelength 650 nm falls on the grating, what is the angle of deviation for the first-order bright band?

10. You use a grating to form a diffraction pattern with monochromatic light of wavelength 592 nm. You measure the angular separation between the central bright line and the first-order line to be 0.065 radian. What is the distance between the lines of the grating?

11. A spectrometer uses a grating with 10,000 lines/cm. When white light shines through the spectrometer, the grating separates the wavelengths. Find the angles at which blue (420-nm wavelength) and red (630 nm) have first-order bands. What is the measure of the angle of separation between the red and blue first-order bands?

12. Monochromatic light of wavelength 535 nm is incident on a single slit of width 15.0 μm. The slit is located 85.0 cm from a screen. What is the angular deviation to the first minimum? How far from the center of the central band is the first minimum?

13. Red light of wavelength 645 nm falls on a single slit, which is located 1.10 m in front of a screen. You measure the distance from the center of the bright central band to the first dark band as 0.95 mm. What is the angular deviation to the first minimum? What is the width of the slit?

14. To measure the wavelength of a laser's output you direct the beam through a single slit of width 28.5 μm. You measure the angular separation between the central bright line and the first-order dark line as 0.83°. What is the wavelength of the radiation?

15. To see finer details of objects with an optical microscope, is red light or blue light better? Explain.

16. In Example 10.11, the length c of the hypotenuse of a right triangle is set approximately equal to the length f of the longest leg. Show that this approximation is valid for small angles θ. Use the Pythagorean theorem to find the relationship between f and c. Then complete the following table.

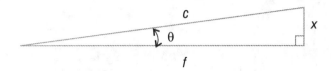

θ, degrees	θ, radians	$\sin \theta$	$\dfrac{f}{c}$
10°	0.174533	0.173648	0.984808
1°			
0.1°			

17. The Hubble space telescope has a diameter of 2.4 m. What is the angular separation of two stars that are just resolved by the telescope using ultraviolet light of wavelength 50 nm? If the stars are 10 light-years away, what is the separation between the stars in light-years? One light-year is the distance light travels in one year. How far apart are the stars in kilometers?

18. The Landsat satellite makes images of the Earth using a 40.6-cm-diameter telescope. Under ideal conditions, what is the angular separation of two objects that are just resolved using visible light of wavelength 550 nm? If the satellite is at 705-km altitude, how far apart are the objects? (This is called the **resolution** of the telescope.)

19. A commercial satellite company plans to launch a satellite with a telescope that can make images with 0.5-m resolution. If the satellite records images with visible light at 550-nm wavelength and is in orbit at an altitude of 250 km, what diameter telescope should the company plan to use?

20. Your eye is an optical system with an aperture (the pupil) approximately 5.0 mm in diameter. Estimate the maximum distance at which you can resolve two objects that are 1.0 meter apart. Assume that diffraction alone limits your resolution and the wavelength of the light is 550 nm.

21. A radar can resolve two objects that are 50 m apart at a range of 1.0 km. What is the minimum diameter of its antenna if the operating frequency of the radar is 6.8 GHz? (GHz $= 10^9$ Hz)

10.3 LASER LIGHT

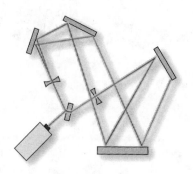

Objectives

- Describe the Thomson, Rutherford, and Bohr models of the atom and the reasons for the major changes to the models.

- Calculate the energy, frequency, and wavelength of a photon emitted by an electron transition in hydrogen.

- Describe the primary difference between the quantum model of the atom and all previous models.

- Explain the functions of the laser medium, optical cavity, and pump in a laser.

- Describe the qualities of laser light that distinguish it from ordinary light.

- Explain why a laser medium must have a metastable energy state.

- Calculate the power density of a laser source.

INTERNET *connection*

To find out more about laser light, follow the links at **www.learningincontext.com**.

In the last section, you learned how a diffraction grating separates the wavelengths of light emitted by a source. The array of wavelengths emitted by a source of light is called its **emission spectrum**. Every substance has a unique emission spectrum.

Scientists have studied emission spectra for hundreds of years. They developed models of the atom to explain observed wavelengths of light emitted by different substances. These models led to an understanding of the structure of the atom and, in 1960, to the development of a new kind of light source—the laser.

Models of the Atom

The first model of the atom was proposed by the English physicist J. J. Thomson. In 1897 Thomson discovered the electron as a fundamental particle of the atom. He also measured the negative charge of the electron and the charge-to-mass ratio. Thomson knew that the overall charge of an atom is neutral and its mass is much greater than that of an electron. So he proposed a model in which most of the mass and the positive charge of an atom are evenly distributed throughout the atom's volume.

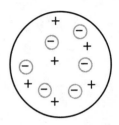

Figure 10.38
In the Thomson model of the atom, electrons are imbedded in a positively charged substance.

The negatively charged electrons are randomly distributed throughout the volume. This became known as the "plum pudding" model, in which electrons were distributed like plums in a pudding.

In 1911, Rutherford discovered that it was possible for atoms to scatter alpha particles through very large angles, even 180° (see Section 9.2). These interactions could not be explained by Thomson's model because they violated Coulomb's law and Newton's laws. The density of the atom would not be great enough to significantly change the direction of any of the alpha particles. To account for his observations, Rutherford proposed a nuclear model of the atom. In this model, more than 99.9% of the mass and all the positive charge of an atom is concentrated in a tiny central core, called the nucleus. Electrons contain the negative charge of the atom but very little of the mass. Electrons are outside the nucleus and very far away. Most of the volume of an atom is empty space.

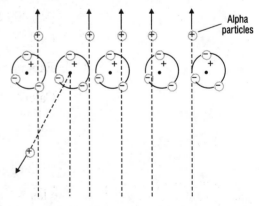

Figure 10.39
Rutherford's model placed most of the mass and the positive charge in the atom's nucleus. This could explain his observation of scattered alpha particles.

Niels Bohr was a Danish physicist working with Rutherford's group trying to determine the structure of the atom. Bohr was aware of Einstein's theory of the photoelectric effect and how sometimes electromagnetic radiation behaves as if it consists of discrete bundles of energy, called photons (see Section 9.1). Bohr combined these ideas with the Rutherford model and developed a new model for the atom. Bohr's model was the first to successfully explain how emission spectra are created. He predicted the observed emission spectrum for hydrogen with an accuracy of about 99.98%. Bohr's model is less useful for more complicated atoms, but his theory about discrete energy levels in atoms was the first step toward the modern quantum theory.

Bohr's Hydrogen Atom

Bohr started with a "planetary model" of the atom, consistent with Rutherford's model in which electrons move in fixed orbits about the nucleus. But this model contains a built-in contradiction. Electrons are charged particles, and, as you learned in Section 9.2, when charged particles are accelerated they radiate electromagnetic energy. If electrons move in circular or elliptical orbits about the nucleus of an atom, their velocities are constantly changing. In other words, the electrons are constantly being accelerated. This means all atoms should constantly radiate electromagnetic waves. In fact, the electrons should lose energy as they radiate,

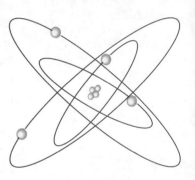

Figure 10.40
In his planetary model of the atom, Bohr hypothesized that electrons orbit the nucleus like the planets orbit the sun.

slow down, follow the force of attraction into the nucleus, and be annihilated. The planetary model would predict that atoms can exist for only a short time!

Bohr made an ingenious hypothesis about the electrons in an atom that allowed him to use the planetary model without the annihilation result. He hypothesized that, in stable atoms, electrons could exist in certain discrete energy states without radiating their energy away. These discrete states are called **energy levels**. An energy level is the total kinetic and potential energy of an electron in its orbit. Energy levels are exactly defined for each atom, and all atoms of the same element have the same set of energy levels. According to Bohr's model, electrons can have only the energies equal to an atom's energy levels. Electrons cannot have intermediate energies between these discrete states.

However, electrons can jump from one energy level to another. An atom emits a discrete photon of radiation when an electron jumps from a higher energy level E_i to a lower energy level E_f. By conservation of energy, the energy of the photon hf is the difference. This is known as the **Bohr frequency condition**. It applies to all atoms, molecules, and nuclei.

$$hf = E_i - E_f$$

Remember, h is Planck's constant. Its value is 6.63×10^{-34} J·s or 4.14×10^{-15} eV·s. f is the frequency of the emitted photon, in Hz.

Bohr calculated the energy levels for hydrogen and matched the observed emission spectrum to the predicted photon frequencies. Hydrogen is the simplest atom, with one proton and one electron. The force holding the electron in an orbit is the Coulomb force. Remember from Section 1.3, this force is $K\dfrac{q_1 q_2}{r^2}$ where K is a constant, q_1 is the charge of the nucleus (e), q_2 is the charge of the electron ($-e$), and r is the radius of the orbit. An electron in a circular orbit is constantly accelerated. The acceleration is called centripetal acceleration. The magnitude of centripetal acceleration is $\dfrac{v^2}{r}$, and the direction is the same as force on the electron—toward the center of the circle. Bohr used Newton's second law of motion for the electron.

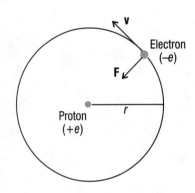

Figure 10.41
In Bohr's model of hydrogen, the force holding the electron in orbit is the Coulomb force. The magnitude is $F = K\dfrac{e^2}{r^2}$.

$$F = ma$$

$$K\frac{e^2}{r^2} = m\frac{v^2}{r}$$

From this equation, you can calculate the electron's kinetic energy KE.

$$KE = \frac{1}{2}mv^2 = \frac{1}{2}K\frac{e^2}{r}$$

The electron is in the electric field of the nucleus. The potential difference at a distance r from the proton is $\Delta V = Ke/r$. You learned in Section 5.3 that the potential energy PE of the electron is the product of potential difference and charge.

$$PE = \Delta V(-e) = -K\frac{e^2}{r}$$

The total energy E of the electron is the sum of the kinetic and potential energies.

$$E = KE + PE = -K\frac{e^2}{r} + \frac{1}{2}K\frac{e^2}{r} = -\frac{1}{2}K\frac{e^2}{r}$$

Since K and e are constants, Bohr's model of the hydrogen atom predicts the total energy of the electron to depend on only the radius of its orbit. If you know the electron's radius r, you can calculate its total energy E, speed v, linear momentum p ($= mv$), and angular momentum L ($= pr$).

This is where Bohr made his hypothesis. He assumed that the angular momentum L can equal only values given by the following.

$$L = n\frac{h}{2\pi} \quad \text{where } n = 1, 2, 3, \dots$$

Again, h is Planck's constant. The integer n is called the **principal quantum number**. Since L can take on only certain values, we say that angular momentum is *quantized*. We write the values of quantized parameters with subscripts, as in L_n:

$$L_n = n\frac{h}{2\pi} \rightarrow L_1 = \frac{h}{2\pi}, L_2 = \frac{h}{\pi}, L_3 = \frac{3h}{2\pi}, \dots$$

If the electron's angular momentum is quantized, so are all the other parameters. The radius r_n and total energy E_n can be calculated by the following equations.

$$r_n = n^2 \frac{h^2}{4\pi^2 Kme^2}$$

$$E_n = -\frac{1}{n^2}\frac{2\pi^2 K^2 me^4}{h^2}$$

When Bohr substituted the values for the constants h, π, K, m, and e, he obtained the following for the quantized energy levels for hydrogen.

$$r_n = n^2 (0.053 \text{ nm})$$

$$E_n = -\frac{13.6 \text{ eV}}{n^2}$$

The value of the principal quantum number n determines the values of radius and total energy. The radius increases quadratically with n. (See Figure 10.42.)

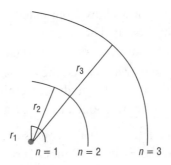

Figure 10.42
Radii of the first three energy levels
for the Bohr hydrogen atom
$r_1 = 0.053$ nm
$r_2 = 4r_1$
$r_3 = 9r_1$

The energy of the electron is negative. This means energy must be added to the electron to remove it from the atom. The lowest energy level E_1 is called the **ground state**. For hydrogen, the ground state is given by $E_1 = -13.6$ eV. Energy levels above the ground state are called **excited states**. When an electron drops from an excited state to a lower state, it emits a photon whose energy equals the difference in the energy states. Total energy is conserved.

Example 10.13 Frequency and Wavelength of a Hydrogen Line

Calculate the frequency and wavelength of light emitted by an electron that drops from the second energy level (or first excited state) to the ground state in hydrogen.

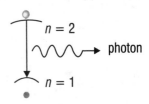

Solution: The ground state is $n = 1$, and the second energy level, or first excited state is $n = 2$. Calculate the energy levels.

$$E_n = -\frac{13.6 \text{ eV}}{n^2}$$

$$E_1 = -\frac{13.6 \text{ eV}}{1^2} = -13.6 \text{ eV} \qquad E_2 = -\frac{13.6 \text{ eV}}{2^2} = -3.40 \text{ eV}$$

The energy of the photon emitted by the electron's transition is the difference in electron energy levels.

$$E_{\text{photon}} = E_i - E_f$$

$$= E_2 - E_1 = -3.40 \text{ eV} - (-13.6 \text{ eV}) = 10.2 \text{ eV}$$

Calculate the frequency and wavelength: $E = hf$ and $c = \lambda f$.

$$f = \frac{E_{\text{photon}}}{h} = \frac{10.2 \text{ eV}}{4.14 \times 10^{-15} \text{ eV} \cdot \text{s}} = 2.46 \times 10^{15} \text{ Hz}$$

$$\lambda = \frac{c}{f} = \frac{3.00 \times 10^8 \text{ m/s}}{2.46 \times 10^{15} \text{ Hz}} = 1.22 \times 10^{-7} \text{ m} \quad \text{or} \quad 122 \text{ nm}$$

Example 10.13 shows how Bohr calculated one line in the emission spectrum of hydrogen. There are several other lines corresponding to electron drops from other energy levels (E_3, E_4, ...) to the ground state.

These lines together are called the Lyman series, after Theodore Lyman who discovered this part of the hydrogen emission spectrum in 1914. Each line in the Lyman series corresponds to an ultraviolet wavelength.

Bohr also calculated the wavelengths of photons emitted when the hydrogen atom drops to the E_2 level (Balmer series) and the E_3 level (Paschen series). The Balmer series corresponds to visible wavelengths, and the Paschen series corresponds to infrared.

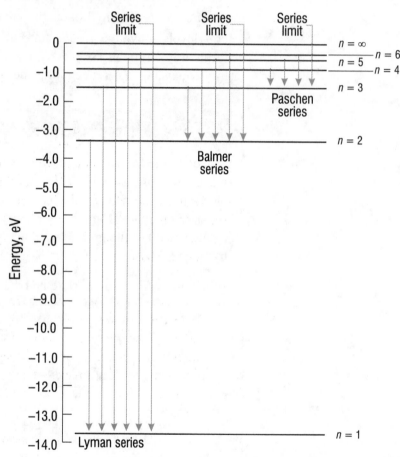

Figure 10.43
Energy levels of hydrogen and some of the transitions that produce the emission spectrum

The Quantum Model of the Atom

Bohr could not explain why his assumption of quantized angular momentum resulted in good agreement with the hydrogen spectrum. But, in 1923, the

French scientist Louis de Broglie extended Bohr's model one step farther. De Broglie reasoned that, if light can behave like both a wave and a particle, an electron might also behave like both a particle and a wave. But how can you calculate the wavelength of an electron? Since the momentum of a photon is $p = h/\lambda$, de Broglie proposed the same relationship for a particle.

$$p = mv = \frac{h}{\lambda}$$

You learned in Section 7.2 that angular momentum L of a particle in orbit is the product of moment of inertia and angular speed:

$L = I\omega = (mr^2)\left(\frac{v}{r}\right) = mvr$. Therefore,

$$L = mvr = pr = \frac{hr}{\lambda}$$

De Broglie combined this result with Bohr's quantization condition for angular momentum.

$$n\frac{h}{2\pi} = \frac{hr}{\lambda} \quad or \quad n\lambda = 2\pi r$$

The right side of the second equation is the *circumference* of the electron's orbit. In words, de Broglie's result says that, if the electron orbiting a nucleus can be modeled as a wave, the Bohr orbits have quantized wavelengths that are integer multiples of the circumference of the orbit. An electron orbit "fits" around a nucleus only if it is composed of complete wavelengths. These are the orbits in the Bohr model in which the electrons do not radiate away their energy.

In the 1920s, an Austrian physicist named Erwin Schroedinger created the modern **quantum model** of the atom by extending de Broglie's wave model. Schroedinger based the entire model of an atom on waves. He formulated a wave equation that provides a purely mathematical model of the atom. The solution of Schroedinger's wave equation is called the *wave function*. For atoms more complicated than hydrogen, the wave function is usually found with computer programs.

Wave functions can predict results of experiments involving objects the size of atoms or smaller, just as Newton's laws can predict results for larger objects like baseballs, cars, airplanes, and spaceships. Scientists have observed wavelike behavior such as diffraction of electrons, protons, neutrons, and atoms. Measured wavelengths of these particles agree with de Broglie's equation, $\lambda = \frac{h}{mv}$. Newton's laws do not work for atomic-sized objects.

As illustrated in Example 10.14 on the next page, the wavelengths of large objects are too small to be measured. This is why we do not observe wavelike behavior of objects in our daily lives.

Example 10.14 Wavelengths of a Tennis Ball and an Electron

Compare the wavelength of a tennis ball traveling at 50 m/s to the wavelength of the electron in the first Bohr orbit of hydrogen. The mass of a tennis ball is 57.6 g (0.0576 kg).

Solution:

$$\lambda_{\text{tennis ball}} = \frac{h}{mv} = \frac{6.63 \times 10^{-34} \, \text{J} \cdot \text{s}}{(0.0576 \, \text{kg})(50 \, \text{m/s})} \quad \left[\text{J} = \text{kg} \cdot \text{m}^2/\text{s}^2 \right]$$

$$\lambda_{\text{tennis ball}} = 2.3 \times 10^{-34} \, \text{m} = 2.3 \times 10^{-25} \, \text{nm}$$

For the electron, the first Bohr orbit means $n = 1$.

$$n\lambda_{\text{electron}} = 2\pi r$$

Since the electron is in hydrogen, the radius r is the Bohr orbit r_{n}.

$$r_{\text{n}} = n^2(0.053 \, \text{nm}) \quad \text{or} \quad r_1 = (1)^2(0.053 \, \text{nm})$$

$$\lambda_{\text{electron}} = \frac{2\pi r_{\text{n}}}{n} = \frac{2\pi(1)^2(0.053 \, \text{nm})}{1} = 0.33 \, \text{nm}$$

The wavelength of the electron is approximately 10^{26} times the wavelength of the tennis ball.

The quantum model of the atom accurately predicts emission and absorption of light by atoms and molecules. Using these predictions in 1960, an engineer and physicist named Theodore Maiman developed a new source of light—the laser.

Lasers

Atoms emit light when electrons drop from excited states to lower energy levels. There are several ways to "excite" atoms (to cause electrons to jump to excited states) of a material. For example, you can add heat to the material, increasing its thermal energy. You can bombard the material with a beam of high-energy electrons. Or you can shine light on the material with photons of exactly the right energy. An electron in an atom can absorb energy and jump to a higher energy level if the energy absorbed equals the difference in the two energy levels of the atom. (See Figure 10.44a.) Absorption works like the reverse of emission.

Suppose an electron of an atom absorbs a photon and jumps from the ground state to an excited state E_2. The absorbed photon energy is $hf = E_2 - E_1$. Normally, the electron returns to the ground state after a short time, emitting a photon of energy $hf = E_2 - E_1$. This process is called spontaneous emission, and it is shown on the energy level diagram in Figure 10.44b.

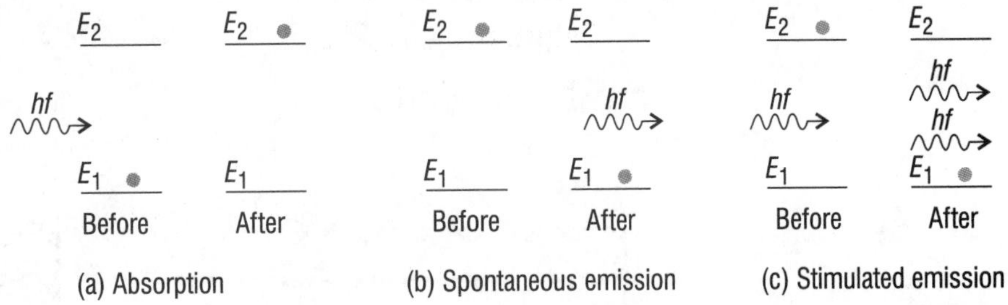

E_2 E_2 • E_2 • E_2 E_2 • E_2

hf → hf → hf → hf → hf →

E_1 • E_1 E_1 E_1 • E_1 E_1 •

Before   After   Before   After   Before   After

(a) Absorption   (b) Spontaneous emission   (c) Stimulated emission

Figure 10.44
Three interactions between photons and atoms:
(a) absorption, (b) spontaneous emission, and (c) stimulated emission

In 1917, Einstein predicted that an electron already in an excited state could be induced, or *stimulated*, to drop to the lower state earlier than normal if the excited atom were near another photon of energy $hf = E_2 - E_1$. When the electron returns to the ground state, it emits a photon. After the atom is driven to the lower energy level, *two* photons are present. This process is called **stimulated emission**. As shown in Figure 10.44c, the emitted photon is exactly the same as the stimulating photon. The two photons have the same energy, direction, and phase. If other excited atoms are nearby, these two photons can now stimulate emission of two more identical photons. This process of stimulated emission can continue, producing an avalanche of photons of the same energy, direction, and phase.

A device that produces **l**ight by **a**mplification of **s**timulated **e**mission of **r**adiation is a **laser**. Because of the way it is produced, laser light has three qualities that distinguish it from ordinary light:

1. **Laser light is monochromatic.** Since emitted photons have the same energy as stimulating photons and emitted photons are used to stimulate emission, all the photons in the laser beam have the same energy and, therefore, wavelength.

2. **Laser light is highly directional.** Emitted photons travel in the same direction as stimulating photons, so all photons in the laser beam have the same direction. If not for diffraction caused by the exit aperture of the laser device, the beam would be almost perfectly parallel.

3. **Laser light is coherent.** Emitted photons are in phase with stimulating photons. The light waves travel in phase, with crests traveling with crests, troughs traveling with troughs.

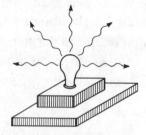

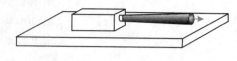

(a) Ordinary light is emitted in all directions.

(b) Laser light is emitted in a virtually parallel beam.

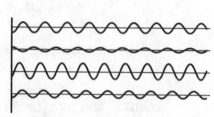

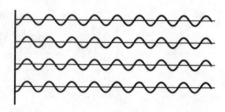

(c) Ordinary light is incoherent.

(d) Laser light is coherent.

Figure 10.45
Comparison between ordinary light and laser light

Laser Components

Lasers have three main components: a laser medium, an optical cavity, and a pump. Figure 10.46 shows these components in a typical arrangement for a laser.

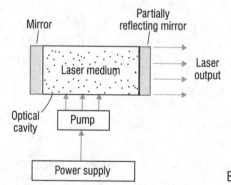

Figure 10.46
Block diagram showing the laser components

The **laser medium** contains the atoms or molecules that have a set of energy levels to produce the wavelength of laser light desired. Remember, two energy levels define the energy and wavelength of the emitted light. In a laser medium, the higher energy level must be a **metastable state**—one in which electrons stay for a much longer time than in other states. Because they stay in a metastable state for a long time, more electrons are available for stimulated emission.

The number of electrons in each energy level determines whether or not a medium can produce laser light. Normally more electrons are in the lower level than the higher level. Figure 10.47a shows a normal distribution of electrons in the laser medium's two energy levels. With this distribution, a photon matching the energy difference would be more likely to be absorbed and not to cause stimulated emission. However, if the distribution of electrons could be inverted, as shown in Figure 10.47b, a photon would be more likely to cause stimulated emission. This distribution is called a **population inversion**. You must create a population inversion in the laser medium to produce laser light.

(a) Normal distribution   (b) Population inversion

Figure 10.47

(a) In the normal distribution, more electrons are in the lower state. A photon is more likely to be absorbed.
(b) In a population inversion, more electrons are in the upper (metastable) state. A photon is more likely to cause stimulated emission.

The laser medium can be a gas, liquid, or solid. It is contained in the **optical cavity**, usually a cylinder with mirrors at each end. Stimulated emission photons travel parallel to the axis of the cavity. They are reflected to travel back and forth between the mirrors, creating additional photons each time. One of the mirrors is designed to be "leaky" so a fraction of the laser light can be emitted from the cavity.

An energy source, or **pump**, is required to raise the energy levels of the atoms or molecules of the laser medium. Energy must be added to electrons to move them to the higher state. As electrons drop to the lower state, they must be replaced to maintain a population inversion. Most lasers use electrical pumps or optical pumps.

An electrical pump uses a potential difference to create a current in the laser medium. Free electrons in the medium are accelerated by the potential difference. They transfer some of their energy when they interact with the laser medium's atoms or molecules.

An optical pump uses photons from flashlamps or other lasers. A flashlamp is a glass tube fitted with electrodes and filled with a gas, such as xenon. A voltage is applied across the electrodes, creating a current in the gas. The current excites atoms of the gas, and the atoms emit photons when they drop to the ground state. These photons are incoherent and have many different wavelengths, but there are enough of the right wavelength and direction to trigger the stimulated emission process in the laser medium. Figure 10.48 shows a helical flashlamp.

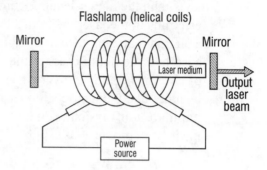

Figure 10.48
Example optical pump using helical coils

Types of Lasers

One of the most common gas lasers uses a mixture of helium and neon as the laser medium. As shown in Figure 10.49, the gas mixture is contained in a glass tube, with a mirror at each end, forming the optical cavity. The medium is electrically pumped with a DC power supply. In a HeNe laser, the pump excites helium atoms. Excited helium atoms collide with neon atoms and transfer energy. Neon atoms are excited to a metastable state. Stimulated emission from this energy level in neon atoms results in laser light of wavelength 632.8 nm.

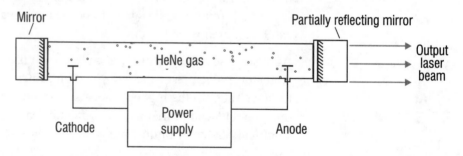

Figure 10.49
HeNe Laser

A neodymium-YAG laser uses a solid medium, in which Nd atoms are distributed through an yttrium aluminum garnet (YAG) glass rod. This laser is optically pumped. The Nd atom contains the metastable state, in which the laser transition corresponds to a wavelength of 1064.1 nm.

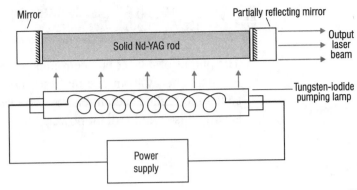

Figure 10.50
Nd-YAG Laser

Another type of laser uses a liquid dye as the medium. These liquids contain organic molecules (the dyes used to color cloth) in a solvent such as alcohol or water. Compared to individual atoms, molecules have many energy levels available for production of photons. Thus, dye lasers can be "tuned" to emit many different wavelengths of laser light. Liquid-dye lasers are optically pumped.

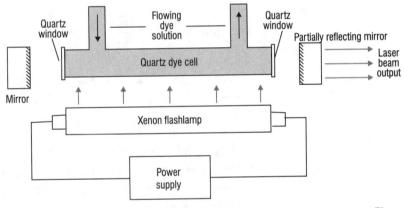

Figure 10.51
Liquid-dye laser

Semiconductors are also used as laser media. Semiconductor lasers are similar to transistors and diodes in construction—two types of semiconductor materials are joined at a junction. Electrons from one material migrate across the junction into the other material, creating a small potential difference. When an external voltage is applied, the electrons are forced back across the junction with a higher energy. When they recombine with atoms, some of the excess energy is emitted as photons.

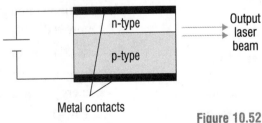

Figure 10.52
Semiconductor laser

Power Density

The output of a laser is electromagnetic radiation. Remember, EM radiation transfers energy from one place to another. For this reason, light is sometimes called radiant energy. The *rate* of radiant energy produced or absorbed is called radiant power.

$$\text{Radiant power} = \frac{\text{radiant energy}}{\text{time interval}}$$

$$\text{Pwr} = \frac{E}{\Delta t}$$

When radiant energy is measured in joules (J), radiant power is measured in watts (W). Remember, 1 W = 1 J/s.

Example 10.15 Radiant Energy of a Light Bulb

How long does it take a 100-W light bulb to radiate 1 J of energy?

Solution: $\text{Pwr} = \dfrac{E}{\Delta t}$

$$\Delta t = \frac{E}{\text{Pwr}} = \frac{1\text{ J}}{100\text{ J/s}} = 0.01\text{ s}$$

A 100-watt light bulb radiates 1 joule of energy in 0.01 second.

The light bulb in Example 10.15 radiates energy in all directions. A laser's output does not spread like the light bulb's. Laser light is highly directional—it is contained in a beam that does not spread rapidly. The **power density** of a laser beam is much higher than normal sources of light. Power density is the ratio of radiant power to the cross-sectional area over which the energy is spread. Power density is sometimes called **irradiance**.

$$\text{Power density or irradiance} = \frac{\text{radiant power}}{\text{area}}$$

In power-density calculations, we use square centimeters to measure cross-sectional areas, instead of the SI unit of square meters. Thus, the units of power density, or irradiance, are watts per square centimeter, W/cm^2.

A normal source of light, like a light bulb, spreads radiant energy over a large area, resulting in a low power density. A laser beam spreads radiant energy over a small area (the beam cross section), resulting in a large power density.

Example 10.16 Power Density of a Light Bulb and a Laser

Compare the power densities of the following sources of light.

(a) A 100-W light bulb at a distance of 5 meters from the bulb.

(b) A 100-W laser at a distance of 5 meters from the laser. At this distance, the laser beam has a radius of 0.1 cm.

Solution: (a) The light bulb spreads radiant energy evenly over the surface of a sphere. The surface area of a sphere is $4\pi r^2$, where r is the radius of the sphere. Substitute $r = 5$ m = 500 cm into the equation.

$$\text{Power density} = \frac{\text{radiant power}}{\text{area}}$$

$$= \frac{100 \text{ W}}{4\pi(500 \text{ cm})^2} = 3.2 \times 10^{-5} \text{ W/cm}^2$$

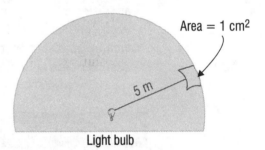

Area = 1 cm^2

5 m

Light bulb

(b) The laser beam has a circular cross section. The area of a circle is πr^2, where r is the radius of the circle. Substitute $r = 0.1$ cm into the equation.

$$\text{Power density} = \frac{\text{radiant power}}{\text{area}}$$

$$= \frac{100 \text{ W}}{\pi(0.1 \text{ cm})^2} = 3200 \text{ W/cm}^2$$

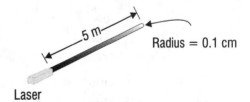

5 m

Radius = 0.1 cm

Laser

The laser beam has 10^8, or 100 million times the power density of the light bulb, even though they have the same radiant power output.

A laser beam combined with a focusing lens can concentrate radiant power in a small region. If the power is focused on a target, the power deposited may be higher than the target can dissipate. In this case the target may burn or melt. The effect of decreasing the spot size on a target is illustrated in Figure 10.53. One watt of radiant power is focused on smaller areas to produce different effects.

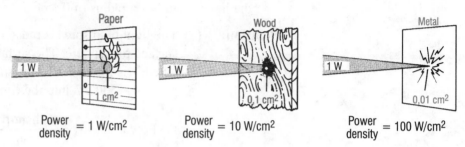

$$\text{Power density} = 1 \text{ W/cm}^2 \qquad \text{Power density} = 10 \text{ W/cm}^2 \qquad \text{Power density} = 100 \text{ W/cm}^2$$

Figure 10.53
A radiant power of 1 W concentrated on target areas of different sizes

A power density of 1 W/cm^2 is just enough to burn paper. When the spot area is decreased by a factor of ten, the power density increases tenfold. A power density of 10 W/cm^2 is enough to burn wood. Decreasing the spot area by another factor of ten increases the power density tenfold again. A power density of 100 W/cm^2 is enough to drill holes in metal.

Applications of Lasers

There are many different laser media with many different uses of the laser output. A few common applications are discussed below.

Helium-neon and semiconductor lasers are used in scanning systems in retail stores. Products have patterns of black and white lines called uniform product codes (UPC) printed on their packaging. When a laser beam is reflected off this pattern as it moves across a screen, information contained in the code can be transferred to the store's computer. The beam reflects off the white lines more strongly than off the black, producing on/off electrical signals, or a digital code. The code contains the identification and price of the product, so the computer will charge you the correct amount for the product, print a sales receipt, and keep track of the store's inventory.

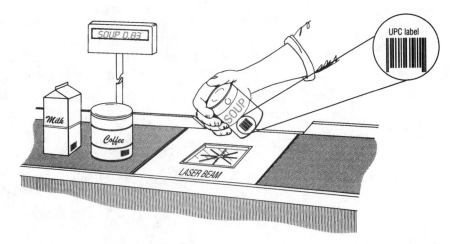

Figure 10.54
Supermarket scanner

Carbon-dioxide gas lasers can produce very high power densities at an infrared wavelength (10.6 μm). These photons are emitted by changing vibrational energies of the entire CO_2 molecule, rather than electron energy levels. These lasers are used in manufacturing to drill, cut, and weld metal. They are also used in medicine as "bloodless scalpels." The laser beam is transported through a glass fiber, so a surgeon can direct the beam to make cuts that are immediately cauterized (sealed). With lower power settings, the laser can vaporize pigments without affecting the surrounding skin, allowing for the removal of tattoos.

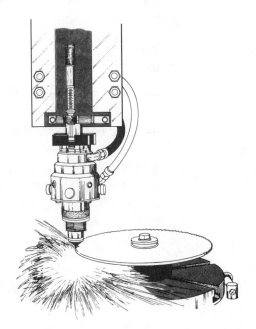

Figure 10.55
CO_2 laser cutting a saw blade

Argon gas lasers operate at two possible wavelengths in the blue-green region at 488 nm and 514 nm. These lasers are used in laser-light shows, semiconductor manufacturing, holography, and eye surgery. An ophthalmologist can repair a detached retina with an argon laser. Ophthalmologists use another type of laser, called an excimer laser, to improve vision by reshaping the lens with laser energy.

Figure 10.56
Laser eye surgery

Semiconductor lasers are used to read and write compact disks and digital video disks. They are also used to align drills and saws in manufacturing and to establish straight lines for surveying and construction. They are used in communication, where laser light is conducted through glass fibers to carry voice and data information. With use of different laser wavelengths and multiplexing (encoding multiple signals so they can be sent at the same time), thousands of conversations or data transmissions can be sent at the same time on a single fiber.

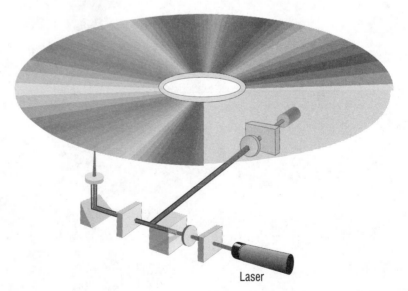

Laser

Figure 10.57
Lasers read and write data on compact disks.

Summary

- The model of the atom evolved to account for discovery of the electron, the nucleus, and the emission spectra of the elements.

- When an electron drops from an energy level E_i to a lower energy level E_f, a photon is emitted of energy $hf = E_i - E_f$. This is the Bohr frequency condition.

- Light has both wavelike and particlelike properties. Particles also have both types of properties. The wavelengths of photons and particles are calculated as the ratio of Planck's constant to momentum. For a particle, $\lambda = \dfrac{h}{mv}$.

- The quantum model of the atom led to the development of lasers. A material can produce laser light if there is at least one metastable energy level in the material's atoms or molecules.

- Laser light is monochromatic (single wavelength), highly directional, and coherent.

- Every laser has a laser medium, an optical cavity, and a pump.

- The power density of a laser beam—or any source of light—is the ratio of radiant power to the cross-sectional area over which the radiant energy is spread.

Exercises

1. Label the following as features of the Thomson, Rutherford, or Bohr model of the atom.

    (a) Electrons have quantized angular momentum.

    (b) The electron is a separate particle in an atom.

    (c) The positive charge and most of the mass are concentrated in a tiny central core.

    (d) Photons are emitted from atoms when electrons in the atoms change energy levels.

2. In the Rutherford and Bohr models, what holds electrons in an atom near the nucleus?

3. According to the Bohr model of the hydrogen atom, how many times larger is the diameter of the third orbit of the electron than the diameter of the first orbit?

4. Calculate the energies of the third and fifth energy levels in hydrogen. Find the wavelength of light emitted when the electron jumps from E_5 to E_3. In what part of the electromagnetic spectrum is this light (ultraviolet, visible, or infrared)?

5. An electron in an excited state of hydrogen drops to the ground state. It emits a photon of wavelength 97.4 nm. In which energy level was the electron before the transition?

6. (a) What is the maximum possible energy of a photon emitted by a hydrogen atom?

    (b) Suppose a hydrogen atom in the ground state *absorbs* a photon of the same energy as in (a). What happens to the electron?

    (c) Suppose a hydrogen atom in the ground state absorbs a photon of *twice* the energy as in (a). What happens to the electron?

7. What is the longest wavelength of visible light in the emission spectrum of hydrogen?

8. What is the longest wavelength of light that can be absorbed by a hydrogen atom in the ground state?

9. Which of the following is quantized?

    (a) The depth of the water in a swimming pool

    (b) The temperature of the water in a swimming pool

    (c) The number of swimmers in a swimming pool

10. The four lowest energy levels of an atom consist of the ground state and three excited states. How many spectral lines can the atom emit from these levels? (Hint—draw an energy-level diagram.)

11. What are the three properties of laser light that distinguish it from light produced by common, everyday sources?

12. Lasers used for CD players are usually semiconductor (gallium arsenide) lasers with wavelengths of 780 nm. What is the difference between the two energy levels for this laser transition? Write your answer in eV.

13. List two types of pumps used in lasers.

14. What is a population inversion in a laser medium? Why is it necessary to have a population inversion for a medium to produce laser light?

The illustration below is a simplified energy-level diagram for neodymium atoms in an Nd-YAG laser rod. Use the diagram to answer Exercises 15–17.

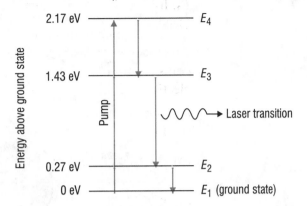

15. Will an Nd atom in the ground state absorb a photon of energy 0.85 eV? Explain.

16. The Nd:YAG laser is optically pumped. Using the energy levels shown, calculate the wavelength of light needed to pump the laser.

17. Which energy level is the metastable state for Nd? What is the wavelength of the laser output? In which region of the electromagnetic spectrum is the output?

18. A HeNe laser produces light at a wavelength of 632.8 nm. In the electron transition that emits photons of laser light, the energy level of the lower state is 18.5 eV above the ground state. How many eV above the ground state is the metastable state?

19. List the commonly used units for each of the following.

    (a) radiant energy   (b) radiant power   (c) radiant power density

20. If you measure the radiant power density, or irradiance, on a surface, you measure

    (a) the total amount of radiant energy deposited on the surface.

    (b) the total amount of radiant energy per second deposited on the surface.

    (c) the total amount of radiant energy per second per square centimeter deposited on the surface.

    (d) none of the above.

21. A CO_2 laser produces a 40-W beam. The beam is focused onto a target with a spot size 0.1 cm in diameter. What is the power density on the target?

22. *This exercise demonstrates why you should protect your eyes when working with lasers, even low-power lasers.*

A laser pointer produces a 2-mW beam. The beam has a circular cross section 2.5 mm in diameter when it enters someone's eye. The person's lens focuses the beam to a spot on the retina. The spot measures 16 μm in diameter.

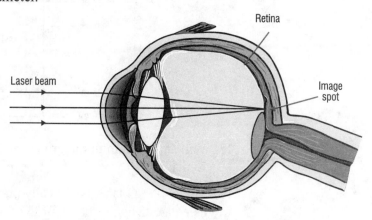

(a) What is the power density of the laser beam just before it enters the person's eye?

(b) What is the power density on the retina, after the beam is focused?

23. An Nd-YAG laser is used in eye surgery to repair a detached retina. The laser produces pulses of light that last for 1.50 ns. An energy of 2.00 mJ is needed in one pulse during the surgery. The laser beam is focused to a tiny spot inside the eye. The diameter of the spot is 18 μm.

(a) What is the power delivered by the laser pulse?

(b) What is the power density of the laser pulse focused on the spot?

24. For a hydrogen atom in the ground state, calculate

(a) the force between the electron and proton.

(b) the centripetal acceleration of the electron.

(c) the speed of the electron. What percent of the speed of light is this?

CHAPTER TEN SUMMARY

Light can be difficult to study and understand because it behaves in different ways in different situations. Over the years, scientists have developed models of light to explain observations. Some of these models have also changed our understanding of atoms and molecules.

To understand how images are formed by mirrors and lenses, you can model light as rays traveling along straight lines. Mirrors and lenses change the direction of incident light rays—mirrors by reflection and lenses by refraction. You can use the laws of reflection and refraction to trace the paths of light rays and predict the location, size, and orientation of images formed by optical systems.

In other situations, light does not appear to travel in straight lines. It bends around the edges of obstacles and spreads out when it travels through narrow slits or apertures. Light produces patterns in these situations. You can understand these patterns if you model light as a wave. Light waves from the same source interfere when they travel different distances to arrive at the same point at the same time. The resulting interference or diffraction pattern can be used to determine the wavelength of the light. Diffraction limits the ability of telescopes and microscopes to resolve two objects—or the smallest detail of one object.

To understand the array of light wavelengths emitted by hydrogen—its emission spectrum—Niels Bohr developed a model of the atom. Bohr's model assumed that the electron in the atom could have only certain discrete, or quantized, energy levels. When the electron changes levels, it emits (or absorbs) a discrete bundle of energy, called a photon. This model was consistent with Einstein's explanation of the photoelectric effect, in which light behaves like a particle.

Louis de Broglie hypothesized that, if light has a particlelike nature, particles such as electrons should have a wavelike nature. This hypothesis led to development of the quantum model of the atom. The quantum model uses a wave function as a mathematical description of the atom, which can predict the energy levels and emission spectra of all the elements and molecules. It also predicts the existence of metastable energy levels. Laser light is produced by stimulated emission from metastable states. Because of the way it is produced, laser light is different from light produced by other sources—it is monochromatic, highly directional, and coherent. These attributes have created many applications for lasers.

Appendix A. Reference Tables

Table A.1 SI Base Units

Quantity	Unit	Symbol
Length	meter	m
Mass	kilogram	kg
Time	second	s
Temperature	kelvin	K
Amount of substance	mole	m
Electric current	ampere	A
Luminous intensity	candela	cd

Table A.2 SI Prefixes

Prefix	Symbol	Value
femto	f	10^{-15}
pico	p	10^{-12}
nano	n	10^{-9}
micro	μ	10^{-6}
milli	m	10^{-3}
centi	c	10^{-2}
kilo	k	10^3
mega	M	10^6
giga	G	10^9
tera	T	10^{12}
peta	P	10^{15}

Table A.3 Derived Units

Quantity	SI		English	
	Name	Symbol and units	Name	Symbol and units
Acceleration		m/s^2		ft/s^2
Area		m^2		ft^2
Angular acceleration		rad/s^2		rad/s^2
Angular speed		rad/s		rad/s
Capacitance	farad	$F \; (= C/V)$		
Density		kg/m^3		$slug/ft^3$
Electric charge	coulomb	C		
Electric field		$N/C \; (= V/m)$		
Electric resistance	ohm	$\Omega \; (= V/A)$		
Energy and work	joule	$J \; (= N \cdot m)$	foot·pound	ft·lb
Force	newton	N	pound	lb
Frequency	hertz	$Hz \; (= s^{-1})$	hertz	$Hz \; (= s^{-1})$
Heat flow rate		J/s		ft·lb/s
Inductance	henry	$H \; (= V \cdot s/A)$		
Length	meter	m	foot	ft
Mass	kilogram	kg	slug	slug
Mass flow rate		kg/s		slug/s
Momentum		kg·m/s		slug·ft/s
Potential difference	volt	$V \; (= J/C)$		
Power	watt	$W \; (= J/s)$		ft·lb/s
Power density		W/cm^2		
Pressure	pascal	$Pa \; (= N/m^2)$		lb/ft^2
Torque		N·m		lb·ft
Velocity		m/s		ft/s
Viscosity		Pa·s		
Volume		m^3		ft^3
Volume flow rate		m^3/s		ft^3/s

Table A.4 Useful Constants

Quantity	Symbol	Value
Elementary charge	e	1.60×10^{-19} C
Gravitational constant	G	6.67×10^{-11} N·m^2/kg^2
Speed of light	c	3.00×10^8 m/s
		9.82×10^8 ft/s
Mass-energy relation	c^2	931 MeV/u
Electron mass	m_e	9.110×10^{-31} kg
		0.000549 u
Neutron mass	m_n	1.675×10^{-27} kg
		1.008665 u
Proton mass	m_p	1.673×10^{-27} kg
		1.007277 u
Hydrogen atom mass	m_H	1.007825 u
Planck's constant	h	6.63×10^{-34} J·s
		4.14×10^{-15} eV·s

Table A.5 Useful Conversions

Mass
1 slug = 14.6 kg
1 u = 1.660565×10^{-27} kg
1 kg weighs 2.21 lb
1 slug weighs 32.2 lb

Length
1 in = 2.54 cm
1 mi = 1.61 km
1 mi = 5280 ft
1 ft = 12 in

Time
1 y = 365 d
1 d = 24 h
1 h = 3600 s

Angular measure
2π rad = 360° = 1 rev

Volume
1 L = 1000 cm^3
1 m^3 = 1000 L
1 m^3 = 264 gal
1 gal = 231 in^3

Force
1 lb = 4.448 N
1 lb = 16 oz

Pressure
1 atm = 14.7 lb/in^2
1 atm = 2116 lb/ft^2
1 atm = 1.013×10^5 Pa
1 atm = 101.3 kPa
1 atm = 760 mm Hg

Energy
1 cal = 4.184 J
1 Btu = 778 ft·lb
1 ft·lb = 1.356 J
1 eV = 1.602×10^{-19} J
1 kW·h = 3.6×10^6 J

Power
1 hp = 746 W
1 hp = 550 ft·lb/s
1 hp = 2545 Btu/h

Appendix B. The Elements

Atomic Number	Element	Symbol	Atomic Mass*	Atomic Number	Element	Symbol	Atomic Mass*
1	Hydrogen	H	1.008	37	Rubidium	Rb	85.468
2	Helium	He	4.003	38	Strontium	Sr	87.62
3	Lithium	Li	6.941	39	Yttrium	Y	88.906
4	Beryllium	Be	9.012	40	Zirconium	Zr	91.224
5	Boron	B	10.811	41	Niobium	Nb	92.906
6	Carbon	C	12.011	42	Molybdenum	Mo	95.94
7	Nitrogen	N	14.007	43	Technetium	Tc	97.907
8	Oxygen	O	15.999	44	Ruthenium	Ru	101.07
9	Fluorine	F	18.998	45	Rhodium	Rh	102.906
10	Neon	Ne	20.180	46	Palladium	Pd	106.42
11	Sodium	Na	22.990	47	Silver	Ag	107.868
12	Magnesium	Mg	24.305	48	Cadmium	Cd	112.411
13	Aluminum	Al	26.982	49	Indium	In	114.818
14	Silicon	Si	28.086	50	Tin	Sn	118.710
15	Phosphorus	P	30.974	51	Antimony	Sb	121.760
16	Sulfur	S	32.066	52	Tellurium	Te	127.60
17	Chlorine	Cl	35.453	53	Iodine	I	126.904
18	Argon	Ar	39.948	54	Xenon	Xe	131.29
19	Potassium	K	39.098	55	Cesium	Cs	132.905
20	Calcium	Ca	40.078	56	Barium	Ba	137.327
21	Scandium	Sc	44.956	57	Lanthanum	La	138.906
22	Titanium	Ti	47.867	58	Cerium	Ce	140.116
23	Vanadium	V	50.942	59	Praseodymium	Pr	140.907
24	Chromium	Cr	51.996	60	Neodymium	Nd	144.24
25	Manganese	Mn	54.938	61	Promethium	Pm	144.913
26	Iron	Fe	55.847	62	Samarium	Sm	150.36
27	Cobalt	Co	58.933	63	Europium	Eu	151.964
28	Nickel	Ni	58.693	64	Gadolinium	Gd	157.25
29	Copper	Cu	63.546	65	Terbium	Tb	158.925
30	Zinc	Zn	65.39	66	Dysprosium	Dy	162.50
31	Gallium	Ga	69.723	67	Holmium	Ho	164.930
32	Germanium	Ge	72.61	68	Erbium	Er	167.26
33	Arsenic	As	74.921	69	Thulium	Tm	168.934
34	Selenium	Se	78.96	70	Ytterbium	Yb	173.04
35	Bromine	Br	79.904	71	Lutetium	Lu	174.967
36	Krypton	Kr	83.80	72	Hafnium	Hf	178.49

*The atomic mass of each element listed is the average of the relative atomic masses of the isotopes of the element.

Atomic Number	Element	Symbol	Atomic Mass*	Atomic Number	Element	Symbol	Atomic Mass*
73	Tantalum	Ta	180.948	95	Americium	Am	243.061
74	Wolfram	W	183.84	96	Curium	Cm	247.070
75	Rhenium	Re	186.207	97	Berkelium	Bk	247.070
76	Osmium	Os	190.23	98	Californium	Cf	251.080
77	Iridium	Ir	192.217	99	Einsteinium	Es	252.083
78	Platinum	Pt	195.078	100	Fermium	Fm	257.095
79	Gold	Au	196.967	101	Mendelevium	Md	258.099
80	Mercury	Hg	200.59	102	Nobelium	No	259.101
81	Thallium	Tl	204.383	103	Lawrencium	Lr	260.105
82	Lead	Pb	207.2	104	Rutherfordium	Rf	(261)
83	Bismuth	Bi	208.980	105	Dubnium	Db	(262)
84	Polonium	Po	208.982	106	Seaborgium	Sg	(263)
85	Astatine	At	209.987	107	Bohrium	Bh	(264)
86	Radon	Rn	222.018	108	Hassium	Hs	(265)
87	Francium	Fr	223.020	109	Meitnerium	Mt	(268)
88	Radium	Ra	226.025	110	Ununnilium	Uun	(269)
89	Actinium	Ac	227.028	111	Unununium	Uuu	(272)
90	Thorium	Th	232.038	112	Ununbium	Uub	(277)
91	Protactinium	Pa	231.036	114	Ununquadium	Uuq	(285)
92	Uranium	U	238.029	116	Ununhexium	Uuh	(289)
93	Neptunium	Np	237.048	118	Ununoctium	Uuo	(293)
94	Plutonium	Pu	244.064				

*The atomic mass of each element listed is the average of the relative atomic masses of the isotopes of the element.

Appendix C. Glossary

absolute pressure The total pressure in an enclosed volume measured above zero, or perfect vacuum. The sum of atmospheric pressure plus gage pressure (1.2)

absolute zero The lower limit of temperature (0 K or –273°C) of any substance, where thermal energy is zero (5.4)

adiabatic process A process in which no heat is transferred to or from a system (5.4)

alpha decay A radioactive decay process in which an unstable nucleus emits an alpha particle (9.2)

alpha particle A particle emitted by some radioactive materials. An alpha particle is a helium-4 nucleus consisting of two protons and two neutrons. (9.2)

alternating current (AC) A current in which the direction of electric charge flow changes regularly in an electric circuit (1.3.)

ammeter A device that measures current (3.3)

ampere (A) The unit of current. Defined as one coulomb per second (2.3)

amplitude The distance from equilibrium to the crest or the trough of a wave (8.1)

angle of incidence The angle between an incident ray and the normal to the surface (10.1)

angle of reflection The angle between a reflected ray and the normal to the surface (10.1)

angle of refraction The angle between a refracted ray and the normal to the surface (10.1)

angular acceleration The ratio of the change in angular speed to the time interval over which the change is measured (3.1)

angular displacement The change in angular position, or angular distance traveled, when an object rotates from one position to another (3.1)

angular impulse The product of the torque exerted on an object and the time interval over which the torque acts (7.2)

angular momentum The product of an object's moment of inertia and its angular velocity (7.2)

angular speed The ratio of angular displacement to the time interval over which the displacement is measured (3.1)

Archimedes' principle An object immersed in a fluid has an upward (buoyant) force exerted on it equal to the weight of the fluid displaced by the object. (1.2)

atomic mass unit (u) A unit of mass used for nuclear calculations. Defined as 1/12 the mass of the carbon-12 isotope (9.2)

atomic number The number of protons in the nucleus of an atom (9.2)

average acceleration The ratio of the change in velocity to the time interval over which the change is measured (3.1)

average speed The ratio of the total distance traveled to the time interval over which the distance is measured (3.1)

average velocity The ratio of the displacement to the time interval over which the displacement is measured (3.1)

barometer An instrument used for measuring atmospheric pressure (1.2)

battery A source of electric potential difference in an electric circuit. Converts chemical energy into electric energy and charge flow (1.3)

beat A pattern of pulsations or variations in loudness produced by two sound waves having slightly different frequencies (8.2)

Bernoulli's principle As the velocity of a fluid increases, the pressure in the fluid decreases. (5.2)

beta decay A radioactive decay process in which an unstable nucleus emits a beta particle (9.2)

beta particle A particle emitted by some radioactive materials. A beta particle can be an electron or a positron. (9.2)

binding energy The energy holding the protons and neutrons together in the nucleus of an atom (9.2)

Bohr frequency condition A condition in which an electron in an atom jumps from one energy level to another and a photon is emitted of frequency $\Delta E/h$, where ΔE is the change in the electron's energy and h is Planck's constant (10.3)

boiling point The temperature at which a material changes state from liquid to gas as thermal energy is added to the material (1.4)

British thermal unit (Btu) A unit of energy in the English system. Defined as the energy required to raise the temperature of one pound of water by one degree Fahrenheit (1.4)

buoyancy or buoyant force The upward force exerted on an object immersed in a fluid (1.2)

calorie (cal) A unit of energy. Defined as the energy required to raise the temperature of one gram of water by one degree Celsius (1.4)

capacitance The ratio of the charge stored on a capacitor to the potential difference across the capacitor (5.3)

capacitor An electrical device that stores charge and energy. The energy is stored in the electric field across the plates of a charged capacitor. (5.3)

Carnot efficiency The maximum possible efficiency of a heat engine (5.4)

chain reaction A process of self-sustained fission reaction in which neutrons are absorbed and cause fissions, which release more neutrons, which cause further fissions (9.2)

closed system A system that does not gain or lose mass (2.2, 5.2, and 7.1)

coefficient of friction The ratio of the maximum force (static or kinetic) of friction to the normal force between the surfaces in contact (4.1)

coherent waves Waves for which there is a fixed relation between their phases. Any difference between phases does not change. (10.2)

concave lens A lens that is thinner at its center than at its edges (10.1)

concave mirror A mirror with an inwardly curved surface ("caved in") as seen by an incident light ray (10.1)

conductor A material containing many free electrons that move through the material easily when an electric field is applied (4.3)

constructive interference Phenomenon in which the interaction of two waves produces an increase in wave amplitude (8.2)

convection The transfer of heat by movement of a fluid (3.4)

convex lens A lens that is thicker at its center than at its edges (10.1)

convex mirror A mirror with an outwardly curved surface as seen by an incident light ray (10.1)

coulomb (C) The SI unit of electrical charge (1.3)

Coulomb's law One charged object attracts another charged object with a force that is directly proportional to the product of the objects' charges and inversely proportional to the square of the distance between the objects' centers. (1.3)

critical angle The angle of incidence for a light ray traveling through a material for which the refracted angle has a measure of 90° (10.1)

current The rate of charge flow in a conductor, measured in amperes. Defined as the ratio of the charge moved through a cross-sectional area to the time interval over which the measurement is made (2.3 and 3.3)

density A property of a material, defined as the mass of a sample of the material divided by the volume (1.2)

destructive interference Phenomenon in which the interaction of two waves produces a decrease in wave amplitude (8.2)

diffraction The bending of light around the edges of an obstacle (10.2)

diffraction grating A optical device that uses a large number of parallel slits (or lines) to transmit (or reflect) light to form an interference pattern (10.2)

direct current (DC) A current in which electric charge flows in one direction in an electric circuit (1.3)

displacement A vector quantity that defines the distance and direction between two points. The magnitude of the displacement vector is the change in position, or distance traveled, when an object moves from the first point to the second point. (3.1)

drag The force that opposes motion when a solid object moves through a fluid or when a fluid flows past a solid object. Drag increases with speed. (4.2)

efficiency The ratio of output work to input work (2.1)

elasticity The tendency of an object or material to return to its original shape after being stretched or compressed (5.2)

elastic potential energy Energy stored by an object due to a change in its shape (5.2)

electrical force A force acting at a distance between two or more charges (1.3)

electrical resistance A measure of the ability of an electrical device to oppose the flow of charge through the device. Defined as the ratio of the potential difference, or voltage drop, across a device to the current through the device (4.3)

electric charge The property of an object that causes electrical force (1.3)

electric field An imaginary construction of vectors to help us visualize and predict electric forces on charged objects placed in the field (1.3)

electric field lines Lines showing the direction and magnitude of the electric field (1.3)

electric potential difference Also called voltage or voltage difference. The ability to accelerate an electric charge between two points in an electric field. Defined as the change in potential energy per unit charge (1.3 and 2.3)

electromagnetic induction The process of generating a current in a wire due to relative motion between the wire and a magnetic field (5.3)

electromagnetic radiation A transfer of energy by means of electromagnetic waves (9.1)

electromagnetic spectrum An arrangement of the continuous wavelengths and frequencies of electromagnetic waves (9.1)

electromagnetic wave A wave that consists of electric and magnetic fields changing in step with each other and that travels through space at the speed of light (9.1)

electromotive force (EMF) The potential difference produced by electromagnetic induction (5.3)

electron volt (eV) An amount of work or energy equal to that gained by an electron when accelerated through a potential difference of one volt (9.2)

elementary charge (q) The charge on one electron or proton, $\pm 1.60 \times 10^{-19}$ C (1.3)

emission spectrum The array of wavelengths emitted by a source of light (10.3)

energy The property of a system or object that enables it to do work (5.1)

energy dissipation A conversion of work or useful forms of energy into thermal or unusable forms of energy (6.1)

energy level A discrete amount of total energy that an electron can have when it is bound to an atom (10.3)

equilibrium A state in which the net force acting on an object is zero; or when the forces are balanced (1.1)

excited state An energy level above the ground state that an electron can occupy in an atom when the atom absorbs the right amount of energy (10.3)

farad (F) The unit of capacitance. Defined as one coulomb per volt (5.3)

first law of thermodynamics Law stating that the increase in internal energy of a system is the heat added to the system minus the work done by the system (5.4)

fission Reproduction in which a heavy nucleus (such as uranium or plutonium) absorbs a neutron, becomes highly unstable, and splits into two or more smaller nuclei plus other nuclear particles and energy (9.2)

fluid A liquid or a gas. A material that can flow, has no definite shape of its own, and conforms to the shape of its container (1.2)

fluid resistance A measure of the ability of an object to oppose the flow of fluid across the object's surface. Defined as the ratio of the pressure drop in the fluid to the volume flow rate (4.2)

focal length The distance from the focal point to the vertex of a spherical mirror. Also the distance from the focal point to the center of a thin lens (10.1)

focal point The point at which a mirror or lens causes parallel light rays to converge or appear to diverge from (10.1)

foot (ft) The base unit of length in the English system (1.1)

foot·pound (ft·lb) The English unit of energy (2.1)

force A push or a pull exerted on an object in a direction (1.1)

free-body diagram A diagram that uses arrows representing vectors to show all the forces acting on an object or system (1.1)

frequency A measure of how often a pattern repeats itself. Defined as the ratio of the number of complete cycles, or oscillations, of the pattern to the time interval over which the cycles are measured (3.3)

friction A force that opposes relative motion of two solids or a solid and liquid (4.1)

fusion A union in which two light nuclei combine to form a single heavier nucleus plus energy (9.2)

gage pressure The pressure in an enclosed volume measured above atmospheric pressure (1.2)

gamma decay A radioactive decay process in which an unstable nucleus emits a gamma ray (9.2)

gamma ray Electromagnetic wave in the wavelength band between approximately 10^{-13} m and 10^{-11} m that is emitted by the nucleus of an unstable atom (9.1 and 9.2)

gravitational acceleration (g) The acceleration experienced by an object when gravity is the only force acting on it. On the surface of the Earth, $g = 9.80$ m/s^2 or 32.2 ft/s^2, and is directed toward the center of the Earth. (4.1)

gravitational force An attractive force acting at a distance between two or more masses (1.3)

gravitational potential energy Energy stored by an object due to the location of the object in a gravitational field (5.2)

ground state The lowest energy level that can be occupied by an electron in an atom (10.3)

heat The energy transferred from one object to another because of a temperature difference (1.4)

heat conduction The process of transferring thermal energy from a hotter object to a cooler object, as kinetic energy is transferred when particles collide (1.4 and 3.4)

heat engine A device that converts thermal energy into mechanical energy (5.4)

heat flow rate The ratio of the heat transferred to the time interval over which the transfer is measured (3.4)

heat of combustion The amount of heat released when one kilogram or one cubic meter of a substance is burned (6.2)

heat of fusion The amount of energy required to melt one gram of a solid substance. Also, the amount of energy released when one gram of a liquid solidifies (1.4)

heat of vaporization The amount of energy required to vaporize one gram of a liquid substance. Also, the amount of energy released when one gram of a gas condenses (1.4)

henry (H) The unit of inductance. Defined as one volt per ampere per second (5.3)

hertz (Hz) The unit of measure of frequency. Defined as one cycle per second, or 1/s (3.3)

horsepower (hp) An English unit of power. Defined as 550 foot pounds per second (5.4)

hydraulic system A system that uses a liquid as a working fluid (1.2)

impulse The product of the force exerted on an object and the time interval over which the force acts (7.1)

incoherent waves Waves for which there is no fixed relation between their phases. There are random differences between their phases. (10.2)

index of refraction A property of a transparent material defined as the ratio of the speed of light in a vacuum (c) to the speed of light in the material (10.1)

inductance The ratio of the induced EMF of an inductor to the rate of change of current through the inductor (5.3)

inductor An electrical device that stores voltage and energy. The energy is stored in the magnetic field of the inductor. (5.3)

inertia A property of an object by which it resists changes in its motion (1.1)

infrared radiation Electromagnetic waves in the wavelength band between approximately 10^{-6} m and 10^{-3} m that can be used to transfer heat from a hot object to a cool object (9.1)

insulation A layer of a material with a high thermal resistance, used to reduce the heat transfer rate from a region (4.4)

insulator A material that does not contain significant numbers of free electrons that can move easily through the material (4.3)

interference The interaction of two or more waves of the same type when they occupy the same space at the same time (8.2)

internal energy The sum of the microscopic kinetic and potential energies of all the atoms and molecules that make up a system (5.1 and 5.4)

isolated system A closed system on which no net external forces act (7.1)

isotopes Atoms that have the same number of protons in their nuclei but differing numbers of neutrons (9.2)

joule (J) The SI unit of energy. Equal to one newton·meter (2.1)

kelvin (K) The interval of temperature measurement on the Kelvin scale (5.4)

kilogram (kg) The base unit of mass in the SI system (1.1)

kilowatt-hour (kWh) The energy consumed by a 1-kW device operated for one hour (6.3)

kinetic energy Energy possessed by an object or system due to motion of the object or system (2.1 and 5.1)

kinetic friction The force required to maintain a constant speed between two surfaces in contact (4.1)

laminar flow Slow, smooth flow of fluid over a surface, in which the paths of individual particles of fluid do not cross. Also called streamlined flow (4.2)

laser A device that is a source of monochromatic, highly directional, coherent light (10.3)

laser medium A solid, liquid, or gaseous material that can be used to amplify the intensity of a laser beam (10.3)

laser pump A source of energy for exciting atoms or molecules of a laser medium (10.3)

law of conservation of angular momentum When no net external torque acts on a closed system, the total angular momentum of the system remains constant. (7.2)

law of conservation of energy The total energy of an isolated system is constant. (5.2)

law of conservation of linear momentum When no net external force acts on a closed system, the total linear momentum of the system remains constant. (7.1)

law of reflection When light reflects from a surface, the angle of reflection equals the angle of incidence. (10.1)

lens A ground or molded piece of transparent glass or plastic used to change the direction of light in optical systems (10.1)

Lenz's law A current produced by electromagnetic induction has a magnetic field that opposes the change in the magnetic field that induced the current. (5.3)

lever arm The shortest distance from an object's axis of rotation to the line of action of an applied force (1.1)

linear momentum The product of the mass of an object and its velocity (7.1)

longitudinal wave A wave that displaces particles in the medium parallel to the direction in which the wave travels (8.1)

magnetic field An imaginary construction of vectors to help us visualize and predict magnetic forces on charged objects moving through the field (5.3)

magnification The ratio of the image size to the object size in an optical system (10.1)

mass A measure of an object's inertia or the amount of matter contained within an object (1.1)

mass defect The difference between the sum of the masses of the nucleons in a nucleus and the actual mass of the nucleus. The mass defect is converted into energy. (9.2)

mass flow rate The ratio of the change in mass to the time interval over which the change is measured (3.2)

mass number The number of nucleons (protons plus neutrons) in the nucleus of an atom (9.2)

mechanical wave A wave that requires a medium for propagation (8.1)

melting point The temperature at which a material changes state from solid to liquid as thermal energy is added to the material (1.4)

metastable state An excited state, or elevated energy level, in an atom; distinguished from other excited states because the electron stays in a metastable state for a much longer time

meter (m) The base unit of length in the SI system (1.1)

metric system A set of measurements in which units are related by powers of ten (1.1)

microwave Electromagnetic wave in the wavelength band between approximately 10^{-3} m and 0.1 m (9.1)

moment of inertia A property that describes an object's resistance to change in rotational motion. For an object in rotational motion, moment of inertia is analogous to the mass for an object in translational motion. (5.1)

monochromatic light Light that has only one wavelength (10.2)

natural frequency The frequency at which an object or system oscillates on its own when set into motion (8.2)

newton (N) The base unit of force in the SI system (1.1)

Newton's first law of motion If the net force on an object or a system is zero, the velocity of the object or system will not change. (1.1)

Newton's second law of motion The acceleration of an object is directly proportional to the net force acting on the object and inversely proportional to the mass of the object. Equivalently stated as: A net force exerted on an object equals the rate of change of the object's linear momentum. (4.1 and 7.1)

Newton's third law of motion When one body exerts a force on another body, the second body exerts an equal and opposite force on the first. (7.1)

Newton's universal law of gravitation One object attracts another object with a force that is directly proportional to the product of the objects' masses and inversely proportional to the square of the distance between the objects' centers. (1.3)

nuclear radiation A transfer of energy away from an unstable nucleus by means of alpha particles, beta particles, or gamma rays (9.2)

ohm (Ω) The unit of electrical resistance. Defined as one volt per ampere (4.3)

Ohm's law The linear relationship between applied potential difference and current through an electrical device, $\Delta V = IR$, where resistance R is constant (4.3)

optical cavity The region between the mirrors of a laser containing the laser medium (10.3)

parallel circuit An electrical circuit in which there are multiple paths for current. Part of the current flows through each branch of the circuit. The total current equals the sum of the currents in the branches. (4.3)

parallel connection A connection of electric circuit elements in which there is more than one path for current. The voltage across each element is the same. (3.3)

Pascal's principle A change in pressure at any point in a confined fluid is transmitted undiminished throughout the fluid. (1.2)

period The time required for one complete cycle of a repeating pattern (3.3)

periodic wave A regular, repeating wave that travels through a medium or space (8.1)

photoelectric effect The liberation of an electric charge by electromagnetic radiation incident on a surface (9.1)

photon A massless particle, the quantum of the electromagnetic field, carrying energy, momentum, and angular momentum (9.1)

Planck's constant (h) A fundamental physical constant, the elementary quantum of action; the ratio of the energy of a photon to its frequency (9.1)

plasma A gas containing free electrons and ions (1.2)

pneumatic system A system that uses a gas as a working fluid (1.2)

Poiseuille's law For a fluid in laminar flow through a tube or pipe, the relationship between volume flow rate, pipe radius, pressure drop, and length of pipe (4.2)

population inversion A state in which more electrons are in an excited energy level than in the next lower level (10.3)

potential energy Energy stored by an object or system due to the location of the object or system (2.1 and 5.1)

pound (lb) The base unit of force in the English system (1.1)

power The rate of doing work or the rate of transferring energy (6.1)

power density For a source of light, the ratio of radiant power output to the cross-sectional area over which the energy is spread. Common units of power density are watts per cm^2. (10.3)

pressure A force applied over an area, defined as the applied force divided by the area on which it acts (1.2)

prime mover The entity responsible for motion in an energy system—*force* in mechanical systems, *pressure* in fluid systems, *potential difference* or *voltage* in electrical systems, *temperature* difference in thermal systems (1.1)

principal quantum number An integer that determines the total quantized energy of an electron in an atom (10.3)

principle of conservation of charge The net electric charge in an isolated system never changes. (1.3)

principle of superposition When two or more waves interfere, the overall wave displacement is the sum of the displacements caused by the individual waves. (8.2)

property A quality or trait belonging to a system, such as mass, volume, weight, diameter, color, speed, height above the ground, and temperature (5.1)

quantized Some properties (such as energy, momentum, angular momentum) can have only certain discrete values separated by small but measurable increments. These properties cannot have values between the quantized values. (10.3)

radian A dimensionless measure of an angle. Defined (for a central angle) as the ratio of the arc length subtended to the radius of the circle for which it is a central angle (2.1)

radiation The transfer of energy by electromagnetic waves (3.4 and 9.1)

radioactive decay A process by which an unstable nucleus emits radiation and becomes more stable (9.2)

radio wave Electromagnetic wave in the wavelength band between approximately 1.0 m and 10^6 m, used to transmit radio and television signals (9.1)

rate The ratio of a measured quantity to the time interval over which the measurement is made. Examples are speed, acceleration, mass flow rate, volume flow rate, current, and heat flow rate. (3.1)

Rayleigh criterion For an optical instrument such as a telescope or microscope, two objects are just resolved if the central bright disk of one object falls on the first dark ring of the other.

ray optics Use of straight lines to model the paths followed by light through a medium or optical system (10.1)

real image An image of an object formed by a mirror or lens when light rays from the object converge. A real image can be seen by placing a screen or piece of paper at the point at which the light from the object converges. (10.1)

reflection The change in direction of a wave or photon of light when it strikes a surface or different medium but remains in the original medium (9.2 and 10.1)

refraction The change in direction of a wave or photon of light as it crosses a boundary into a different medium (10.1)

resistivity A property of a material that describes its ability to resist flow of electric charge (4.3)

resistor An electrical device that has a specific value of resistance (4.3)

resolving power For an optical instrument such as a telescope or microscope, the minimum separation of two objects for which the images appear separate and distinct (10.2)

resonance A condition between a source of vibration and an object or system in which the frequency of the source equals the natural frequency of the object or system (8.2)

resultant vector A single vector representing the sum of two or more addend vectors (1.1)

scalar quantity A quantity that can be described by a magnitude (1.1)

second (s) The base unit of time in the SI and English systems (1.1)

second law of thermodynamics (1) The natural direction of heat flow is from a high-temperature body to a low-temperature body. (2) A heat engine can convert only some of the heat taken from a reservoir into work. The rest is rejected as heat at a lower temperature. (5.4)

semiconductor A material intermediate between a conductor and an insulator in its ability to conduct charge (4.3)

series circuit An electric circuit in which there is only one path for current. Charge flows through each device in the circuit, one at a time. (4.3)

series connection A connection of electric circuit elements in which there is only one path for current. The current through each element is the same. (3.3)

slug The base unit of mass in the English system (1.1)

Snell's law The ratio of the sines of the angles of incidence and refraction equals the inverse ratio of the indices of refraction. (10.1)

solenoid A series of loops of wire that acts like a magnet when a current flows through it (5.3)

specific heat (1.4) The amount of energy that must be added to a material to raise the temperature of a unit mass of the material one degree (1.4)

standing wave Waves with stationary nodes that are created by reflections interfering with incident waves (8.2)

static friction The force required to start relative motion between two surfaces in contact (4.1)

steady flow A process in which the same amount of fluid enters and leaves a system in a given time interval (2.2)

stimulated emission A release of a photon from an atom or molecule, caused by another photon whose energy exactly matches the difference in energy levels of the atom. The emitted photon has the same energy, direction, and phase as the incident photon. (10.3)

Stokes' law The relationship between the drag force and speed for a small sphere moving through a viscous fluid (4.2)

strong nuclear force The force of attraction that holds protons and neutrons together in the nucleus of an atom (9.2)

temperature A property of an object that measures its "hotness." Temperature is proportional to the average kinetic energy of the random motion of the atoms and molecules in an object. (1.4)

terminal speed The constant speed achieved by a falling object when the downward force of gravity equals the upward drag force (plus the buoyant force if it exists) (4.2)

thermal conductivity A property of a material that measures its ability to conduct heat (3.4)

thermal energy The total energy of random motion of vibration of all the particles that make up an object (1.4)

thermal equilibrium A balance in thermal energy transfer between two objects; when the objects have the same temperature (1.4)

thermal resistance A measure of the ability of an object to oppose the flow of heat through the object. Defined as the ratio of the temperature drop across the object to the heat flow rate (4.4)

thermodynamics The science dealing with internal energy, heat, and work (5.4)

thermometer A device that measures temperature (1.4)

time interval The elapsed time or the difference between two clock readings (3.1)

torque A quantity that causes rotation in mechanical systems. The product of the applied force and the lever arm (1.1)

total internal reflection A phenomenon in which an incident light ray strikes a boundary with a medium of lower index of refraction at a large enough angle that no light is refracted (10.1)

transverse wave A wave that displaces particles in the medium perpendicular to the direction in which the wave travels (8.1)

turbulent flow Irregular flow of fluid over a surface, with eddies and whorls causing fluid to move in different directions (4.2)

ultraviolet radiation Electromagnetic waves in the wavelength band between approximately 10^{-9} m and 10^{-7} m (9.1)

vector quantity A quantity that must be described by both a magnitude and a direction (1.1)

virtual image An image that apparently causes light to diverge from a mirror or lens. A virtual image cannot be seen on a screen or piece of paper since no light actually converges at the image location. (10.1)

viscosity A property of a fluid that describes the internal friction or opposition to relative motion within the fluid (4.2)

visible light Electromagnetic waves in the wavelength band between approximately 400 nm and 700 nm that can be detected by the human eye (9.1)

volt (V) The unit of measure of electric potential difference (1.3)

voltmeter A device that measures potential difference or voltage (3.3)

volume flow rate The ratio of the change in volume to the time interval over which the change is measured (3.2)

watt (W) The SI unit of power. Defined as one joule per second (6.1)

wavelength The shortest length of the repeating pattern in a wave (8.1)

wave pulse A single disturbance that travels through a medium (8.1)

weight The force on an object caused by the Earth's gravity (1.1)

weight density A property of a material, defined as the weight of a sample of the material divided by the volume (1.2)

work The amount of energy gained or lost by an object when a force moves the object through a distance. Defined as the product of the force applied (in the direction of motion) and the distance the object moves (2.1 and 5.1)

work-energy theorem The work done on an object equals the change in kinetic energy of the object. (5.1)

work function The minimum energy needed to remove an electron from the Fermi level of a metal to infinity (9.1)

X ray Electromagnetic wave in the wavelength band between approximately 10^{-11} m and 10^{-8} m (9.1)

Appendix D. Selected Answers to Exercises

Section 1.1 (Pages 23-26)

1. pounds, newtons
5. zero
7. 117 newtons
9. The magnitude is 13.2 and direction is 35° above the positive *x*-axis.
11. The net force is 44 newtons upward. The vertical speed of the balloon will increase.

13. 6.6 km
15. (a) 96 lb·ft
    (b) 0 lb·ft
21. 6960 N at 21° above the horizon
23. 41 N
25. 4.1 N; 0.90 N·m; 0 N·m

Section 1.2 (Pages 44-46)

1. solid, liquid, gas, plasma
3. mass
5. pneumatic, hydraulic
7. (a) $1 \times 10^3 \dfrac{kg}{m^3}$
   (b) 37.1 N
   (c) 8.34 lb
   (d) $440 \dfrac{lb}{ft^2}$
11. The volumes are the same.
13. (a) egg
    (b) salt water
    (c) salt water

15. (a) 13,801 kPa
    (b) 1180 kPa
    (c) 1281 kPa
17. (a) 2450 kPa
    (b) 6.9×10^5 N
19. (a) $1.24 \dfrac{g}{cm^3}$
    (b) 1.24
    (c) No

Section 1.3 (Pages 61-63)

1. 9 times (decreases to $\frac{1}{9}$ of the original force); 100 times (decreases to $\frac{1}{100}$ of the original force)
5. 105 N
7. There is a potential difference between A and B.
9. 8.0×10^{-7} C

11. $1.5 \times 10^4 \dfrac{V}{m}$
13. (a) 1.9 V
    (b) alternator
15. alternating
17. alternating

Section 1.4 (Pages 76-79)

1. Sum or total
3. 0°C
5. 106°F
7. Heat will flow out of the gas.
9. Heat will flow out of the ice cube.
11. The wax will absorb energy.
19. 2400 kcal
21. 1.8×10^4 cal

Section 2.1 (Pages 93-94)

1. moves
3. (a) -2.5×10^6 J
   (b) 2400 J
   (c) -4.5×10^5 ft·lb
   (d) -5.8×10^6 ft·lb
9. 3.6×10^4 ft·lb: -3.6×10^4 ft·lb
11. 2573 J
13. 51 N·m
15. 75%

Section 2.2 (Pages 103-105)

1. Increase
5. (a) positive
   (b) negative
   (c) negative
   (d) positive
7. $6550 \dfrac{\text{lb}}{\text{ft}^2}$
9. 8.7×10^5 ft·lb
11. 0.057 hp
13. 17 J
15. (a) $14.4 \dfrac{\text{lb}}{\text{ft}^2}$
   (b) 1.14×10^7 ft·lb
   (c) 3170 ft·lb
   (d) 5.76 hp

Section 2.3 (Pages 116-117)

1. no
3. 0.6 J
5. (a) 4.0×10^4 N·m
   (b) 4.5×10^4 J
   (c) 89%
7. (a) 1.9×10^{-19} J
   (b) 5.0×10^{-19} J
9. (a) 3.13×10^8 J
   (b) 3.9×10^8 J
11. 4×10^{-13} J

Section 3.1 (Pages 136-137)

1. $\dfrac{m}{s}; \dfrac{m}{s^2}; \dfrac{rad}{s}; \dfrac{rad}{s^2}$

5. (a) $920 \dfrac{rev}{min}$

 $97 \dfrac{rad}{s}$

 (b) $126 \dfrac{rad}{s}$

7. $190\ s$

9. $181 \dfrac{rad}{s}$

11. (a) $7.42 \dfrac{rev}{s}$

 (b) $46.6 \dfrac{rad}{s}$

13. $272 \dfrac{ft}{s^2}$

15. $50.6 \dfrac{m}{s}$

Section 3.2 (Pages 146-148)

1. (a) mass flow rate
 (b) volume flow rate
 (c) mass flow rate
 (d) volume flow rate
 (e) mass flow rate
 (f) neither
 (g) volume flow rate
 (h) volume flow rate

3. $1.7 \dfrac{kg}{min}$

5. (a) $\approx 0.14 \dfrac{gal}{min}$

 (b) $0.55 \dfrac{in^3}{s}$

7. (a) $\dfrac{m \cdot kg}{s^2}$ or N

 (b) $5.8 \times 10^4\ N$

9. (a) $9 \dfrac{in}{s}$

 (b) $16\ in^2$

 (c) $140 \dfrac{in^3}{s}$

 (d) $37 \dfrac{gal}{min}$

Section 3.3 (Pages 155-156)

1. charge
3. amperes
5. hertz; frequency

7. $3.1 \times 10^{-14}\ C$
9. $0.8\ s$

Section 3.4 (Pages 164-165)

1. There must be a temperature difference within the object.

3. high

9. $7.8 \frac{cal}{s}$

11. $2960 \frac{J}{s}$

13. a. 1.62×10^6 cal

    b. 32 min

Section 4.1 (Pages 181-183)

1. Yes

5. $g = \dfrac{F}{m} = \dfrac{N}{kg} = \dfrac{\frac{kg \cdot m}{s^2}}{kg} = \dfrac{m}{s^2}$

7. (a) 0.17 kg

   (b) $118 \frac{m}{s^2}$

9. (a) $9.80 \frac{m}{s^2}$

   (b) $0 \frac{m}{s}$

   (c) $9.80 \frac{m}{s^2}$

   (d) $9.8 \frac{m}{s}$

11. (a) increase

    (b) decrease

13. no

Section 4.2 (Pages 196-199)

1. increases

3. turbulent

5. (c) and (d)

7. (a) 0.048 N to the left.

   (b) 4.8×10^{-5} N

   (c) 9.1×10^{-7} N

   (d) air

9. $1.9 \times 10^{-3} \frac{m}{s}$

11. (a) $\dfrac{Pa \cdot s}{m^3}$

    (b) $1.55 \times 10^8 \dfrac{Pa \cdot s}{m^3}$

    (c) $9.7 \times 10^{-6} \dfrac{m^3}{s}$

    (d) $4.9 \times 10^{-6} \dfrac{m^3}{s}$

15. (a) $3.1 \frac{m}{s}$

    (b) $3.7 \frac{m}{s}$

Section 4.3 (Pages 212-215)

1. charge
3. (b)
5. Resistor A
7. (a) 7.5 A
   (b) 6 V
   (c) $I_1 = 6$ A; $I_2 = 1.5$ A
11. The resistivity of metal A is lower than that for metal B.
13. (a) Current doubles.
    (b) Current is halved.
15. 570 A

17. (b) 24 V
    (c) $I_1 = 2$ A; $I_2 = 1.2$ A
19. (a) 3.7×10^{-4} Ω
    (b) 0.0148 Ω
    (c) 2800 A
21. (a) $\dfrac{10}{17}$
    (b) $\dfrac{350}{17}$; $\dfrac{10}{17}$
    (c) $R_2 = xR_{total}$

Section 4.4 (Pages 224-226)

1. heat
7. $300 \dfrac{\text{kcal}}{\text{h}}$

9. (a) $2.6 \times 10^{-3} \dfrac{\text{h} \cdot {}^\circ\text{F}}{\text{Btu}}$
   (b) $27{,}000 \dfrac{\text{Btu}}{\text{h}}$

11. about 26°F
13. (a) 105 ft^2
    (b) $-760 \dfrac{\text{Btu}}{\text{h}}$
    (c) 9 inches

Section 5.1 (Pages 240-242)

3. by a factor of 4
5. $KE_{initial} = 9.65 \times 10^5$ J
   $KE_{final} = 5.00 \times 10^5$ J
   $W = -4.65 \times 10^5$ J
7. $5.29 \dfrac{\text{m}}{\text{s}}$ or $19.0 \dfrac{\text{m}}{\text{h}}$
9. radians per second $\left(\dfrac{\text{rad}}{\text{s}}\right)$
11. 9.62×10^6 ft·lb
13. -4.17×10^4 J

15.

Wheel Design	Angular Speed (rad/s)	Angular Speed (rpm)
Solid	9.2	88
Annular	8.7	83
Hoop	6.5	62

Use the solid design.

17. (a) $I = 1.777 \times 10^{18}$ kg·m^2
    $\omega = 7.27 \times 10^{-5} \dfrac{\text{rad}}{\text{s}}$
    $KE = 4.70 \times 10^9$ J
    (b) $7.27 \times 10^{-5} \dfrac{\text{rad}}{\text{s}}$
    (c) 1.07×10^8 J
    (d) 4.59×10^9 J

Section 5.2 (Pages 258-261)

1. No. Energy is the property of an object or system that enables it to do work. Work done by an external force on an object or system changes its energy.
3. (a) 7200 J
   (b) 4100 J
5. (a) 1900 J
   (b) no
7. (a) no
   (b) yes
   (c) yes
9. (a) 5.06×10^{-2} J
   (b) $KE = 5.06 \times 10^{-2}$ J
   $v = 0.26 \dfrac{m}{s}$
   (c) 0.75 cm
11. The greatest gravitational potential energy is at C. The greatest kinetic energy is at A.
13. 1.32×10^{10} ft·lb; 1.32×10^{10} ft·lb; 2.1×10^{10} ft·lb
15. P_1; $P_1 = P_2 + \rho g(h_2 - h_1)$

Section 5.3 (Pages 275-276)

1. electric field; magnetic field
3. parallel plates; insulator
5. The charge in (b) is greater.
7. 3.3×10^{-6} F, or 3.3 μF
9. capacitor; inductor
11. 3.4×10^{-2} F, or 34 mF
13. current
15. 3.7 H
17. 31.3 H
19. 0.91 J

Section 5.4 (Pages 292-294)

1. internal energy
3. (a) positive; increases
   (b) negative; decreases
7. a higher; greater than
9. first
11. It does not matter.
13. (a) 2.67 J
    (b) 12.17 J
15. (a) −507 J
    (b) 1950 J
17. 830°C

Section 6.1 (Pages 304-306)

1. (c)
3. 408 W
5. $137.5 \dfrac{ft \cdot lb}{s}$
   186.5 W
7. (a) 10 W
   (b) 30 J
9. 10%
11. 37 pounds

13.
Translational System	Rotational System
$Pwr = \dfrac{W}{\Delta t}$	$Pwr = \dfrac{W}{\Delta t}$
$Pwr = \dfrac{F \Delta d}{\Delta t}$	$Pwr = \dfrac{\tau \theta}{\Delta t}$
$Pwr = Fv$	$Pwr = \tau \omega$

15. (a) 9.21×10^6 J
    (b) 461 kW
17. 267 lb·ft

Section 6.2 (Pages 314-315)

1. Fluid pressure is constant.

3. by; on

5. $3.0 \times 10^{-3} \frac{m^3}{s}$

7. (a) 598 kPa

   (b) $109 \frac{m^3}{s}$

9. (a) 14 kPa

   (b) 7.1 W

Section 6.3 (Pages 321-322)

1. (a) no
   (b) yes
   (c) yes
   (d) yes
   (e) no
   (f) no
   (g) yes
   (h) no

3. (a) no
   (b) yes
   (c) yes
   (d) yes

   (e) yes
   (f) yes
   (g) no
   (h) no

5. 1000 W, or 1 kW

7. 70.7 V

9. They use the same amount of energy.

11. 1.27×10^6 J, or 1.27 MJ

13. (a) 74.6 kWh

    (b) $6.34

15. 1.8 hours

Section 7.1 (Pages 336-338)

1. mass; velocity

5. (a) $31,250 \frac{kg \cdot m}{s}$ to the north

   (b) $141 \frac{km}{h}$ to the north

7. (a)

9. The system does not lose or gain mass, and no net external forces act on the system.

11. $0.83 \frac{m}{s}$

13. 48.4 N

15. (a) −1980 lb

    (b) −890 lb

    (c) Graph 1 is for bumper A. Graph 2 is for bumper B.

Section 7.2 (Pages 349-350)

1. angular velocity; moment of inertia

3. $F = \dfrac{\Delta p}{\Delta t}$; $\tau = \dfrac{\Delta L}{\Delta t}$

   Torque is analogous to force; angular momentum is analogous to linear momentum.

7. $4.69 \dfrac{\text{kg} \cdot \text{m}}{\text{s}}$; $1.36 \times 10^{-2} \dfrac{\text{kg} \cdot \text{m}^2}{\text{s}}$

9. -168 N·m

13. (a) decreases
    (b) increases
    (c) stays the same
    (d) increases

Section 8.1 (Pages 364-368)

1. by a transfer of matter, or by wave action

3. The direction of the particle motion: in a transverse wave it is perpendicular to the direction the wave is traveling, and in a longitudinal wave it is parallel to the direction the wave is traveling.

5. (c) wavelength
   (d) amplitude
   (c) wavelength
   (b) period
   (a) frequency
   (e) wave speed

7. (a) 2.4 ms
   (b) 417 Hz

   (c) $3.3 \dfrac{\text{m}}{\text{s}}$

9. $2.5 \dfrac{\text{m}}{\text{s}}$

11. amplitude

13. 107 kHz

15. (a) 4 V
    (b) 0.8 ms
    (c) 1.25 kHz

17. (a) $\sin 42° = 0.699$
        $\cos 42° = 0.743$
        $\tan 42° = 0.900$
    (b) 77.0 ft
    (c) 85.5 ft

Section 8.2 (Pages 380-382)

1. interference

3. destructive interference

5.

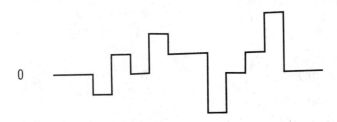

(Continued on next page)

7.

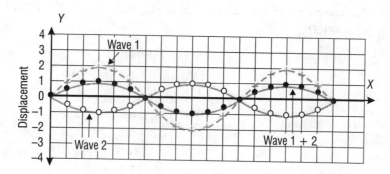

9. beats

11. (a) 2.2 s

    (b) 16 m

13. farther apart

Section 9.1 (Pages 401-403)

1. electrical resistance in the wire; electromagnetic radiation

3. (a) X rays

    (b) radio waves

    (c) All have the same speed.

5. 0.305 m

7. (a) 2.40×10^{-15} J

    (b) 3.31×10^{-10} m

9. (a) 3.16×10^{-20} J

    (b) 2.64×10^{5} m/s

11. (a) 3.139×10^{-19} J

    (b) $4.78 \times 10^{17} \dfrac{\text{photons}}{\text{s}}$

13. (a) 75 mW

    (b) $-1.047 \times 10^{-27} \dfrac{\text{kg} \cdot \text{m}}{\text{s}}$

    (c) $-2.094 \times 10^{-27} \dfrac{\text{kg} \cdot \text{m}}{\text{s}}$

    (d) 7.507×10^{-10} N

Section 9.2 (Pages 418-421)

1. $Z = 11$; $A = 11 + 12 = 23$

3. 92.1 MeV

5. 64.7 MeV

7. (a) 5

    (b) 2

    (c) 4

9. The atomic number increases by 1. The mass number does not change.

11. $^{226}_{88}\text{Ra} \rightarrow ^{222}_{86}\text{Rn} + ^{4}_{2}\text{He}$; radon-222

13. $^{22}_{11}\text{Na} \rightarrow ^{22}_{10}\text{Ne} + ^{0}_{+1}\text{e}$; neon-22

15. (a) $^{238}_{92}\text{U} + ^{1}_{0}\text{n} \rightarrow ^{96}_{39}\text{Y} + ^{141}_{53}\text{I} + 2\left(^{1}_{0}\text{n}\right)$

    (b) 0.1914 u

    (c) 178.3 MeV

17. (a) $^{239}_{94}\text{Pu} + ^{1}_{0}\text{n} \rightarrow ^{96}_{42}\text{Mo} + ^{141}_{52}\text{Te} + 3\left(^{1}_{0}\text{n}\right)$

    (b) 0.1858 u

    (c) 173.0 MeV

19. (a) 23.8 MeV

    (b) 3.26 MeV

    (c) 4.03 MeV

21. (a) $2.96 \times 10^{19} \dfrac{\text{fissions}}{\text{s}}$

    (b) 0.33 kg

Section 10.1 (Pages 446-449)

1. incidence; reflection

5. 6 cm

7. (b) between 3.8 cm and 4.3 cm; real
   (c) 4.1 cm
   (d) between 0.3 and 0.5

9. $n = \dfrac{v}{c}$ or $v = nc$
   (a) 3.93×10^8 m/s
   (b) 4.38×10^8 m/s
   (c) 4.56×10^8 m/s

11. $\theta_2 = 37.7°$

13. (b) 1.58

15. 61.0°

17. 1.44

19. The material compositions of the lenses are different. One material has a higher index of refraction than the other.

21. (a) 53.3 cm
    (b) −1.67; enlargement

25. (a) 0.0508 m; 0.0501 m; 0.0007 m or 0.7 mm
    (b) 0.013 m or 13 mm

Section 10.2 (Pages 465-467)

1. The wavelength of light is very short. Most sources emit light incoherently.

3. (a) neither—they travel the same distance
   (b) slit B—one wavelength λ
   (c) slit A—one-half wavelength $\frac{1}{2}\lambda$

5. 8.7×10^{-6} m or 8.7 μm

7. red; blue

9. (a) 2.22×10^{-6} m
   (b) 0.297 radian or 17°

11. $\theta_{blue} = 0.43$ radian or 25°; $\theta_{red} = 0.68$ radian or 39°; 0.25 radian or 14°

13. 8.6×10^{-4} radians; 7.5×10^{-4} m or 0.75 mm

15. blue light

17. 2.5×10^{-8} radians; 2.5×10^{-7} light-years; 2.4×10^6 km

19. 0.34 m or 34 cm

21. 1.1 m

Section 10.3 (Pages 487-490)

1. (a) Bohr
   (b) Thomson
   (c) Rutherford
   (d) Bohr

3. 9

5. fourth

7. 657 nm

9. (c)

11. monochromatic, highly directional, coherent

13. electrical and optical

15. No

17. E_3; 10,700 nm or 1.07 μm; infrared

19. (a) J
    (b) W
    (c) $\dfrac{W}{cm^2}$

21. $5000 \dfrac{W}{cm^2}$

23. (a) 1.33×10^6 W
    (b) $5.2 \times 10^{11} \dfrac{W}{cm^2}$

Appendix E. Preparatory Math Skills

1. On a separate piece of paper...

    a. Make a scale drawing of 20 grams, using a scale of 1 in = 4 gm.

    b. Make a scale drawing of 5.3 kilograms, using a scale of 1 cm = 2 kg.

    c. Make a scale drawing of 4000 pounds, using a scale of 1 in = 500 lb.

    d. Make a scale drawing of 4000 pounds, using a scale of 1 cm = 500 lb.

2. Given the scale drawings below, use your inch ruler to measure the line length and then calculate the magnitude represented by the line length.

    a. Scale: 1 in = 30 lb

    _____

    Line length represents _____ pounds.

    b. Scale: 1 in = 10 kg

    _____

    Line length represents _____ kilograms.

    c. Scale: 1 in = 200 Newtons

    _____

    Line length represents _____ Newtons.

    d. Scale: 2 in = ½ mile

    _____

    Line length represents _____ miles.

1. Measure each of the angles shown below. On a separate sheet of paper, identify each angle and record its measurement. For example, $\angle BAC =$ _____°.

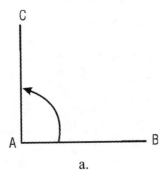

a.

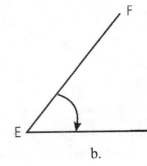

b.

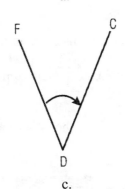

c.

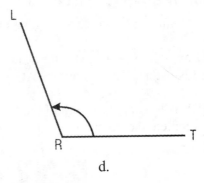

d.

2. Draw and label each of the following angles.

Example: $\angle BAC = 90°$

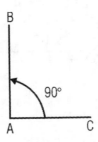

a. $\angle CDF = 50°$

b. $\angle XYZ = 115°$

c. $\angle RST = 13°$

d. $\angle JIH = 67°$

3. Use the drawing below to answer the questions that follow:

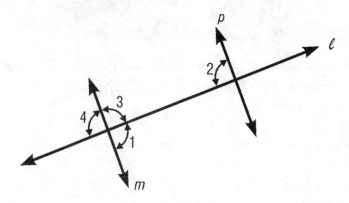

a. If $\angle 1 = 90°$, what can you say about lines ℓ and m?

b. If line p is perpendicular to line ℓ ($p \perp \ell$), what is the measure of $\angle 2$?

c. If $\angle 1 = 90°$, what is the measure of $\angle 3$?

d. If $\angle 1 = 90°$, what can you say about the measure of $\angle 4$?

e. Since $\angle 1$ and $\angle 2$ are right angles, what statement can you make about lines m and p?

4. Draw $\angle BAC = 45°$. Use the scale: 1 cm = 5 N. Draw line AB to a length representing 15 Newtons. Then draw line AC to a length that represents 8 Newtons.

5. Below is a simple sketch of the frame and drive shaft for a rear-wheel-drive automobile. Complete the statements that follow.

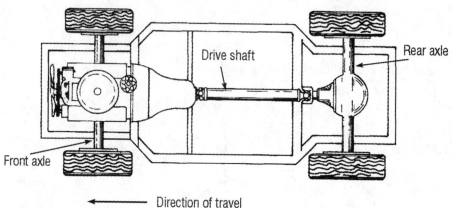

a. The drive shaft is _____ to the rear axle.
   1. parallel
   2. perpendicular
   3. at an angle of 30°
   4. at an angle of 45°

b. The rear axle and the front axle are _____ to each other.
    1. parallel
    2. perpendicular
    3. at an angle of 30°
    4. at an angle of 45°

c. The drive shaft is _____ to the direction of travel of the car.
    1. parallel
    2. perpendicular
    3. at an angle of 30°
    4. at an angle of 45°

d. When the tires on the car have spun around 360° (one revolution), the distance they have moved on the ground is about the same as their _____.
    1. radius
    2. diameter
    3. circumference
    4. semicircle

6. For the following triangles, *solve* for $\angle x$.

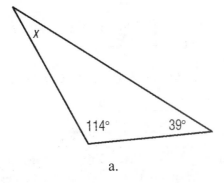

a.

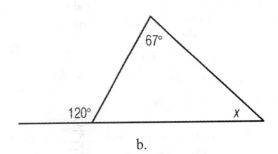

b.

1. $5 \text{ lb} \times 10 \text{ ft} =$ _____

2. $10 \text{ lb} \div 2 \text{ ft}^2 =$ _____

3. $100 \text{ N} \div 5 \text{ m}^2 =$ _____

4. $1000 \text{ cm}^3 \times 13.6 \dfrac{\text{g}}{\text{cm}^3} =$ _____

5. $16 \dfrac{\text{miles}}{\text{hour}} \times 0.5 \text{ hour} =$ _____

6. $5 \text{ hours} \times 60 \dfrac{\text{minutes}}{\text{hour}} =$ _____

7. $62.4 \dfrac{\text{lb}}{\text{ft}^3} \times 10 \text{ ft} =$ _____

8. $10 \dfrac{\text{N}}{\text{m}^3} \times 2 \text{ m} =$ _____

Practice Exercises 4
Learning How to Write Numbers in Scientific Notation

1. The following numbers are all larger than one. Change each to **scientific notation**—with only *one* digit remaining to the left of the decimal point in the final answer.

   Example: $3860 = 3.86 \times 10^3$

   a.   38,600 = _____

   b.   157,300 = _____

   c.   300,000,000 = _____

   d.   147 = _____

   e.   93,000,000 = _____

2. The following numbers are all less than one. Change each to **scientific notation**—with only *one* digit (other than zero) remaining to the left of the decimal point in the final answer.

   Example: $0.015 = 1.5 \times 10^{-2}$

   a.   0.0036 = _____

   b.   0.715 = _____

   c.   0.000025 = _____

   d.   0.002 = _____

   e.   0.00083 = _____

3. The following numbers are written in power-of-ten notation. Change each to decimal notation.

   Examples: $8.36 \times 10^{-1} = 0.836$
   $3.01 \times 10^3 = 3010$

   a. $81.5 \times 10^{-1} =$ _____

   b. $47.71 \times 10^{-4} =$ _____

   c. $326.1 \times 10^{-4} =$ _____

d. $4.771 \times 10^4 =$ _____

e. $389 \times 10^{-5} =$ _____

f. $3 \times 10^8 =$ _____

4. Change the following numbers to power-of-ten notation by filling in the correct prefixes.
Example: $3860 = 3.86 \times 10^3$

    a. $38,600 =$ _____ $\times 10^2$

    b. $157,300 =$ _____ $\times 10^4$

    c. $23,600 =$ _____ $\times 10^5$

    d. $0.00147 =$ _____ $\times 10^{-3}$

    e. $0.056 =$ _____ $\times 10^{-2}$

    f. $0.0791 =$ _____ $\times 10^{-3}$

    g.   Indicate which of the numbers above have been rewritten in scientific notation.

5. Multiply or divide the expressions below with a calculator. Then write the answers in **scientific notation**.

    a. $(1.25 \times 10^{12}) + (8.7 \times 10^{11}) =$ _____

    b. $(3.2 \times 10^6) \times (5.9 \times 10^4) =$ _____

    c. $26 \div (4.6 \times 10^{14}) =$ _____

    d. $(4.9 \times 10^{-32}) \times (1.6 \times 10^{33}) =$ _____

    e. $12^{45} =$ _____

Practice Exercises 5
Learning How to Measure Angles in Radians

1. Answer the following questions about angles and measuring angles.

    a.   How many degrees are in a circle?

    b.   If a pie is cut in half (across a diameter), then each of those halves is cut in half, and then each of those pieces is cut in half, how many pieces of pie are cut? How many degrees does each piece span?

    c.   How many degrees are between each of the numbers on the face of a clock? (That is, how many degrees are between the 12 and the 1, between the 1 and the 2, and so on?)

    d.   On the face of a clock, if you start at 12 o'clock and move clockwise, how many degrees will you cross between 12 and 3? Between 12 and 6? Between 12 and 9? Between 12 and all the way around to 12 again?

2. Convert $60°$ to radians.

3. Convert $150°$ to radians.

4. Convert $\dfrac{\pi}{3}$ to degrees.

5. Convert $\dfrac{5\pi}{4}$ to degrees.

Practice Exercises 6
Area and Volume Measurement

1. Find the area of a flat aluminum plate, 4 in. by 8 in.

2. Find the volume of a pool that is 10 m in length, 15 m wide, and 1.5 m deep.

3. A fire extinguisher has a radius of 3 in. and a height of 24 in. How many cubic inches of water can it hold?

4. A very popular 8-cylinder automobile engine is manufactured with each cylinder having a 4-inch diameter and a height of 3.48 inches. What is the total volume of this popular engine?

Practice Exercises 7
Ratio and Proportion

1. Read the statements in the following chart. Then write the ratios described by the statements in the blanks. Write each ratio as (1) a fraction, (2) a quotient, and (3) with a colon.

Statement	Fraction	Indicated division	Colon
a. Jana is three times as tall as Mark.			
b. A gallon of milk costs twice as much as a gallon of gasoline.			
c. Her brother is half as old as my brother.			

2. What is the ratio of **shaded** to **unshaded** areas in the following figures?

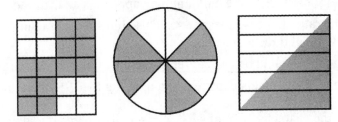

3. What **percentage** of each figure in Exercise 2 is **shaded**?

4. What **percentage** of each figure in Exercise 2 is **unshaded**?

5. Does adding the percentages in Exercises 3 and 4 give 100% for each figure?

6. Solder is a mixture of lead and tin. "Soft" solder has 6 parts tin and 4 parts lead.
   a. How many grams of tin are in 1 kilogram of soft solder?
      (Hint: 6 parts + 4 parts = 10 parts = whole.)
   b. How many grams of lead are in 1 kilogram of soft solder?

7. Which of the following ratios is proportional to 40/5?
   a. 20/10
   b. 8/1
   c. 5/40
   d. 80/11

8. Which of the following ratios is proportional to 7/63?
   a. 14/126
   b. 1/8
   c. 1/7
   d. 9/1

9. What is the constant of the ratios $\dfrac{12}{1}$ and $\dfrac{144}{12}$?

10. What is the constant of the ratios $\dfrac{1}{8}$ and $\dfrac{8}{64}$?

11. A force of 70 Newtons compresses a spring 2 cm. A second force compresses the same spring only 1 cm. How much force is applied the second time?

    (Hint: Use the proportion $\dfrac{70 \text{ N}}{2 \text{ cm}} = \dfrac{x(\text{N})}{1 \text{ cm}}$.)

12. Blueprints and floor plans of buildings are not drawn actual size but are "scaled down." For example, a 1-foot distance in the building may appear as a ¼" distance on the drawing.

   a. What is the ratio that describes the scale used in such a drawing? (Show the ratio both with and without dimensions.)

   b. How long a line would be used to represent a wall that is 24' long?

   c. How long is a duct that is depicted on a drawing by a 9½-inch line?

13. A catalog lists the characteristics of several manually operated winches. One of the features listed is the gear ratio. The worm gear shown below is advertised to have a gear ratio of 41:1. That is, 41 turns of the hand crank are needed to produce one turn of the large gear.

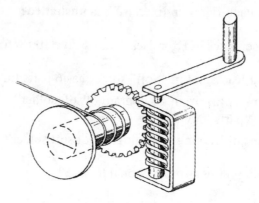

   a. The drum attached to the large gear has a diameter of 1½" and is used to reel in a length of cable. About how many times would the hand crank have to be turned to reel in 18" of cable? (Round to the nearest whole turn of the crank.)

   b. Suppose you are able to turn the hand crank at a rate of 40 turns per minute. About how many minutes would it take to wind 18" of cable? (Round to the nearest 0.1 minute.)

14. A pressure intensifier is used to convert available air (pneumatic) pressure to high hydraulic pressures, such as those needed in hydraulic lifts and actuators. The ratio of input piston areas to output piston areas is *inversely proportional* to the ratio of input to output pressures.

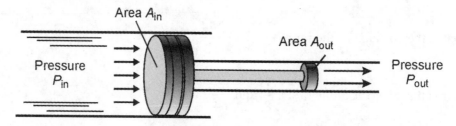

   A water-jet cutting mechanism requires 10,000 psi water pressure at the output. The manufacturing plant can supply 80 psi air pressure as input to a pressure intensifier. If the circular input piston can be no larger than 12 in. diameter, what must be the diameter of the circular output piston to achieve the desired output pressure?

Practice Exercises 8
Unit Conversion

SI Prefixes

Factor by which the unit is multiplied	Prefix Name	Prefix Symbol
10^{12}	tera	T
* 10^{9}	giga	G
* 10^{6}	mega	M
* 10^{3}	kilo	k
10^{2}	hecto	h
$10^{1} = 10$	deca	da
10^{-1}	deci	d
* 10^{-2}	centi	c
* 10^{-3}	milli	m
* 10^{-6}	micro	μ
* 10^{-9}	nano	n
10^{-12}	pico	p
10^{-15}	femto	f
10^{-18}	atto	a

*Most commonly used

1. Place the names and symbols for the following factors in the spaces provided. The answer to the first one is provided.

Factor	Name	Symbol
10^{3}	kilo	k
10^{-3}	________	________
10^{6}	________	________
10^{-6}	________	________
10^{-2}	________	________
10^{9}	________	________
10^{-9}	________	________
10^{-12}	________	________

2. For each value given below, change the power-of-ten notation to a number. Then add the correct prefix symbol to the unit.

$$5.6 \times 10^3 \text{ meters} = \underline{\text{5.6 kilometers (km)}}$$

$$6.8 \times 10^3 \text{ calories} = \underline{\hspace{5cm}}$$

$$10 \times 10^{-2} \text{ meters} = \underline{\hspace{5cm}}$$

$$5 \times 10^{-3} \text{ meters} = \underline{\hspace{5cm}}$$

$$3.14 \times 10^{-9} \text{ seconds} = \underline{\hspace{5cm}}$$

3. Use the table on the preceding page to identify the correct prefixes for the power-of-ten numbers given below.

$$10^{-3} \text{ meters} = \underline{\hspace{5cm}}$$

$$10^{-3} \text{ grams} = \underline{\hspace{5cm}}$$

$$10^{-6} \text{ calories} = \underline{\hspace{5cm}}$$

$$10^{-2} \text{ meters} = \underline{\hspace{5cm}}$$

4. Rewrite "15,600 grams" using power-of-ten notation and a unit prefix name that involves kilograms.

5. Given the equation: $v_f = v_i + at$

where v_f = Speed (ft/s or m/s),
v_i = Initial speed (ft/s or m/s),
a = Acceleration (ft/s^2 or m/s^2), and
t = Time (s).

Substitute the proper units for v_i, a, and t, first in the English system and then in SI. Show that each term has dimensions of ft/s or m/s, hence speed—the correct units for v_f.

6. Given the equation: $R_E = \dfrac{\rho\ell}{A}$

where R_E = Electrical resistance in ohms (Ω),
ρ = Electrical resistivity in ohm $\cdot$ cm,
ℓ = Length in cm, and
A = Cross-sectional area in cm^2.

Substitute the proper units for ρ, ℓ, and A into the equation. Show that the terms on the right reduce to ohms (Ω). This is the correct unit for the resistance R_E on the left side.

7. Convert 150 centimeters to an equal length in millimeters. A table of conversions gives 1 cm = 10 mm. This solution is partially set up as follows:

$$150 \text{ cm} \times \frac{10 \text{ mm}}{1 \text{ cm}} =$$

8. Convert 21 liters to an equal volume in gallons. A table of conversions gives 1 gal = 3.785 liters.

9. Convert 40 centimeters to an equal length in meters. A table of conversions gives 1 m = 100 cm.

10. Convert 5 hours to an equal time in seconds. A table of conversions gives 1 h = 3600 s.

11. Convert 10.5 mi/h to an equal speed in ft/s. A table of conversions gives 1 mi = 5280 ft and 1 h = 3600 s.

Practice Exercises 9
Algebra Review

1. The ratio of the speed of light in a vacuum ($c = 3 \times 10^8$ m/s) to the speed of light in a particular medium (v) results in a constant known as the index of refraction (n). This can also be represented with the formula $n = \frac{c}{v}$. Find the speed of light in glass ($n = 1.5$).

2. On a certain golf course, the traditional play is to take two strokes to go around a small lake. Each stroke requires a distance of about 250 yards, as shown below. You wonder how strong a drive would be needed to make it across the lake in one stroke. Determine how far a single stroke would have to go to cross the lake toward the green. (**Hint:** For a right triangle, $a^2 + b^2 = c^2$.)

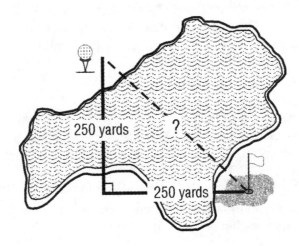

250 yards

?

250 yards

3. Your medical insurance policy requires you to pay the first $100 of your hospital expenses (this is known as a deductible). The insurance company will then pay 80% of the remaining expense. The amount that you must pay can be expressed by the following formula:

$$E = [(T - D) \times (1.00 - P)] + D$$

where E is the expense to you (how much you must pay),
   T is the total of the hospitalization bill,
   D is the deductible you must first pay, and
   P is the decimal percentage that the insurance company pays after you meet the deductible.

Suppose you are expecting a short surgical stay in the hospital, for which you estimate the total bill to be about $5000. Use the formula to estimate the expense to you for the total hospital bill.

4. Greenshield's formula can be used to determine the amount of time a traffic light at an intersection should remain green. This formula is shown below.

$$G = 2.1n + 3.7$$

where G is the "green time" in seconds and
   n is the average number of vehicles traveling in each lane per light cycle.

Find the green time for a traffic signal on a street that averages 19 vehicles in each lane per cycle.

5. White light is incident on the surface of a soap bubble. A portion of the surface reflects green light of wavelength $\lambda_0 = 540$ nm. Assume that the refractive index of the soap film is near that of water, so that $n_f = 1.33$. Estimate the thickness (in nanometers) of the soap bubble surface that appears green in 2nd order ($m = 2$).

Use $2n_f t + \dfrac{\lambda_0}{2} = m\lambda_0$.

6. In close-up photography, the distance of the object from the lens determines how far the lens must be from the film. This requires special lenses and focusing mechanisms. These distances (all measured in the same units) are controlled by the formula

$$\frac{1}{f} = \frac{1}{p} + \frac{1}{q}$$

where f is the focal length of the lens,
   p is the distance of the object being viewed from the center of the lens, and
   q is the distance of the image formed on the film from the center of the lens.

a. Rewrite the formula, isolating the variable representing the object distance.
b. Determine the object distance predicted by the equation for a lens with a focal length of 50 mm and a lens-to-film distance of 6.2 cm.

1. A pendulum clock can maintain accurate time because it has a finely adjustable period of swing. The period of swing of a pendulum is given by the formula

$$T = 2\pi \times \sqrt{\frac{L}{g}}$$

   where T is the period (see note below) of the pendulum in seconds,
   L is the length of the pendulum in centimeters, and
   g is the acceleration due to gravity, 980 cm/s².

   Note: The **period** is defined as the time required for one complete swing, back and forth.

   a. What would be the period of a pendulum that is 25.00 cm long?
   (Use your calculator's value for π with this formula.)

   b. Suppose you want the same pendulum to have a period of 1.000 second. If the length were shortened to 24.90 cm, would the period be closer to or farther from the desired value of 1.000 second?

2. You agree to sell your car for $2600 and allow the buyer to finance it by paying 1% per month interest on the unpaid balance. You would like to amortize the loan in 24 months (finish receiving payment with 24 equal monthly payments). Use the formula below to determine the monthly payment you should ask for.

$$R = P \times \frac{i}{\left[1 - (1+i)^{-n}\right]}$$

   where R is the monthly payment,
   P is the loan amount ($2600),
   I is the periodic interest rate (0.01 per month), and
   n is the number of payments (periods) (24 payments).

3. A shipper uses a cube-shaped box that is advertised to have 700 cubic inches of enclosed volume. What is the largest ball (sphere) one could place in this box?

4. Electrical resistors are coded with colored bands to indicate the value of resistance in ohms. Each color represents a number:

Color	Number
Black	0
Brown	1
Red	2
Orange	3
Yellow	4
Green	5
Blue	6
Violet	7
Gray	8
White	9

The resistance value is determined by obtaining the first and second digits from the first and second color bands and multiplying by 10 raised to the nth power, where n is the number represented by the third color band. For example, a resistor banded red-brown-orange would have a resistance of 21 (from the red and brown bands) $\times 10^3$ (from the orange band) ohms, or 21,000 ohms.

Determine the resistance values for the following color band combinations:

a. Green-brown-orange

b. Red-red-blue

c. Black-gray-black

d. Yellow-green-brown

5. Some infrared temperature detectors use the fact that energy is radiated from hot "black" objects according to the formula

$$R = (5.670 \times 10^{-12}) \times (273°C + T)^4$$

where R is the total energy radiated in watts per cm^2 from a perfect radiator and
T is the temperature in degrees Celsius.

a. What would be the total energy radiated from such an object that had a temperature of 300°C?

b. What would be the total energy radiated from such an object that had a temperature of 37°C?

6. When computing statistics, one must often evaluate the expression "*n*!" or "*n* factorial." (You may have such a key on your calculator.) Factorial expressions are simply a decreasing series of numbers multiplied together. For example, $4! = 4 \times 3 \times 2 \times 1 = 24$. The value of 5! is 120 ($5! = 5 \times 4 \times 3 \times 2 \times 1$). However, manually evaluating factorials of even slightly larger numbers (try 15!) becomes very tedious and results in very large numbers. So, for large values of *n*, Stirling's formula is often used, as shown below.

$$n! \approx \sqrt{(2\pi n)} \times \left(\frac{n}{e}\right)^n$$

where *e* is a constant that has a value of about 2.718.

Use Stirling's formula to obtain an approximate value for 30! If your calculator has an *x*! key, enter 30 and press *x*! (or 2nd *x*!) and compare the result with Stirling's formula.

Practice Exercises 11
The Basics of Graphing

1. Information about the total highway mileage traveled by vehicles in the United States is shown below.

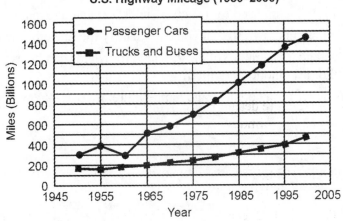

U.S. Highway Mileage (1950–2000)

a. What types of vehicles are referred to by this graph?

b. What span of time is covered by the graph?

c. The total mileage traveled each year is increasing. Which type of vehicle is increasing its total mileage faster?

d. Use the graph to estimate how many miles trucks and buses will travel in the year 2005. Do you think this would be a reliable estimate? Why?

2. There are many relationships between weather and crop performance. A relationship pertaining to corn yields in a certain region is pictured below. It compares crop yield with average temperature for the month of July, for various rainfalls.

Crop yield compared to average temperature and rainfall

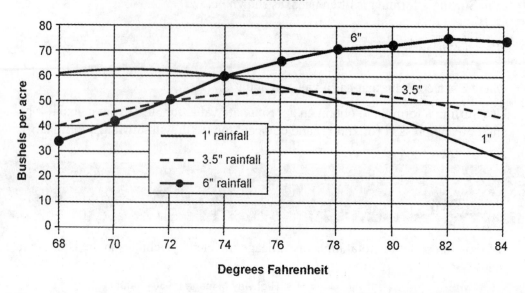

a. What units are being used for (1) crop yields, (2) average temperature, and (3) rainfall?

b. How is the graph drawn so that you can identify the lines for the three different rainfalls?

c. For an average temperature of 82°F, what crop yields can be expected for a 6" monthly rainfall? For a 1" monthly rainfall?

d. Which is better for a cool average temperature of 70°F—heavy rainfall or light rainfall?

3. A large company produces a certain machine part. The company can produce the part either by casting or by forging. The tooling cost for casting is quite expensive, but the labor and material cost is relatively low compared to the forging method. With the forging method, the tooling cost is lower but the labor and material cost is higher. A graph of these relationships is as follows.

Total Cost of Forging or Casting the Part

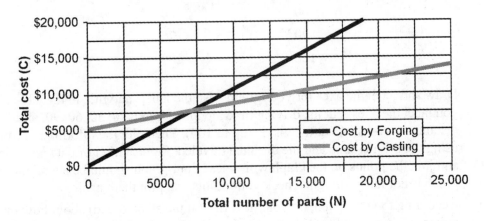

a. For an order of 15,000 parts, what is the cost of producing the part by casting? By forging?

b. For an order of 5000 parts, what is the cost of producing the part by casting? By forging?

c. At what size order, the breakpoint, are the cost of forging and the cost of casting the same?

d. Can the "breakpoint" determined above be used as a guideline for the production staff? What would that guideline be?

4. Traveling at 50 miles per hour, you record the mileage on your odometer every 30 minutes, as shown below.

Time (min)	Distance traveled (mi)
0	0
30	25
60	50
90	75
120	100

a. Draw and label the axes for your graph. Use the labels and title in the table above to help you label the axes. Put the driving time along the x-axis (0, 30, 60, 90, and 120) and distances traveled along the y-axis (up to 100). Then plot the information from the table, using the driving time and the distance traveled. Plot each set of data given in the table and join the points on the graph with lines. Your graph should be a straight line. If your graph is not fairly straight, check your points and plot them again.

b. According to your graph, on your next trip (at the same speed) about how many miles can you travel in 50 minutes? How many in 100 minutes? Remember that you are interpolating with your graph; the result is only an estimate.

c. Suppose you wanted to show the bottom axis in hours, rather than minutes. Relabel your bottom axis in hours without replotting your points.

d. Now use your graph to tell how far you could travel in 3 hours. Do you think this is a reasonable extrapolation of your graph?

5. As a lab technician, you must perform various tests of material properties. A stress analysis on wire samples is one such test. Shown below are the results of a stress analysis on a length of copper wire. The stretch of the wire is measured as different weights are hung from it.

Stress analysis on copper wire	
Load (lb)	Stretch (inches)
0	0.00
2	0.02
4	0.04
6	0.06
8	0.08
10	0.10
12	0.13
14	0.64

a. Construct a graph of the stretch in the copper wire at each load. Label the load along one axis and the stretch along the other axis.

b. Interpret the graph to estimate the load limit for this wire. Show the load at which the wire will stretch to the point of breaking.

c. Can you estimate what the stretch might be at 3 pounds? At 16 pounds? If so, what is your estimate? If not, explain why you are not able to estimate.

1. In electrical circuits with varying currents and voltages, the combined effect of resistance and reactance is called impedance. The impedance is related to the resistance and the reactance by the formula shown below.

$$Z^2 = R^2 + X^2$$

where Z is the impedance, in ohms,
R is the resistance, in ohms, and
X is the reactance, also in ohms.

a. The relationship above is equivalent to the Pythagorean formula, which relates the sides of a right triangle. Draw and label a right triangle to represent the relation among the impedance, the resistance, and the reactance.

b. A loudspeaker is labeled as having an impedance of 8.0 ohms. Your measurement with an ohmmeter shows a resistance of 1.5 ohms. What is the reactance of the speaker?

2. You need to string a cable across Murky Creek and need to determine the distance across. Suppose the two points can be labeled A and D, as shown in the sketch below. You find that, starting at point A, you can walk due south for 21 meters then turn due east and walk 22.5 meters across the bridge. Finally, walking due north 9 meters you reach the desired point D.

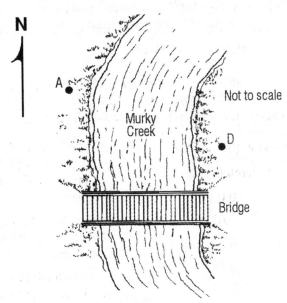

a. On your paper, make a sketch of the distances and directions traveled, similar to the sketch above. The final point should be labeled D.

b. The segment joining point A to point D on your scale drawing is the distance you need to string cable. How many meters is it across Murky Creek, from point A to point D?

3. A manual has the illustration shown here as a guideline for the safe use of an extension ladder. Suppose your ladder has a maximum extended length of 24 feet.

  a. Using the guideline of having 3 feet extending above the top landing, what is the distance to the top support for your ladder?

  b. Using the guideline shown in the drawing, what is the maximum landing height that you can safely reach with your ladder?

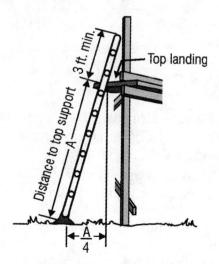

4. You want to build a picture frame from a kit. Each of the four frame pieces is 12 inches long (on the longest edge). To check for "squareness" you plan to measure the diagonals. How long should the diagonal measurement be (at its longest point) for this frame?

Practice Exercises 1: Learning How to Draw and Measure to Scale

1. Answers will vary.

2. a. 90; b. 15; c. 800; d. 5/8

Practice Exercises 2: Learning How to Draw and Measure Angles

1. a. 90°; b. 50°; c. 45°; d. 110°

2.

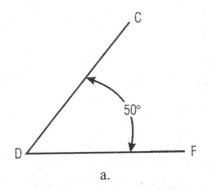

a.

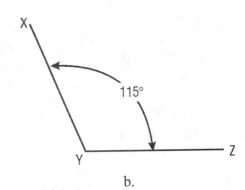

b.

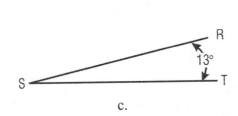

c.

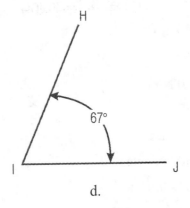

d.

3. a. They are perpendicular $(\ell \perp m)$ because they intersect at a right angle (90°).

   b. $\angle 2 = 90°$; the reverse reasoning of part (a).

   c. $\angle 3 = 90°$; because $\angle 1$ and $\angle 3$ together make a straight angle (180°), so $\angle 1 + \angle 3 = 180°$ $\Rightarrow 90° + \angle 3 = 180° \Rightarrow \angle 3 = 90°$.

   d. $\angle 4 = 90°$; if $\angle 1 = 90°$ then $\angle 3 = 90°$ (from part (c)), then since $\angle 3$ and $\angle 4$ make up a straight angle then $\angle 4 = 90°$.

   e. Lines m and p are parallel $(m \| p)$ because each line is perpendicular $(\perp)$ to the same line, ℓ.

4.

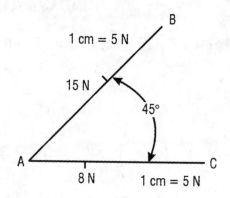

5. a. 2; b. 1; c. 1; d. 3

6. a. $114° + 39° + x = 180°$
        $153° + x = 180°$
        $x = 27°$

    b. $(180° − 120°) + 67° + x = 180°$
        $60° + 67° + x = 180°$
        $127° + x = 180°$
        $x = 53°$

Practice Exercises 3: Learning How to Multiply and Divide Numbers and Units

1. 50 lb • ft

2. 5 lb/ft^2

3. 20 N/m^2

4. 13,600 g

5. 8 miles

6. 300 minutes

7. 624 lb/ft^2

8. 20 N/m^2

Practice Exercises 4: Learning How to Write Numbers in Scientific Notation

1. a. 3.86×10^4

    b. 1.573×10^5

    c. 3×10^8

    d. 1.47×10^2

    e. 9.3×10^7

2. a. 3.6×10^{-3}
   b. 7.15×10^{-1}
   c. 2.5×10^{-5}
   d. 2×10^{-3}
   e. 8.3×10^{-4}

3. a. 8.15
   b. 0.004771
   c. 0.03261
   d. 47710
   e. 0.00389
   f. 300,000,000

4. a. 386
   b. 15.73
   c. 0.236
   d. 1.47
   e. 5.6
   f. 79.1
   g. d and e

5. a. 2.12×10^{12}
   b. 1.89×10^{11}
   c. 5.65×10^{-14}
   d. 7.84×10^{1}
   e. 3.66×1048

Practice Exercises 5: Learning How to Measure Angles in Radians

1. a. 360°

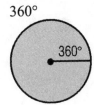

b.   8 sections (equal size)

$$\frac{360°}{8} = 45° \text{ per piece}$$

c.   There are 12 sections to a clock. So, $\frac{360°}{12} = 30°$.

d.   12 and 3
   3 sections $3 \times 30° = 90°$ (forms a right triangle)
   12 and 6
   6 sections $6 \times 30° = 180°$ (forms a straight triangle)
   12 and 9
   9 sections $9 \times 30° = 270°$
   12 to 12
   12 sections $12 \times 30° = 360°$ (forms a full circle)

2. $45° \times \dfrac{\pi \text{ radians}}{180°} = \dfrac{\pi}{4} \text{ radians}$

3. $150° \times \dfrac{\pi \text{ radians}}{180°} = \dfrac{5\pi}{6} \text{ radians}$

4. $\dfrac{\pi}{3} \text{ radians} \times \dfrac{180°}{\pi \text{ radians}} = 60°$

5. $\dfrac{5\pi}{4} \text{ radians} \times \dfrac{180°}{\pi \text{ radians}} = 225°$

Practice Exercises 6: Area and Volume Measurement

1.   The aluminum plate has an area of 32 in^2.

2.   The pool's volume is 225 m^3.

3.   The fire extinguisher has a volume of 678 in^3 of water.

4.   The total volume is 349.67 or 350 in^3.

Practice Exercises 7: Ratio and Proportion

1.

Statement	Fraction	Indicated division	Colon
a. Jana is three times as tall as Mark.	³⁄₁	$3 \div 1$	$3 : 1$
b. A gallon of milk costs twice as much as a gallon of gasoline.	²⁄₁	$2 \div 1$	$2 : 1$
c. Her brother is half as old as my brother.	½	$1 \div 2$	$1 : 2$

2. a. $\dfrac{12}{8} = \dfrac{3}{2}$

    b. $\dfrac{4}{4} = \dfrac{1}{1}$

    c. $\dfrac{1}{1}$

3. a. $\dfrac{12}{20} = \dfrac{3}{5} = 0.6 \Rightarrow 60\%$

    b. $\dfrac{4}{8} = \dfrac{1}{2} = 0.5 \Rightarrow 50\%$

    c. $\dfrac{1}{2} = 0.5 \Rightarrow 50\%$

4. a. $\dfrac{8}{20} = \dfrac{2}{5} = 0.4 \Rightarrow 40\%$

    b. $\dfrac{4}{8} = \dfrac{1}{2} = 0.5 \Rightarrow 50\%$

    c. $\dfrac{1}{2} = 0.5 \Rightarrow 50\%$

5. Yes

6. a. $\dfrac{6 \text{ parts tin}}{10 \text{ parts total}} \times 1 \text{ kg} = 0.6 \text{ kg}$

    $0.6 \ \cancel{kg} \times \dfrac{1000 \text{ g}}{1 \ \cancel{kg}} = 600 \text{ g of tin in 1 kg of soft solder}$

b. $\dfrac{4 \text{ lead}}{10 \text{ total}} \times 1 \text{ kg} = 0.4 \text{ kg}$

$0.4 \text{ kg} \times \dfrac{1000 \text{ g}}{1 \text{ kg}} = 400 \text{ g of lead in 1 kg of soft solder}$

7. b.

8. a.

9. 12

10. ⅛

11. $\dfrac{70 \text{ N}}{2 \text{ cm}} = \dfrac{x}{1 \text{ cm}}$

$70 \text{ N} \cdot \text{cm} = (2 \text{ cm})x$ Use cross multiplication.

$x = 35 \text{ N}$

12. a.   1' : ¼"

      12" : ¼"   Restate as a ratio with the same units.

      48 : 1   Multiply both sides by 4 to get whole numbers.

   b. $\dfrac{48}{1} = \dfrac{24'}{x}$ (Using 48 : 1 ratio)

      $48x = 24' \cdot 1$

        $x = 0.5'$, or 6"

     A 6" line on the paper would represent a 24' wall.

   c. $\dfrac{48}{1} = \dfrac{x}{9.5"}$

      $1 \cdot x = 48 \cdot 9.5"$

        $x = 456"$, or 38'

     So, a 9½" line on the paper corresponds to 38' in full scale.

13. a.   Diameter = 1.5" → Circumference = 1.5(π)"

     Each turn of the large gear reels in 1.5(π)" of cable. Since 18" is needed,

     $\dfrac{18"}{1.5" \pi} = 382$ turns (rounded) of the *large* gear are required.

     $\dfrac{41 \text{ turns of the small gear}}{1 \text{ turn of the large gear}} = \dfrac{x}{382 \text{ turns of the large gear}}$

     Solving for *x*, we find $x = 157$ turns of the small gear (rounded).

   b. $\dfrac{40 \text{ turns}}{1 \text{ minute}} = \dfrac{157 \text{ turns}}{x}$

     $(40 \text{ turns})x = (157 \text{ turns})(1 \text{ minute})$

     $x = 3.9$ minutes (rounded)

     It will take about 3.9 minutes.

14. The circular input piston will have an area of $A_{in} = \pi(\text{radius})^2 = \pi(\frac{12 \text{ in}}{2})^2 = 113 \text{ in}^2$. The ratio of pressures is inversely proportional to the ratio of the areas. Thus,

$$\frac{\text{Input pressure}}{\text{Output pressure}} = \frac{\text{Output area}}{\text{Input area}}$$

$$\frac{P_{in}}{P_{out}} = \frac{A_{out}}{A_{in}}$$

$$\frac{80 \text{ psi}}{10,000 \text{ psi}} = \frac{A_{out}}{113 \text{ in}^2}$$

$$A_{out}(10,000 \text{ psi}) = (80 \text{ psi})(113 \text{ in}^2)$$

$$A_{out} = \frac{(80 \ \cancel{\text{psi}})(113 \text{ in}^2)}{10,000 \ \cancel{\text{psi}}}$$

$$A_{out} = 0.904 \text{ in}^2$$

The area of the output piston should be a little less than 1 square inch.

Next, calculate the diameter of the output piston using the formula for the area of a circle.

$$A_{out} = \pi(\text{radius}_{out})^2$$

$$A_{out} = \pi\left(\frac{d_{out}}{2}\right)^2$$

$$\frac{A_{out}}{\pi} = \left(\frac{d_{out}}{2}\right)^2$$

$$\sqrt{\frac{A_{out}}{\pi}} = \frac{d_{out}}{2}$$

$$d_{out} = 2 \cdot \sqrt{\frac{A_{out}}{\pi}}$$

$$d_{out} = 2 \cdot \sqrt{\frac{0.904 \text{ in}^2}{\pi}} = 1.07 \text{ in.}$$

So, the output piston must have a diameter of a bit more than an inch.

Practice Exercises 8: Unit Conversion

1. See table.

2. 6.8 kilocalories (kcal)
   10 centimeters (cm)
   5 millimeters (mm)
   3.14 nanoseconds (ns)

3. millimeters (mm)
   milligrams (mg)
   microcalories (μcal)
   centimeters (cm)

4. 1.56×10^1 kg

5. $v_f = v_i + at$ $\qquad\qquad$ $v_f = v_i + at$

$$\frac{\text{ft}}{\text{s}} = \frac{\text{ft}}{\text{s}} + \left(\frac{\text{ft}}{\text{s}^{\cancel{2}}}\right)(\cancel{\text{s}}) \qquad \frac{\text{m}}{\text{s}} = \frac{\text{m}}{\text{s}} + \left(\frac{\text{m}}{\text{s}^{\cancel{2}}}\right)(\cancel{\text{s}})$$

$$\frac{\text{ft}}{\text{s}} = \frac{\text{ft}}{\text{s}} \qquad\qquad\qquad \frac{\text{m}}{\text{s}} = \frac{\text{m}}{\text{s}}$$

6. $R_E = \dfrac{\rho\ell}{A}$

$$\Omega = \frac{(\Omega \cdot \cancel{\text{cm}})\,\cancel{\text{cm}}}{\cancel{\text{cm}^{2}}}$$

$$\Omega = \Omega$$

7. $150 \; \cancel{\text{cm}} \times \dfrac{10 \text{ mm}}{1 \; \cancel{\text{cm}}} = 1500 \text{ mm}$

8. $21 \; \cancel{\text{L}} \times \dfrac{1 \text{ gal}}{3.785 \; \cancel{\text{L}}} = 5.55 \text{ L}$

9. $40 \; \cancel{\text{cm}} \times \dfrac{1 \text{ m}}{100 \; \cancel{\text{cm}}} = 0.40 \text{ m}$

10. $5 \; \cancel{\text{h}} \times \dfrac{3600 \text{ s}}{1 \; \cancel{\text{h}}} = 18{,}000 \text{ s}$

11. $\dfrac{10.5 \text{ mi}}{\cancel{\text{h}}} \times \dfrac{5280 \text{ ft}}{1 \; \cancel{\text{mi}}} \times \dfrac{1 \; \cancel{\text{h}}}{3600 \text{ s}} \times = 15.4 \; {}^{\text{ft}}\!/_{\text{s}}$

Practice Exercises 9: Algebra Review

1. $$n = \frac{c}{v} \triangleleft$$

$$1.5 = \frac{3 \times 10^8 \text{ m/s}}{v}$$

$$v \times 1.5 = \frac{3 \times 10^8 \text{ m/s}}{\cancel{v}} \times \cancel{v}$$

$$1.5v = 3 \times 10^8 \text{ m/s}$$

$$\frac{\cancel{1.5}v}{\cancel{1.5}} = \frac{3 \times 10^8 \text{ m/s}}{1.5}$$

$$v = 2 \times 10^8 \text{ m/s}$$

The speed of light in glass is 2×10^8 m/s.

2. $$a^2 + b^2 = c^2$$

$$(250 \text{ yd})^2 + (250 \text{ yd})^2 = c^2$$

$$125{,}000 \text{ yd}^2 = c^2$$

$$\sqrt{125{,}000 \text{ yd}^2} = \sqrt{c^2}$$

$$354 \text{ yd} = c \ \ (\text{rounded})$$

c is the hypotenuse of the right triangle.

The hole is about 350 yards away. To clear the water, the ball does not have to go 350 yards in the air, but if it gets over the water it will probably roll that far.

3. $E = [(T - D) \times (1.00 - P)] + D$
$E = [(\$5000 - \$100) \times (1.00 - 0.8)] + \$100$
$E = (\$4900 \times 0.2) + \$100$
$E = \$980 + \$100$
$E = \$1080$

You will pay \$1080 for the hospital bill.

4. $G = 2.1n + 3.7$
$G = 2.1(19) + 3.7$
$G = 39.9 + 3.7$
$G = 43.6$

The light should stay green for about 44 seconds.

5.
$$2n_f t + \frac{\lambda_0}{2} = m\lambda_0$$

$$2n_f t + \frac{\lambda_0}{2} - \frac{\lambda_0}{2} = m\lambda_0 - \frac{\lambda_0}{2}$$

$$2n_f t = \lambda_0\left(m - \frac{1}{2}\right)$$

$$\frac{2n_f t}{2n_f} = \lambda_0\left(m - \frac{1}{2}\right) \times \frac{1}{2n_f}$$

$$t = \frac{\lambda_0}{2n_f}\left(m - \frac{1}{2}\right)$$

$$t = \frac{540 \text{ nm}}{2(1.33)}\left(2 - \frac{1}{2}\right)$$

$$t = \frac{540 \text{ nm}}{2.66}(1.5)$$

$$t = 305 \text{ nm}$$

Factoring out λ_0 simplifies the result but is not necessary.

6. a.
$$\frac{1}{f} = \frac{1}{p} + \frac{1}{q}$$

$$\frac{1}{f} - \frac{1}{q} = \frac{1}{p} + \frac{1}{q} - \frac{1}{q}$$

$$\frac{q}{fq} - \frac{f}{fq} = \frac{1}{p}$$

$$\frac{q - f}{fq} = \frac{1}{p}$$

$$p \times \left(\frac{q - f}{fq}\right) = \frac{1}{p} \times p$$

$$p \times \left(\frac{q - f}{fq}\right) \times \left(\frac{fq}{q - f}\right) = 1 \times \left(\frac{fq}{q - f}\right)$$

$$p = \frac{fq}{q - f}$$

b. $50 \cancel{mm} \times \dfrac{1\ cm}{10\ \cancel{mm}} = 5\ cm$

$$p = \dfrac{(5\ cm)(6.2\ cm)}{6.2\ cm - 5\ cm}$$

$$p = \dfrac{31\ cm^2}{1.2\ cm}$$

$$p = 25.8\ cm$$

Practice Exercises 10: Powers and Roots

1. a. $T = 2\pi \times \sqrt{\dfrac{L}{g}}$

$$T = 2\pi \times \sqrt{\dfrac{25.00\ cm}{980\ cm/s^2}}$$

$T = 1.0035\ cm$ (rounded)

   b. $T = 2\pi \times \sqrt{\dfrac{24.90\ cm}{980\ cm/s^2}}$

$T = 1.0015\ cm$ (rounded)

The 24.90-cm pendulum is closer to the desired value of 1.000 second.

2. $R = P \times \dfrac{i}{\left[1 - (1 + i)^{-n}\right]}$

$$R = \$2600 \times \dfrac{0.01}{\left[1 - (1 + 0.01)^{-24}\right]}$$

$$R = \$2600 \times \dfrac{0.01}{\left[1 - 0.7876...\right]}$$

$R = \$122.391$ (rounded)

Therefore, the monthly payments will be \$122.39.

Note: The "…" in the problem indicates that those numbers are not being rounded, but kept in the calculator. You should only round at the last step.

3. The volume of a cube is given by the formula $V = s^3$, where s is the length of one side of the cube. A sphere of diameter s will just fit within the box. Solve for s and substitute the given volume.

$V = s^3$ — Given equation.

$\sqrt[3]{V} = \sqrt[3]{s^3}$ — Take the cube root of both sides.

$\sqrt[3]{V} = s$ — Simplify.

$s = \sqrt[3]{700 \text{ in}^3}$
$\ \ = 8.88$ in. — Substitute value for V and solve.

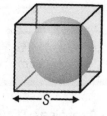

So this box could hold a sphere with a diameter as large as 8.88 inches.

4. a. Green-brown-orange
       5-1-3 $\rightarrow$ 51 $\times$ 10^3 Ω = 51 kΩ
    b. Red-red-blue
       2-2-6 $\rightarrow$ 22 $\times$ 10^6 Ω = 22 MΩ
    c. Black-gray-black
       0-8-0 $\rightarrow$ 08 $\times$ 10^0 = 8 $\times$ 1 = 8 Ω
    d. Yellow-green-brown
       4-5-1 $\rightarrow$ 45 $\times$ 10^1 = 450 Ω

5. a. $R = (5.670 \times 10^{-12}) \times (273°C + T)^4$
       $R = (5.670 \times 10^{-12}) \times (273 + 300)^4$
       $R = (5.670 \times 10^{-12}) \times (573)^4$
       $R = (5.670 \times 10^{-12}) \times (1.078 \times 10^{11})$
       $R = 0.611$ watts/cm^2
    b. $R = (5.670 \times 10^{-12}) \times (273 + 37)^4$
       $R = (5.670 \times 10^{-12}) \times (310)^4$
       $R = (5.670 \times 10^{-12}) \times (9.235 \times 10^9)$
       R = 5.236×10^{-2} watts/cm^2 (or 0.05236 watts/cm^2)

6. $n! \approx \sqrt{(2\pi n)} \times \left(\dfrac{n}{e}\right)^n$

   $30! \approx \sqrt{2\pi(30)} \times \left(\dfrac{30}{2.718}\right)^{30}$

   $30! \approx \sqrt{60\pi} \times (11.04...)^{30}$
   $30! \approx (13.73...) \times (1.933 \times 10^{31})$
   $30! \approx 2.6534 \times 10^{32}$ (rounded)

Entering 30! into a calculator gives a result of 2.6525×10^{32} (rounded). In the "grand scheme of things," these are pretty close!

Practice Exercises 11: The Basics of Graphing

1. a. Passenger cars and trucks and buses
   b. 1950 to 2000
   c. Passenger cars
   d. About 550. This estimate should be fairly reliable because over the last 50 years the increase has been consistent.

2. a. (1) bushels per acre, (2) Fahrenheit, (3) inches
   b. Each line is formatted differently so the user can distinguish between them.
   c. 6" about 75 bushels per acre
      1" about 37 bushels per acre
   d. Light rainfall (1" rainfall results in about 62 bushels per acre.)

3. a. 15,000 parts   casting: about $10,500
                        forging: about $16,000
   b. 5000 parts   casting: about $7000
                   forging: about $5500
   c. About 7500 parts
   d. Yes. If producing less than 7500 parts, it is more cost effective to use the forging method. If over 7500 parts are being produced, casting will save money.
      Parts < 7500 → forging
      Parts > 7500 → casting

4. a.

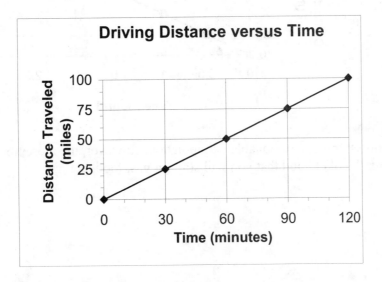

   b. In 50 minutes you would travel about 42 miles.
      In 100 minutes you would travel about 84 miles.

c.

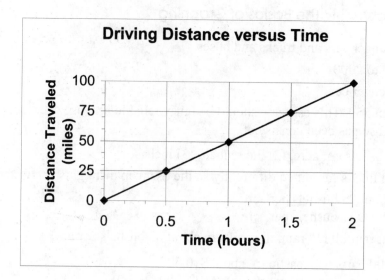

d.

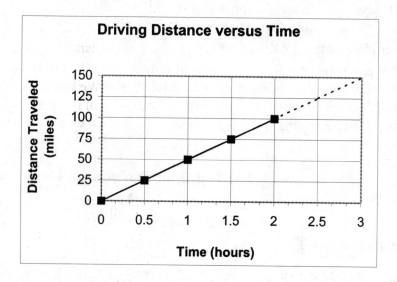

150 miles; this is a reasonable extrapolation. However, the more time spent in the car, the greater the likelihood that you will stop for gas, food, etc.

5. a.

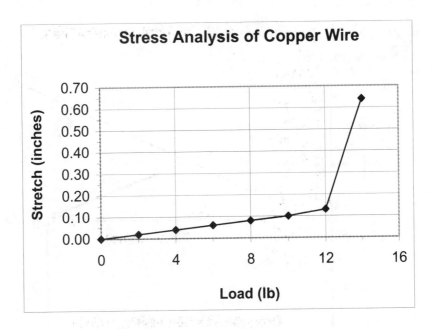

Stress Analysis of Copper Wire

Stretch (inches) vs *Load (lb)*

b. Somewhere between 12 and 14 pounds the stretch distance increases drastically.

c. 3 pounds → about 0.03 inch
   At 16 pounds an accurate estimation is not possible. We know that it would exceed 0.64 inch, but we know little beyond that. The problem is that there is not a consistent pattern at and around this point to project the stretched distance. The "point of breaking" in a material can be modeled with a piece of silly putty. Take a piece and pack it tightly together. Then slowly pull on both ends. You'll notice that initially there is resistance to the stretching. But once it gets to a certain point the resistance greatly decreases as you pull it apart.

Practice Exercises 12: Getting to Know Trigonometry

1. a. The labels for the legs can be reversed, but the hypotenuse must correspond to the impedance Z.

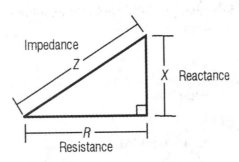

Impedance Z

X Reactance

R Resistance

b. $X^2 = Z^2 - R^2$

$X = \sqrt{(8.0 \text{ ohms})^2 - (1.5 \text{ ohms})^2}$

$X = 7.9 \text{ ohms (rounded)}$

2. a.

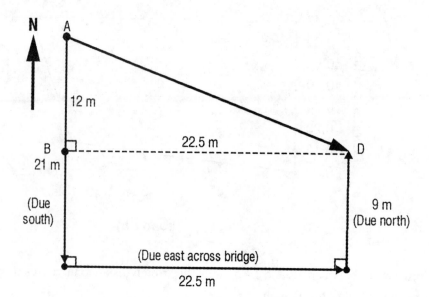

b. Using the right triangle ABD shown in the drawing above:

$AD = \sqrt{(AB)^2 + (BD)^2}$

$AD = \sqrt{(21-9)^2 + (22.5)^2}$

$AD = \sqrt{12^2 + (22.5)^2}$

$AD = 25.5 \text{ m}$

3. a. To have 3 feet above the top landing with a 24-foot ladder, you can have no more than 21 feet (that is, 24 ft – 3 ft) between the point at which the ladder touches the ground and the top support.

b. The drawing with the exercise shows a right triangle whose base is one-quarter the length of the hypotenuse. The hypotenuse was determined in part (a) to be 21 feet. Then use the Pythagorean formula to solve for the remaining leg.

$c^2 = a^2 + b^2$ (Solve for one leg, b.)

$b = \sqrt{c^2 - a^2}$

Here $c = 21$ ft and $a = \dfrac{c}{4} = \dfrac{21}{4} = 5.25$ ft

$b = \sqrt{(21)^2 - (5.25)^2}$

$b = 20.33$ ft or 20' 4" (rounded)

This ladder's maximum safe landing height is 20' 4" from the ground.

4. Since the frame will be square, each pair of sides forms a right triangle. The diagonal will be the hypotenuse, so you can use the Pythagorean formula.

$$c^2 = a^2 + b^2$$

$$c = \sqrt{(12 \text{ in})^2 + (12 \text{ in})^2}$$

$$c = \sqrt{288 \text{ in}^2}, \text{ or } 17 \text{ in. (rounded)}$$

Or you may use the fact that the right triangle formed is a 45°-45° triangle. Then the hypotenuse is $\sqrt{2}$ times the length of one leg, or $12\sqrt{2}$ inches, yielding the same answer as above.

Appendix F: Career Links

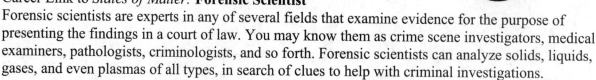

Page 27
Career Link to *States of Matter:* **Forensic Scientist**
Forensic scientists are experts in any of several fields that examine evidence for the purpose of presenting the findings in a court of law. You may know them as crime scene investigators, medical examiners, pathologists, criminologists, and so forth. Forensic scientists can analyze solids, liquids, gases, and even plasmas of all types, in search of clues to help with criminal investigations.

Page 66
Career Link to *Measuring Temperature:* **Veterinarian**
Zoos, veterinary facilities, and medical research laboratories must provide precise temperature control for animals to provide for their general health and well-being. This involves a wide array of temperature sensors for measuring and documenting the changing air and water temperatures as well as various methods for controlling the temperature of the animal's environment.

Page 98
Career Link to *Work Done in Fluid Systems:* **Commercial Diver**
Commercial divers rely on fluid system diagnostics and pump design to provide purified, high-pressure, compressed air for self-contained underwater breathing.

Page 109
Career Link to *Work in Electrical Systems:* **Lighting Engineer**
A lighting engineer for a television network must rely on battery-powered lighting for outdoor events such as late-breaking news stories, postgame interviews, and other unscheduled broadcasts for which commercially supplied electricity is unavailable.

Page 141
Career Link to *Measuring Fluid Rates:* **Research Scientist**
As a research scientist for an engineering products company specializing in fluid modeling and flow analysis, one must be familiar with measuring fluid rates in addition to CFD, computational fluid dynamics.

Page 162
Career Link to *Convection:* **Irrigation Specialist**
Irrigation specialists might use the concept of convection as they apply irrigation water techniques to protect cut foliage crops and subtropical plants from freezing during winter months.

Page 174
Career Link to *Friction Forces:* **Race Car Driver**
A race car driver and his crew are probably familiar with the following concept: Soft compound tires are required to be wider in order for the sidewall to support the weight of the car. Softer tires have a larger coefficient of friction, therefore better traction. A narrow, soft tire would not be strong enough, nor would it last very long. Wider tires, assuming all other factors are equal, commonly have stiffer sidewalls and experience less roll. This gives better cornering performance.

Page 191
Career Link to *Poiseuille's Law:* **Medical Laboratory Technician**
A vascular medical lab technician uses several Dopplers to perform testing for vascular disease. For example, a carotid Doppler is used for the technician to gain an image of the blood flow through the carotid artery of the neck.

Page 230
Career Link to *Kinetic Energy:* **Mathematician**
A mathematician working for the military might use the concept of kinetic energy while working on the Kinetic Energy Interceptor program. This program is designed to use kinetic energy interceptors capable of shooting down enemy ballistic missiles.

Page 264
Career Link to *Capacitance:* **HVAC Technician**
Capacitors are an important part of almost every electric motor. Repair personnel who work on electric motors in air conditioners, elevators, refrigerators, water pumps, and so on must measure, install, repair, and/or replace capacitors.

Page 301
Career Link to *Drag Force:* **Commercial Pilot**
During flight, a pilot must be familiar with the concept of drag force (in addition to weight force and thrust force) in order to maintain altitude and speed.

Page 318
Career Link to *Power in a Resistance:* **Power Systems Electricians**
Power system electricians facilitate the distribution of electricity over great distances and must overcome the electrical resistance that is inherent in all transmission lines. They minimize electrical resistances in conductors to reduce losses in the power delivered to the customer, but maximize electrical resistances that serve as insulators to prevent high voltage dissipation of the power to the ground and nearby personnel.

Page 327
Career Link to *Momentum:* **Personal Trainer**
A personal trainer may work with clients on how not to use momentum when they lift weights. If you jerk the weights to be able to lift more, you are not building muscle and are increasing risk of injury. Personal trainers also discourage ballistic stretching, which relies on momentum caused by repetitive bouncy movements.

Page 332
Career Link to *Newton's Third Law of Motion:* **Police Officer**
When a police officer fires a gun during a training exercise, the force of the gas produced by burning gunpowder hurls out the bullet. By Newton's law, the gun itself recoils backward.

Page 361
Career Link to *Sound:* **Audiologist**
An audiology exam tests your ability to hear sounds. Sounds vary according to the intensity (volume or loudness) and the tone (the speed of sound wave vibrations). Hearing occurs when sound waves are conducted to the nerves of the inner ear and from there to the brain. Sound waves can travel to the inner ear by air conduction (through the ear canal, eardrum, and bones of the middle ear) or bone conduction (through the bones around and behind the ear).

Page 376
Career Link to *Natural Frequency:* **Instrument Maker**
The frequencies to which musical instruments naturally respond are called *natural frequencies*. The art of making musical instruments comes from creating shapes and enclosing volumes of air to stir up these natural forms of vibration.

Page 397
Career Link to *X Rays:* **Speech-Language Pathologist**
A speech-language pathologist may evaluate and treat swallowing disorders resulting from neurological incidents such as stroke, multiple sclerosis, or Parkinson's disease. Through the use of a modified barium swallow study, the pathologist will be able to visualize the actual swallowing muscles through the X rays.

Page 410
Career Link to *Radioactivity:* **Environmental Engineer**
Environmental engineers must work with municipalities along Lake Michigan in southeastern Wisconsin to help them remove salt and other pollutants from radioactive drinking water tapped from low levels of sandstone.

Page 434
Career Link to *Refraction:* **Optometrist**
When determining a prescription for a patient's glasses or contacts, an optometrist will perform a "refraction test." Through the results from this test, the doctor can diagnose nearsightedness, farsightedness, astigmatism, or presbyopia.

Page 439
Career Link to *Lenses:* **Photographer**
A photographer must recognize the effects of lens characteristics and how it can make the difference between good and bad photography. A photographer should be familiar with lens design and aberrations, astigmatism, chromatic aberration, coma, curvilinear distortion, and spherical aberration.

Page 451
Career Link to *Wave Interference:* **Polishing Technician**
Interferometry is used to measure with atomic-scales the precision of ground optics that will be used in various laser and other optical systems.

Appendix G. Index

mass number, 405

matter: gas state of, 28; liquid state of, 28; plasma state of, 28; solid state of, 28; states of, 27

Maxwell, James Clerk, 451

mean free path, 213

measuring: current and voltage, 151; fluid rate, 141; force, 6; temperature, 66

mechanical resistance, 168

mechanical system, 2; energy in, 230, 243; force in, 4; power in, 298; rate in, 122; resistance in, 170; work in, 84

mechanical wave, 352, 355

melting point, 74

metastable state, 478

metric system, 6

microwave radiation, 393

mirror, 428; concave, 429; convex, 429; plane, 428; spherical, 428

mirror equation, 432

models of the atom, 469

molecule, random motion of, 278

moment of inertia (I), 233

momentum, 324; angular (L), 339, 340; angular, units, table, 340; and Newton's second law, 328

momentum, linear (p), 326, 327; units, *table*, 331

monochromaticity, 477

motion, Newton's first law of, 171, 326; Newton's second law of, 171; Newton's third law of, 332

N

natural convection, 162;

natural frequency, 376

net force, 11

neutron, 50, 405

Newton, Isaac, 12

newton (N), 6

Newton's: first law of motion, 12, 326; second law of motion, 171; second law, momentum and, 328; third law of motion, 332; second law for rotation, 341; universal law of gravitation, 48

newton-meter (N·m), 18, 85

node, 373

normal 427

normal force, 175

nuclear equation, 411

nuclear fission, 413

nuclear force, strong, 407

nuclear fusion, 415

nuclear radiation, 385, 404

nucleus, 405

O

object, 428

Ohm, Georg Simon, 203; law, 203

open fluid system, 96

opposing torques, 21

optical fiber, 439

optical system, 422, 424

optics: ray, 426; physical, 450; wave, 450

output voltage, 215

P

parallel circuit, 209

parallel connection, 151

Pascal, Blaise, 37; principle, 37

pascal (Pa), 31

Paschen series, 474

pendulum, 382

period (T), 153, 358

periodic wave, 355

phase, wave, 373

photoelectric effect, 398